D0064853

SCIENCE
AND
THE FUTURE OF MANKIND

WORLD ACADEMY OF ART AND SCIENCE

1

SCIENCE AND THE FUTURE OF MANKIND

edited by

HUGO BOYKO

INDIANA UNIVERSITY PRESS

BLOOMINGTON

ORIGINALLY PUBLISHED BY DR. W. JUNK IN THE NETHERLANDS
FIRST PUBLISHED IN THE UNITED STATES 1964
LIBRARY OF CONGRESS CATALOG CARD NUMBER 64-63014
MANUFACTURED IN THE UNITED STATES OF AMERICA

Contents

On December 24, 1960, the appeal of the International Conference on Science and Human Welfare (Oct. 1956) was realized by the constitution of the WORLD ACADEMY OF ART AND SCIENCE, which will function as an informal "World University" of the highest scientific and ethical level. The structure of the Academy and its aims are laid down in the Statutes which, in their final form, will be included as an Appendix in the next volume.

The two main purposes of the Academy are:

1. Gradually to build up a TRANSNATIONAL FORUM, in which the vital problems of mankind can be responsibly discussed and thoroughly studied by the best brains of our generation and of the following ones, from an objective, scientific and global point of view.
2. To act as an impartial advisory body in the service of Human Welfare, OUTSIDE OF ALL GROUP-INTERESTS.

This book is the Academy's first small step in this direction.

Further details concerning the organization and the activities of the World Academy will be found in the Appendices to this and to the following volumes.

Plato[1]:

"Until philosophers are kings, or the kings and princes of this world have the spirit and power of science, and political greatness and wisdom met in one, neither states nor the human race itself will ever have rest from their evils."

Remark: The great Greek belongs to that small group of congenial giants in Asia, Africa and Europe, who saw the "Need" a few thousand years earlier than we, although the "Means" which they considered may differ greatly from those at our disposal.

Plato was also the founder of an Academy with a similar "Goal" in mind as ours. This Academy proceeded with its work through nine centuries (!) namely from 387 B.C. until 529 A.D., when it was closed by religious intolerance. Its main aim was the scientific and philosophical training of potential political leaders.

The Editor

[1]. From the 7th letter to Dion and his family at Syracuse.

Foreword

by

LORD BOYD ORR

Civilization has evolved by the stimulus of new knowledge which gave man increased power over the forces of nature. In the last few decades science has advanced more than in the previous 2,000 years. This impact of modern science on human society is bringing about great changes. The adjustment of the structure of human society to these changes has raised grave political and economic problems. If these problems cannot be solved by harnessing the new powers of science to serve mankind our civilization will be destroyed by the tremendous new forces science has let loose.

All nations and races have made some contribution to the growth of knowledge and, in this now small world, all nations will ultimately share the same fate. It is a matter of urgency that scientists and men of learning of all countries who should recognize no political boundaries get together in an International Council to consider the problems science has raised, and in view of the impending further advance of science to suggest what political and economic changes might be made to ensure that our civilization might evolve to a wonderful new era of permanent peace, economic prosperity, and a higher level of culture than has yet been attained, which modern science has made possible.

This is the great objective of this new movement[1] which will have the support of all people of vision and goodwill who think of the kind of world we would like to pass on to our children and grandchildren.

1. See page 367.

Introduction

This book is a new beginning in our world. Basically speaking, the twenty scientists who wrote it are not the sole authors. The whole of these essays, however original each of them may be in its line of thought, reflects the thinking of hundreds of thousands of scientists as well as the more or less vague feeling of countless others working in all branches of human activity.

This book is like the first step a child takes in the upright position in surroundings still new to him – in a world into which man now steps as creator or as destructor, without having yet fully grasped this fact.

This book has been written to express this common thinking and feeling and to try to find a way leading to creation and not to destruction. All the essayists are acknowledged leaders in their spheres of work, and the names of most of them are known to intellectuals the world over. Some of them have become symbols of spiritual life in our times. But together with these authors stand many of the best and noblest men of our times, firmly resolved to work actively in spreading the thought of this group.

What is this leading thought? It is very simple. Many scientists feel that they are partly responsible for the paths that mankind has been treading in the last decades, and they feel obliged to shoulder this responsibility not only in theory, but in practice.

This feeling is shared by most thinking men and women, including many of the political leaders, for the most outstanding and most cultured among them know that according to the tendency of their education they are not capable by themselves to evaluate the true magnitude of the responsibility which is weighing them down. Together with the great statesmen of our time we have to look for the way to make possible "Life with the bomb" – as C. F. VON WEIZSÄCKER has formulated it.

Just as every species, confronted with surrounding factors which endanger its existence, must either adapt itself to them or perish, so mankind in its whole organizational structure must adapt itself to the wholly new conditions created by science and technology in the last decades.

Our time is not only the period filled with threats of destruction by atom bomb, bacterial warfare, death rays, brain-washing and the Lord knows what more future discoveries. It is also the time – if we will it, and who does not? – of new creation of forces only dimly perceived as yet, forces which are able to intensify the joy of living for everybody everywhere, without at the same time taking away from the joy of living of any group anywhere.

Atomic energy, bacteria, the different rays, the entirely new ways of education towards mutual understanding, and last not least the huge increase in the potential of the earth's productivity through genetics, irrigation with sea-water, making the deserts productive – all this and much more means that we have powers to our hand which can in a far simpler and far more economical way be used for good than for evil. But for this purpose the will, existent already with nearly all individuals, must be forged into a common will usable only in this one direction, inflexible against If and But.

The forum to be created for this purpose will construct the way. Now, that I am writing these words the World Academy of Art and Science is in process of being founded.

And this book is the first concrete and preparatory step.

This Academy is meant as a "transnational Forum" (transnational was coined for us by ROBERT OPPENHEIMER) of the highest scientific and ethical level for our and the following generations, to discuss objectively and scientifically the vital problems of mankind beyond all group interests and from a global point of view. It is meant as an advisory body for UNO, governments and peoples, in this decisive transitional period of our development, and it is meant as a body whose advice will be heard, and that soon.

Outsiders will consider many of the preceding words to be those of a dreamer. They are not. They have a most realistic back-ground. EINSTEIN's view expressed thirty years ago, "Scientists of the World must unite" – an appeal which has the same object in view that we have, has today entered into the phase of realization.

The special agencies of UNO are everywhere in the vanguard to demand global common work of science. Many international conferences have already milled through the organizational problems. Scientific Unions have already worked in these lines for many years, even though so far on the basis of national representation. The conferences of the last few years have made every effort to free themselves of national shackles, and their great value lies in that they have made clear, even to such as live far from the centres of politics and science, how immense are the dangers that mankind is threatened with in consequence of its organizational structure in small and large groups – suddenly grown obsolete.

Such conferences were official ones like those of UNESCO, and also unofficial ones, such as the famous Pugwash Conference called by BERTRAND RUSSELL and CYRUS EATON (from 6 to 11 July 1957), which had the RUSSELL-EINSTEIN appeal of the year 1955 for its basis. All these conferences saw as their great task in shaking world publicity out of its lethargy again and again, and to hold against the fatalism of the many and the satanism of the few – the warning of those who know.

All these conferences had temporary success. They were only meant to be temporary. With one exception: The "International Conference on Science and Human Welfare," held in Washington in October, 1956.

Under the leadership of JOHN A. FLEMING and RICHARD M. FIELD a resolution was tabled which for the first time decided on creating something permanent as the result of all these conferences and individual strivings; an overall inventory on the natural resources at our command, and a permanent forum where the deepest thought, the greatest knowledge, and the best know-how of our and the following generations should freely and constructively discuss the vital problems of mankind: this very transnational forum which we have missed so sorely up to now and which is to show the way towards using the vast achievements of our time for construction and not for destruction, for the happiness of all and not for the suffering of all.

Understandably, of the many outstanding scientists of our time only a very few could make their voices heard between these covers. It is also a matter of course, that even on this narrow basis the mosaic of the book is composed of many colours. Genetics, political science, engineering, and so on, elucidate our problems from very different angles. Some of us will be delighted at the variety of knowledge, others may possibly miss the one common scientific subject, but all of us see the common direction, "the striving of the best minds for a harmonic solution to the conflicts existing today: the conflicts within our own minds – the conflicts between man and man and between nation and nation – the contrast between our education of yesterday and the demands of tomorrow – the contrasts between centrifugal group interests and mutual, unifying work for the common object: Our future on this very tiny planet."

Our earth has grown so small. And man so great. The Earth knows nothing of its smallness – nor does Man of his Greatness.

Our form of organization, traditionally only a few thousand years old, is divided into national states and groups of states, trying unsuccessfully to shut each other out by impossible border lines. The smallness and narrowness of our stateborders become clear when we apply the only objective measure, that of speed.

A table at the end of this introduction is meant to show this development graphically, giving comparative times for circling the world.

Thus for instance the whole of our earth would be a far smaller state than was Israel 3,000 years ago; for it took fourteen days to get from the northern border to Elath, and for HOMER's Odysseus the Aegaean Islands were a world of greater space than to-morrow our whole planetary system will be.

This table shows the gradual historical shift in the potential borders of a great Power, and we leave it to the reader to decide whether the most recent expansions still be understood under the traditional concept of the state as an organizational structure.

But this is already one of the vital problems to be discussed by the World Academy or by a group of experts. The Academy will never profess to be allknowing. But it will further mutual work of all those who know, with every means at its disposal.

We must work together to safeguard our future – the future of mankind. To find the way for a common work for a common goal there is no need for a revolution. There is need merely of deep knowledge, of objective thought, of constructive discussion, and of willingness for understanding.

These will lead to such foundations in science, in philosophy, in psychology, in technology, in the arts, as will form the suitable bases for gradually building up a commonwealth aiming at the truly ideal state – the ideal organizational form for mankind as a whole.

The need for such a common political organization in the near future is today clear to everybody. What we cannot know is whether it will be formed peacefully or by violence. Will the trial be made by force, it will in all probability destroy whatever will have been achieved until then, including our progeny.

How different is the vision of a peaceful solution for which this book and the World Academy as a whole is meant as a pathfinder.

We believe, we still believe in spite of all threats from both sides, that we shall increase our greatness and that it is not yet too late to do so by peaceful means. The desire and the will of all has become so strong, it is ever increasing – it will surely vanquish all opposition.

Statesmen and scientists, philosophers and artists, and every worker among us, from the unskilled Chinese coolie and the illiterate shepherd of the poorest steppes, up to the chief engineer of the greatest industrial works and the leader in industry – they will all help pave the way.

Jerusalem, October 1960 THE EDITOR

TABLE

Shrinking of our planet by man's speed to travel round the globe

YEAR	TIME NEEDED	MEANS	AIM	POTENTIAL STATE SIZE
500,000 B.C.	a few hundred thousand years	on foot (over land, ice-bridges)	by chance	none
20,000 B.C.	a few thousand years	on foot and by canoe	by chance	a small valley, vicinity of a small lake, etc.
3,000 B.C.	a few hundred years	small sails and paddles, relays of runners	partly by chance, (storms etc.) partly intentional for big distances (hundreds of kilometers)	small part of continent
500 B.C.	a few tens of years	big sail ships with paddles, horses, relays of runners, cars, camels and riders	partly by chance, partly intentional for big distances, thousands of kilometers	big parts of a continent with coastal colonies
1,500 A.D.	a few years	big sailing ships with *compass*	intentional	big parts of continents with transoceanic colonies
1900 A.D.	a few months	*steamboat*, railway (Suez-Canal, Pana-ma-*Canal*)	intentional	big parts of continents with transoceanic colonies
1925 A.D.	a few weeks	steamboat, transcontinental railways, auto, *airplanes*	intentional	whole continents and transoceanic commonwealth
1950 A.D.	a few days	steamboat, transcontinental railways, auto, *jet planes*	intentional	the globe
1960 A.D.	a few hours [2]	steamboat, transcontinental railways, auto, space *rockets*	intentional	the globe and more [1]

1. The actual development of state size according to communication possibilities securing law, order and economic development is today about 30–500 years behind.
2. From a UPI, Reuter telegramme in the Press of August 5th, 1960: "The rocket-powered X-15 carried test pilot Joe Walker over the Californian desert at more than three times the speed of sound yesterday to establish a world's air speed record of 2,150 miles an hour" (= 3460 km).

This is more than twice as much as the speed of earth rotation at the equator, and means – if continued – a mere air-flight round the globe in less than 12 hours at the equator, and in higher latitudes, of course, much less. The speed of Space-vehicles circling the globe is many times higher even than that. (Hugo Boyko).

The Need

Die Internationale der Wissenschaft[1]

von

ALBERT EINSTEIN

1) Als während des I. Weltkrieges die nationale und politische Verblendung ihren Höhepunkt erreicht hatte, prägte EMIL FISCHER in einer Akademiesitzung mit Nachdruck den Satz: "Sie können nichts machen, meine Herren, die Wissenschaft ist und bleibt international." Das haben die Grossen unter den Forschern stets gewusst und leidenschaftlich gefühlt, obschon sie in Zeiten politischer Verwicklungen unter ihren Genossen kleineren Formats isoliert blieben.

2) Die Entdeckung der atomistischen Kettenreaktionen braucht den Menschen so wenig Vernichtung zu bringen wie die Erfindung der Zündhölzer. Wir müssen nur all das tun, was den Missbrauch der Mittel beseitigt. Beim heutigen Stand der technischen Mittel kann uns nur eine übernationale Organisation schützen, verbunden mit einer hinreichend starken Exekutivgewalt. Wenn wir dies eingesehen haben, werden wir auch die Kraft finden, die für die Sicherung des Menschengeschlechts nötigen Opfer zu bringen. Jeder einzelne von uns wäre Schuld daran, wenn das Ziel nicht rechtzeitig erreicht würde. Die Gefahr ist, dass jeder untätig darauf wartet, dass andere für ihn handeln.

3) Den in unserem Jahrhundert erzielten Fortschritten der Wissenschaft wird jeder Mensch Respekt zollen, der

1. Quotations from: ALBERT EINSTEIN: Mein Weltbild. (Herausgegeben von Carl Seelig). Reprinted by kind permission of Europa Verlag Zürich.

einigen Einblick hat, ja selbst der oberflächliche Beobachter, der nur technische Anwendungen zu sehen bekommt. Man wird aber die Leistungen der letzten Zeit nicht überschätzen, wenn man die Probleme der Wissenschaft im grossen nicht aus dem Auge verliert. Es ist wie beim Eisenbahnfahren: achtet man nur auf die nächste Umgebung, so scheint man im Flug fortzukommen. Achtet man aber auf grosse Formen, wie auf hohe Gebirge, so ändert sich die Situation nur ganz langsam. Ähnlich ist es, wenn man die grossen Probleme der Wissenschaft im Auge hat.

4) Es ist meiner Meinung nach nicht vernünftig, von "our way of life" oder dem der Russen überhaupt zu sprechen. In beiden Fällen handelt es sich um eine Sammlung von Traditionen und Gewohnheiten, die kein organisches Ganzes bilden. Es ist gewiss besser, sich zu fragen, was für Einrichtungen und Traditionen für die Menschen schädlich und welche nützlich sind, welche das Leben glücklicher, welche es schmerzlicher machen. Man muss dann das als besser Erkannte einzuführen versuchen, unabhängig davon, ob es gegenwärtig bei uns oder sonstwo realisiert ist.

5) Wenn ich bezüglich des Fortschreitens der allgemeinen internationalen Organisation voll zuversichtlicher Hoffnung bin, so beruht dies weniger auf dem Vertrauen auf die Einsicht und die Noblesse der Gesinnung als vielmehr auf dem gebieterischen Druck der wirtschaftlichen Entwicklung. Da diese in so hohem Masse auf der Gedankenarbeit selbst der rückschrittlich gesinnten Wissenschaftler ruht, werden auch diese gegen ihren Willen die internationale Organisation der Wissenschaft schaffen helfen.

The Need of a World Academy of Art and Science

by

HUGO BOYKO

In October 1956 an International Conference on Science and Human Welfare was convened at Washington, D.C.

Two main tasks filled its program:

1) To organize a global working team in order to create an inventarium of all natural resources known already to us or to be expected with great probability, and
2) The creation of a World Academy of Art and Science.

There is nothing exceptional nowadays in an international conference of Scientists. In the course of the last 50 years many such conferences and congresses have been convened in a growing succession in the framework of the various branches of science.

With this task however this Conference leaped far ahead, going beyond the frame of a regular scientific conference, in its former sense. This conference is the logical outcome of a development to which human way of thinking and physical achievements have led in the course of a few thousand years, bursting wide open our limits as accepted up to now.

However, each of us feels also that something about the aims and the nature of this conference is yet vague, but this is easily comprehensible if we realize that the main subject of the Conference was the future of man.

What was intended to achieve there was merely to seek a way for, as smooth as possible, a further development of all

1. See also p. 367.

peoples and in all countries, the way to a future in which all mankind will be able to enjoy the immense achievements of the human brain; and to seek for a forum in which this way may be discussed on an unpolitical, objective, scientific and highly ethical basis. The time of our own generation and the time of the two or three following ones form the threshold of a period when history has ceased to be the history of single peoples, states or groups. From now on the history of every single state, even the smallest, is linked firmly with that of all others. Mankind has become a whole and undividable unit, struggling as yet against such a realization. If we desire it or not we have all become neighbours and even the remotest of them, our geographical antipodes, have moved into calling distance; quite apart from the fact that through the speed of our planes today, and more so of those of tomorrow, we are able to grasp one anothers hand virtually in a few hours time.

We are starting to trespass the accepted borders of earth, space, matter and even of energy, and – if we are not mistaken – even the threshold of Life and Death. In quick succession ever new vistas keep opening up the unknown territories; already we see in a virus a being which does not permit any more a distinct limit; it can at one moment appear as a lifeless crystall, in the next as a living being of extra-ordinary vitality.

If already these decisive dividing lines of nature seem to disappear before our very eyes and in our comprehension, how small and insignificant and negligible seem the dimensions of the political frontiers. Frontiers which are needed still for the sake of our smaller or larger groupings either for defence or for a better economic development.

The principles however of these limitations and borders seem to be proved nonsensical by the development of modern technique. This again is an example of how the tempestuous technical development tends to throw mankind off its psychological equilibrium and possibly even to destroy it physically.

Only farseeing statemanship in cooperation with the leading scientists in all branches of science will be able to regain the equilibrium.

It will be one of the main tasks to bring such a cooperation into being. This task will remain a necessity until a new form of organizational structure of mankind may develop, a structure adequate not only to mankind's weakness but also to its greatness.

It will not be an easy task to find a way by which such an ideal forum can be erected, which is meant to include the most farseeing brains of science, philosophy and statesmanship and probably for the benefit of mankind, also the most prominent poets and artists.

It is of secondary importance whether we should call such a forum an International Academy of Art and Science or any other adequate name. But it is of imminent importance to recognize the urgency of its creation and, after its creation, to see to it that such a body be trusted in its objectivity with worldwide confidence. If we succeed in promoting this confidence then such a body may act as an advisory influence with the various developments of peoples and governments, and this may well be equivalent to a new era in history.

But before we go into the various approaches to the aim, that is before we discuss the various organizational set-ups which such a forum should have, we must discuss once more the problems which indicate the necessity of such an organization. We want to do this because we want to be certain of our own judgment in order to be able to implant our own convictions and certainty on others.

Quite some part of what I shall have to mention here has been common knowledge amongst broad minded people for some time already. Nevertheless it seems necessary to mention these points too as they form the basis of our deductions.

It has taken thousands of years for man to reach the existing stage of his development. The field of our knowledge is being steadily enlarged and we cannot yet guess where the limitations of our potential comprehension may be lying. We know, however, that we are steadily widening the borders, given us by nature, widening them with increasing rapidity by intensifying the capacity of our sensitive organs or by even producing additional ones. The microscope, the electroscope and radar with all their potentialities are suitable examples of this kind. As a parallel we have the enhancing of our physical qualities, starting with the lifting of weights of many tons with the pressure of one single finger on an electric button, up to flying through space.

The achievements of crossing such natural borders in the course of our one own generation has no parallel since man tamed and produced fire for the first time.

The number of men, however, who are leading mankind on such new ways, or who have original creative minds in any one field is very small indeed. As yet nobody has written the whole story of the eminent historical role played by the scientists, the philosophers, the inventors, and the artists. The importance of this small group of people for the higher values of living is as yet not recognized as it should be. The technician alone is valued more than all the other creators for his achievements, because his achievements are the easiest understood and can be employed in everyday life.

On the whole there are very few people who realize that only the creative mental powers of this small group have been responsible for all the upward trends in the development of men and it is they who are lifting the entity on to higher levels in the art of living. Satisfaction can naturally also be reached by frugality of needs. But let us not forget that uncounted generations of research were essential even for the manufacturing of DIOGENES' famous empty barrel. He himself did neither seek the right wood for it nor did he bend it with the help of heat, nor did he smelt the metal and invent the bands around the sections of wood; he only settled himself in the ready barrel.

Every scientific and technical progress is but the result of a long chain of researches prepared and done by countless generations of Scientists. How quickly is a paper taken in hand to write some notes on it. Who stops to think of the many scientists - botanists, physicists, engineers, chemists - who made the manufacture of this little strip of paper possible.

Would there still be a living specimen of man if not for the few who were ever ahead of their times; scientists of prehistoric periods who invented the methods to make fire, to use stone tools, to sow grains for survival?

We have lived to see enormous social upheavals and developments in the course of the last few generations.

Now is the time ripe that the main call should be: Scientists of all countries, unite! Create a forum which can be looked upon by mankind with trust, and which is able and willing to give advice in all the most vital questions with objectivity and from the highest ethical level.

It is evident that we ourselves shall here have to recognize the necessity of such a unification and of such an extranational and extra-political forum, and to see its far-reaching consequences, before we can try to convince others of its necessity.

Nevertheless we can see already that our small group, which has seen, recognized and advocated this need for the last 10, 15, 20 years, is rapidly growing, so that it represents nowadays already a general urge, even if not generally recognized as such. The seed of this thought started during the first world war, but it needed a second world war to make it grow to its strength and size of today.

Immediately after the last world war this trend of thought produced the formation of the U.N. and its Economic and Social Council, of U.N.E.S.C.O., F.A.O., W.M.O., W.H.O., and others. It has been expressed inside and outside the International Unions of Science frequently and with lucidity. Quite a number of prominent brains have been working in the same direction, independent of one another.

A host of various great names present themselves before our inner eye in this respect. The greatest scientist of our times, EINSTEIN, also belonged to the representatives of this trend of thought.

Soon these thoughts were expressed similarly by statesmen of high standing in open public discussions; still up to now we are alone each of us, even if each one represents the focal center and hope of many thousands.

There exists a number of physical laws which are applicable equally in the era of mental and spiritual trends. I am deeply convinced that we may achieve by the combined effort of strong single forces, which are all of them pulling in the same direction, a resultant multiplied force of great effect and most valuable consequence. We are only starting today to realize this for ourselves but already we are spreading and influencing a large and wide community. The time is near, when the leading statesmen – even perhaps of our own generation – will willingly get in closest contact with the representatives of this strongest creative element of mankind, as soon as these represent an organized body for this purpose. And both together they will then try to find the right ways of development for mankind and the true progress on a global scale and on scientific premises.

The first reason for building such an organization as we have in mind lies in the recognition that such a forum would constitute a very positive step forward, based on thoroughly peaceful methods. This aspect is of the utmost importance and significance for all groups of mankind and for all countries: the highly developed ones as well as the underdeveloped.

But there are quite a number of other reasons beyond this one: As by our own efforts our planet has shrunk to such small dimensions we have to draw several consequences therefrom. First of all, there must be from now on in history a somehow centralized handling of the mutual affairs of mankind as an inevitable necessity.

This is recognized and accepted already and the U.N. and her Special Agencies are the best proof of this fact. There are, however, as we know, psychological differences between races and peoples, language difficulties and economic group interests and various other obstacles still in the way of this natural development. These differences and difficulties have to be thoroughly investigated and this brings us again to the result, that it seems one of the most important things to make scientific research of these differences and obstacles.

A thorough research on the various and very different human environments, climate, vegetation, food, etc. is a necessity, how they influence the behaviour and even the way of thinking of the various populations.

Some years ago (August 1956) the first Bio-climatological Congress was convened in Paris at U.N.E.S.C.O.-House. There a new biological approach even to the geo-physical concept of climate has been accepted, and an International Committee has been set up to elaborate biological climate standards among living things, mostly plants, and this new branch of science, called ecological climatography seems to become also of decisive value for evaluating the need of man, so different in different climates.

In its widest sense all this may be named *human ecology*.

We should not forget that the peace – or war – problem is fundamentally a scientific problem and in the first line a biological problem. So, for instance, if we know the psychological difference between the big groups of mankind and also their causes, a big step forward would have been made.

If we know how to enlarge the food-potential of our earth and also the potential of all the other natural resources, another big step has been made.

But in this last example we see how complicated these problems are. The higher the standard of living, the more differentiated will be the wants of the population, and this is not only a question of production but rather more of distribution of these goods. Here again the conflicting interests of single countries manifest themselves and can only be overcome by cooperation and common planning.

However, common planning does not mean total planning because total planning is inconceivable as long as there is no complete knowledge, and such a thing does not and will never exist.

Only the uneducated individual or the semi-educated one can see the solution in total planning, or, on the other hand somebody who wants to achieve total power. One thing is sure: the final result will be coercion and terror.

It is of course quite easy to convince a public assembly of the fact that such a total planning would be the desired aim of mankind. But to try to carry this out, and necessarily by sheer force and terror, can only bring utter disaster. There against a partial planning as based on our acquired knowledge is conceivable and to be advocated.

Much is already being done in this direction. But regrettably many of these plans are still closely linked with political motives and only partly based on objective scientific considerations. Here too the lack of such a non-political extra-national, purely scientific institution, if only as an advisory council, is being felt.

This present state of affairs may be traced back to the leadership principle, evolved almost 3000 years ago and at that time truly a great achievement. This was expressed in a bulletin of the American Institute of Geonomy and Natural Resources as follows: "Our generation having made the first step into the Atomic Age, has also to make a further step in the development of leadership principles; from the prehistoric muscle-magician stage to the stage of orators and politicians, first developed in ancient Greece, now to the leadership of the best and broadest-minded brains among statesmen and scientists, and this step has to be made now, before it is too late."

What we need is an institution of the highest scientific authority held in the highest esteem by all peoples as a strictly objective advisory body for countries and peoples, and gradually growing into an influential position in all questions decisive for the future of mankind.

Only in such a forum can new principles of leadership be studied without being suspected of being in the service of any power-politics. Only in such a forum can such advice be found which may give the highest possible source of life-values for a specific generation or for certain specified regions.

I am quite optimistic in regard to the question whether we may conceivably satisfy the demands of an increasing world-population. From my own ecological knowledge I venture to prophecy that we shall be able to overcome the discrepancy between potential food production and size of population. The population-potential of the globe depends less on the increased square-miles of soil available than on the creative power of our brains.

The lack of a right balance in most countries at present is due primarily to the two world wars and secondly to the fact that farreaching measures have been taken without necessary scientific foundations.

The great efforts of U.N.E.S.C.O. and of F.A.O., for instance in India must necessarily take far longer to produce effects according to their nature in respect to increased production of food, than will many of the quicker acting measures of modern hygiene.

Japanese cultivation-methods for rice as introduced by F.A.O., have raised rice production in many Indian areas fourfold already; but it still will take years before the discrepancy between the number of the population and available quantities of foodstuffs will be eradicated.

It is the task of scientists to uncover such causes and to seek solutions of such vast problems, untouched by any suspicion of powerpolitics.

The tasks of those, however, who are meant to lead humanity into a brighter future, are far more extensive and far-reaching. They will have to foster all those matters which are apt to unite all human beings, be it a common language – to name one example of importance – a language for scientists, or be it by the means of expression which are at our disposal to an extent never before attained and much too little exploited – the film, the radio, poetry, and creative art, and last but not least the elite of the press.

As far as a common language in science is concerned, it is quite obvious and understandable that each group of the same language wants to see its own language accepted. But he who deals with this question objectively and outside of all national and political points of view must admit that every additional language which is added to the admitted language for scientific use, is liable to decrease the value of all scientific publications, and in consequence thereof, also the value of science itself.

Let us take up another example from the vast schedule of tasks which have to be dealt with by such an extra-national forum. The establishment of new branches of science is often hampered by many obstacles. Every official bureau is conservative according to its very nature. This is the case even in the most developed and advanced countries. The history of science and of technique is full of researches, inventions, discoveries, which have only been brought to light by some chance, and very often long after the death of the person responsible for the discovery or piece of research. There are many cases when a *national* forum would not be the place to offer constructive criticism or active help out of subjective causes. Very often also, the path to an international meeting is closed to a person because the expense of travelling does not allow more than a few to take part in such assemblies. Only a fighter might be able to overcome these handicaps, but only then at the cost of years or decades, or overwhelming material sacrifices. Unfortunately we find that among many serious scientists the fighting spirit is not strongly developed.

It is therefore one of the tasks of such an extra-national

Academy of Art and Science to support and foster morally such new branches of research, and to recommend their material support if they promise valuable results in a desired direction.

We should also most emphatically support the border-sciences and all work in synthesis in science, as both are of great importance today and are frequently badly treated by official authorities.

However, it will not be only a matter of supporting science as such but also its representatives – the scientists – by emphasizing the value of them and of science in general within the framework of the general organizational structure of mankind; a fact which is not yet recognized by the great majority. And the same applies to Art.

The intellectual resources of many countries are often wasted and even sometimes suppressed by too low salaries and standards of living. In many countries one is apt to forget that though a tractorist is able to raise production in comparison to the primitive ploughman, this does not therefore mean a principal difference of achievement. The really significant achievement lies in the creative thought, in the invention of the physical principles; it lies with the geologist, the metallurgist who produces the chemical premises, with the ecologist who carries out research on the need of plants and finally with the engineer who could build the tractor with the basic knowledge at hand.

As a rule one is apt to see but the last member of the chain and the other members of it remain largely anonymus.

Another important point is, that we must also find the right balance of the sciences against one another and their integration in our educational system, a problem of the utmost significance.

The biological branches of science, for instance, rate far behind those which deal with the easier accessible physical, chemical and technical problems, and this both in moral as in material renumeration.

Such a pooling center of science as a world advisory body must embrace the brightest and freest minds in all branches of science, but will have to be subdivided into different teams and working groups.

In nearly all of them the biological point of view will have to be dealt with to a much higher degree than was the case up to now.

It is one of the most crucial mistakes in the history of mankind that this has not been done with the necessary intensity up to now. The history of science itself gives us the cause of this mistake.

Since prehistoric times – many thousands of years ago – mathematics, physics, and a little later also chemistry, have been developed. Gradually we are unveiling the secrets of matter and energy. We conquer the depths of the oceans, the air, and are even beginning to conquer space outside our own planet.

But just now, with the brightest outlook before us which mankind ever had, we are faced with the possibility of destroying ourselves. Why? Because Biology, the knowledge of life in general: plants, animals, and men because of its more complicated nature, has been the stepchild of science until the last hundred years, except for the very superficial medical knowledge we had before. Until the last few decades biology was in fact confined to a descriptive science only.

Physiology is not older than about 100 years and ecology not older than 50 years. We are only now beginning to see the wonders of life a bit more clearly.

In physics we are overwhelmed, and rightly so, by the greatness of the discoveries of Atoms, their structure and movements.

But yet how simple is the movement of an atom, or of a sun system, compared with the smallest movement of our little finger. How many millions of different atoms and molecules have to be coordinated for it! What a complex of physical and chemical processes has to be completed in this short second from the time the idea creates the will in the brain cells, leads to the nerve cells and on to the muscle cells, and then stops it.

Most of the basic problems of mankind are of a biological nature: overproduction and underproduction of foodstuffs and organic rawmaterials, overpopulation and underpopulation, economic prosperity and depression, mass-apathy and mass-emotion, and finally war and peace are fundamentally biological problems. As soon as this will be understood and as soon as the leading statesmen will be willing to contemplate it on this scientific level, in cooperation with such an objective scientific Institution representing all branches of science, we shall have found the way to the highest art of living.

For the discussion of such and similar objects and for adequate recommendation we are in need of such an extranational and objective forum.

Now, as the first nucleus of the "World Academy of Art and Science" has started already with its activities, the next task will be to achieve the unshakable confidence in its scientific and ethical authority and objectivity. This may require several years and, apart of a sound and controlled financial basis, a most careful selection and way of election of members. In this task hundreds of top scientists and other personalities esteemed by the world for their high intellectual and ethical standard, further the Special Agencies of U.N.O., the International Scientific Unions and Societies, and the national Academies will be of great assistance.

The Needs will dictate the priority of the main problems. In these first years they will have to be discussed and decided upon; the working groups, as the principal Means to carry out the scientific work, will have to be organized; the financial basis will have to be secured, and the organizational structure to be brought into that balance ordained by its Goal.

May I repeat: The great and new task of this Institution lies in that it is supposed to be an extra-national, a transnational, and truly objective forum for the vitally important problems of mankind. The problems today will be less in the foreground of discussion than the problems of tomorrow; and in our opinion this future is outlined already in distinguishable contours.

We do not know yet when the political unification of mankind will become a fact, but we know with certainty that this unification is imminent in the course of the next few generations.

We do not know which way will bring this about, a peaceful or a forceful one. Independent of the possibility of a third or fourth World War it must be the task of the World Academy to lead the way to a worldwide and peaceful co-operation.

In these last few decades science has created new and unforeseen ways for the development of mankind. However, we are as yet overshadowed by the clouds of foregone millennia and our best inventions are used more for the *de*struction than for *con*struction.

It is up to us scientists to lead on the path that will make these new inventions enrich our life and that of coming generations, not destroy it.

Scientists of all parts of the world!

Let us create the scientific basis which is necessary to enable us to live and work together peacefully! Let us use all our imagination to make an art of living.

Non-Scientists and Scientists alike! Let us all help to make this forum a true "Agency for Human Welfare" irradiating hope and belief, and let us work together for a brighter future, a future truly adequate to "Homo sapiens."

Thoughts on Art and Science

by

Robert Oppenheimer

SCIENCE AND OUR TIMES

Our times have been deeply marked by science. What we think of it will shape the future. It is a great testament to man's power and his reason; it is equally a testament to their limits.

No one can have had the experience of new discovery, can have witnessed the transmutation of mystery to understanding and order and then to greater mystery, without learning both of our helplessness and our great strength. Science sustains a view of man, piteously and even comically impotent, yet with a dignity and hope quite special to him. This is the view of man of the days of the Enlightenment, and of the founding of this Republic. It seems quite in harmony with the teachings and spirit of the Stoics, with the blend of stoic tradition and Christian sensibility that characterized the emergence of the modern world. A sunny, hopeful view of science prevailed even in the early years of this century, during our childhood, though a few anxious observers had found the seeds of misgiving. Think, for instance, of Henry Adams, and his related concern for the rise of the specialist, and of the machine.

Among the founders of the United States it is natural for us to remember Franklin and Jefferson; they were both in some real sense men of science as well as statesmen. They looked to science as an essential part of this country's heritage. They saw first that in practical terms it was a strong tool against misery and poverty and squalor. They rightly understood that science would contribute to the well-being and the civility of life. They saw it in intellectual terms as a guard against ignorance and superstition. They saw it in political terms as a guard against tyranny, barbarism, repression and bigotry, that they associated with centuries past, with their religious wars, the inquisition, and what they thought of as the dark ages. For them it was incompatible only with an authoritarianism, by which, they were determined, this country should never be darkened.

The nearly two centuries that have elapsed since then have more than fulfilled the promise they saw. In the last years we have moved, through discoveries in chemistry, biochemistry, and genetics, by great steps nearer to an understanding of the origin of life, and its characteristic stability, variety, mutability, and form. We understand how, under the conditions prevailing on earth very long ago, organic materials characteristic of life would almost necessarily be formed from inorganic matter. In the coding, information bearing and information transmitting characteristics of some nucleic acids, we have a beginning of an understanding of how living matter instructs its progeny to be a mould, an elephant, a tulip, or a man. We understand stars and galaxies today better than we understood the minerals of this earth a century ago. We even understand much of the evolution and history of stars, as they brighten and darken, fade, explode, and form again from dust. We are in the midst of finding an answer to the ancient questions of the constitution of matter. In this field we are today so beset by novelty, paradox, and puzzlement that we cannot escape the sense of a vast, strange new order waiting to be discovered. For the first time, we are beginning to learn some of the subtleties of perception and of memory. We know that the very maintenance of the rational faculties – the ability, for instance, to add and to subtract – and of memory itself, requires the constant flow of unnoticed sensory stimuli.

The practical consequences of the application of science are everywhere about us; they have contributed to the largely new world in which we live. Some of these consequences are profoundly troublesome, of part of that I shall speak. Many appear today as mixed blessings: the automobile, the television tube, the antibiotics, call perhaps for somewhat greater wisdom than we have shown. But characteristically and overwhelmingly the applications of science have alleviated man's sufferings, moderated his harshest limitations, and responded to his long-sustained aspirations. We live longer, labor less brutally, more seldom suffer starvation, find frequent comfort and relief in illness, travel, communicate, and learn with undreamed of ease; and we need no slave or peon.

It is a mark of our time that these changes must spread throughout the world; the world cannot endure half-darkness and half-light. This is of course not all that we see stirring the peoples of Asia and Africa today; but surely it is a great part and a most enduring part, of the need and the reality of change. What we have learned will not easily be lost; knowledge once given will not easily be lost in world-wide darkness as long as man endures; the powers that it gives offer too much to mankind for the sciences to desist or regress. It is truc that there once were what we call the dark ages. They touched only one of the world's civilizations; the knowledge they ignored for the most part survived elsewhere and the sciences that languished had, in Greek and Hellenistic times, only the frailest of beginnings, had not begun to attain the instruments, the power, the success, the application, nor the explosively cumulative character that mark them today. In this one limited sense, man's course cannot now be retrograde; in this one sense progress is inevitable.

It is my purpose here to identify two among many of the ways in which the great growth of science has created new problems for us. Both problems seem grave to me. They do not appear to me to be very directly related, except that it is we, in our time, who must learn to live with them. One has to do with the powers that knowledge makes possible, and one with the effect of this explosive growth of knowledge on the nature of our culture. What is troublesome in the new situation may not be easy to alter. We must start by trying to understand it.

It is not new that knowledge brings power, and that among the powers may be the power to do evil. In modern science there is much such knowledge. It cannot be lost; it leads to powers the exercise of which spells disaster. The most familiar, though not the deepest example is the discovery of nuclear weapons, and the associated machinery of war. These have brought to a large part of mankind an appalling prospect of devastation and death, an apocalyptic vision of what would be terrible reality. Much has been said of the prospect that man, along with many other forms of life, might lose his genetic inheritance, would disappear as a species. In time, not a long time, that may come to be possible. What is more certain and more immediate is that we lost much of our human inheritance, much that has made our civilization and our humanity, very much of our life.

In the great strides in the biological sciences, and far more still in the early beginnings of an understanding of man's psyche, of his beliefs, the learning, his memory, and his probable action, one can see the origin of still graver problems of good and evil. Today we know very little of these matters. We have little patches of illumination and understanding, unrelated to any assured corpus of reasonably certain knowledge. If today we have technical means for better predicting man's behaviour, the improvement is at best marginal. How shall we meet with wisdom the greater and more certain knowledge of how to make people think and do? Foreshadowing of this time we see both in brainwashing, and in propaganda, that unhallowed marriage of crude psychological lore with the advanced technology of communication.

The problem of these great powers is not made easier by the autonomy of the three-score governments that make up the world, nor by the little understood and intricate dispersal of power that characterizes some of the best of them, nor by the absence of any common code of conduct or common view of men between them. The problem is not made easier by the Communist powers, by their denial of any essential community with other societies, their long tradition of hostility, and their extreme, morbid preoccupation with power. It is not made easier by the experience of vast continents, where history of European rule has induced a passion for national enhancement, and a low and bitter appraisal of the Western heritage. In any real or immediate sense, it does not appear to be a soluble problem. The threat of the apocalypse will be with us for a long time; the apocalypse may come.

We can see perhaps only the dimmest outline of a course that, in the long term, may be hopeful: the creation of honest and viable international communities with increasing common knowledge and understanding. Of all such communities, those dealing with the sciences and their applications, those in which hope and danger are most intimately mixed, seem, if the most difficult to create, the most hopeful for our future. Such were indeed the hopes entertained at the War's end by many who had worked on the atomic project. They were in large part embodied in the ACHESON-LILIENTHAL report, early in 1946, on how – in the words of that time – "cooperation might replace rivalry" in the development of atomic energy. Perhaps the world was not ripe nor ready. Perhaps we were not fully ready. Certainly the Soviet government was not ready.

Shall we find other opportunities? We may. Looking at the broad ranges of science, with all its portents of benefit and misery, I should think that the answer was "yes."

The second element of novelty that science has brought to us, like the first, is a change in scale; it is not something wholly new; and like the first, it is an inherent, necessary accompaniment of the great success of the sciences. It is not new that what has been learned in the recent past is more than was learned in all of man's earlier history. Men said that in the eighteenth century, and they were right. It continues to be true.

Positive knowledge, what is recorded in the technical books and learned journals, all of it that is new and true and not trivial, is of course not wisdom; it can on occasion almost appear incompatible with wisdom. I think that such positive knowledge doubles in less than a generation, perhaps in a decade. This means that most of what there is to know about the world of nature was not discovered when a man went to school; it means that universal knowledge, always, even in LEONARDO's day, a dream, but not an irrelevant dream, has become a mockery; it means that the specialized sciences, genetics, for instance, or astrophysics, or mathematics, are like the fingers of a hand; they all arise from the common matrix of common sense, from man's daily experience, his history, his tradition, and his words. Each is now developing a life, an experience, and a language of its own, and between the tips of the fingers there is rare contact. For many centuries mathematics and physics grew in each other's company in happy symbiosis. Today at their growing tips they hardly touch. Logic, psychology, philosophy were long studies in the same rooms, and often by the same men. Today, they rarely speak to each other, and are more rarely understood or even heard. The deep, detailed, intimate, almost loving knowledge of a specialized science is lost in synoptic views of science as a whole. These changes mean that ignorance is a universal, pervasive feature of our time. It is clear that they have an essential relevance to the problems of education.

In a free world, if it is to remain free, we must maintain, with our lives if need be, but surely by our lives, the opportunity for a man to learn anything. We need to do more: we need to cherish man's curiosity, his understanding, his love, so that he may indeed learn what is new and hard and deep. We need to do this in a world in which the changes wrought by the applications of science, and the din of communication from remote and different places, complement the unhinging, unmooring effects of the explosive growth in knowledge itself. For the un-understood rumours of change from the frontiers of physics or from psychology, can be more deeply disturbing than that what we heard in the last 15 years of China or Kenya: they lead to despair of man's reason. The rumoured uncertainties of an endless quest for knowledge make, for the bewildered, as inhuman a view of man's frailty as the rumoured magic of science makes of his triumphs.

Such a culture can hardly be architectonic in structure. The world that we study is an orderly world, and this order illuminates and organizes our understanding; but it is not an hierarchical nor an architectonic order. It has no central chamber of man's common understanding, a common repository of all essential knowledge. It has instead the structure of a vast, manifold, many-dimensional network of bonds. We deceive ourselves, if we attempt to model our culture on Athens in the fifth century (B.C.) or the thirteenth century (A.D.) in Europe.

The bonds of understanding reflect the order and define the structure of our world. The man who bears in himself more than one passion for knowledge creates such a bond. Men who, working in separate rooms of the house of science, find common understanding, create another. Occasionally between the sciences, and more rarely between a science and other parts of our experience and knowledge, there is a correspondence, an analogy, a partial mapping of two sets of ideas and words. We learn then to translate from one language into another. Ours is thus a united world, united by countless bonds. Everything can be related to anything, everything cannot be related to everything. It may perhaps then be a beginning of wisdom to learn of the virtues, of the restraint and tolerance, and of the sense of fraternity that will be asked of us, if, in this largely new world, we are to live, not in chaos, but in community.[1]

1. This contribution was originally the Address held by the author at the Roosevelt University Founders and Friends Dinner in Chicago, Ill., May 22, 1956.

PROSPECTS IN THE ARTS AND SCIENCES

The words "*prospects in the arts and sciences*" mean two quite different things to me. One is prophecy: What will the scientists discover and the painters paint, what new forms will alter music, what parts of experience will newly yield to objective description? The other meaning is that of a view: What do we see when we look at the world today and compare it with the past? I am not a prophet; and I cannot very well speak to the first subject, though in many ways I should like to. I shall try to speak to the second, because there are some features of this view which seem to me so remarkable, so new and so arresting, that it may be worth turning our eyes to them; it may even help us to create and shape the future better, though we cannot foretell it.

In the arts and in the sciences, it would be good to be a prophet. It would be a delight to know the future, I had thought for a while of my own field of physics and of those nearest to it in the natural sciences. It would not be too hard to outline the questions which natural scientists today are asking themselves and trying to answer. What, we ask in physics, is matter what is it made of, how does it behave when it is more and more violently atomized, when we try to pound out of the stuff around us the ingredients which only violence creates and makes manifest? What, the chemists ask, are those special features of nucleic acids and proteins which make life possible and give it its characteristic endurance and mutability? What subtle chemistry, what arrangements, what reactions and controls make the cells of living organisms differentiate so that they may perform functions as oddly diverse as transmitting information throughout our nervous systems or covering our heads with hair? What happens in the brain to make a record of the past, to hide it from consciousness, to make it accessible to recall? What are the physical features which make consciousness possible?

All history teaches us that these questions that we think the pressing ones, will be transmuted before they are answered, that they will be replaced by others, and that the very process of discovery will shatter the concepts that we today use to describe our puzzlement.

It is true that there are some who profess to see in matters of culture, in matters precisely of the arts and sciences, a certain macro-historical pattern, a grand system of laws which determines the course of civilization and gives a kind of inevitable quality to the unfolding of the future. They would, for instance, see the radical, formal experimentation which characterized the music of the last half-century as an inevitable consequence of the immense flowering and enrichment of natural science; they would see a necessary order in the fact that innovation in music precedes that in painting and that in turn in poetry, and point to this sequence in older cultures. They would attribute the formal experimentation of the arts to the dissolution, in an industrial and technical society, of authority, of secular, political authority, and of the catholic authority of the church. They are thus armed to predict the future. But this, I fear, is not my dish.

If a prospect is not prophecy, it is a view. What does the world of the arts and sciences look like?

There are two ways of looking at it: *the world of arts and sciences*. One is the view of the traveller, going by horse or foot, from village to village to town, staying in each to talk with those who live there and to gather something of the quality of its life. This is the intimate view, partial, somewhat accidental, limited by the limited life and strength and curiosity of the traveller, but intimate and human, in a human compass. The other is the vast view, showing the earth with its fields and towns and valleys as they appear to a camera carried in a high altitude rocket. In one sense this prospect will be more complete; one will see all branches of knowledge, one will see all the arts, one will see them as part of the vastness and complication of the whole of human life on earth. But one will miss a great deal; the beauty and warmth of human life will largely be gone from that prospect.

It is in this vast high altitude survey that one sees the general surprising quantitative features that distinguish our time. This is where the listings of science and endowments and laboratories and books published show up; this is where we learn that more people are engaged in scientific research today than ever before, that the Soviet world and the free world are running neck and neck in the training of scientists, that more books are published per capita in England than in the United States, that the social sciences are pursued actively in America, Scandinavia, and England, that there are more people who hear the great music of the past, and more music composed and more paintings painted. This is where we learn that the arts and sciences are flourishing. This great map, showing the world from afar and almost as to a stranger, would show more; it would show the immense diversity of culture and life, diversity in place and tradition for the first time clearly manifest on a world-wide scale, diversity in techniques and language, separating science from science and art from art, and all of one from all of the other. This great map, world-wide, culturewide, remote, has some odd features. There are innumerable villages. Between the villages there appear to be almost no paths discernible from this high altitude. Here and there passing near a village, sometimes through its heart, there will be a superhighway, along which windy traffic moves at enormous speed. The superhighways seem to have little connection with villages, starting anywhere, ending anywhere, and sometimes appearing almost by design to disrupt the quiet of the village. This view gives us no sense of order or of unity. To find these we must visit the villages, the quiet, busy places, the laboratories and studies and studios. We must see the paths that are barely discernible; we must understand the superhighways, and their dangers.

In the natural sciences there are and have been and are likely to continue to be heroic days. Discovery follows discovery, each both raising and answering questions, each ending a long search, and each providing the new instruments for a new search. There are radical ways of thinking unfamiliar to common sense and connected with it by decades or centuries of increasingly specialized and unfamiliar experience. There are lessons of how limited, for all its variety, the common experience of man has been with regard to natural phenomena, and hints and analogies as to how limited may be his experience with man. Every new finding is a part of the instrument kit of the sciences for further investigation and for penetrating into new fields. Discoveries of knowledge fructify technology and the practical arts, and these in turn pay back refined techniques, new possibilities of observation and experiment.

In any science there is harmony between practitioners. A man may work as an individual, learning of what his colleagues do through reading or conservation; he may be working as a member of a group on problems where technical equipment is too massive for individual effort. But whether he is a part of a team or solitary in his own study, he, as a professional, is a member of a community. His colleagues in his own branch of science will be grateful to him for the inventive or creative thoughts he has, will welcome his criticism. His world and work will be objectively communicable; and he will be quite sure that if there is error in it, that error will not long be undetected. In his own line of work he lives in a community where common understanding combines with common purpose and interest to bind men together both in freedom and in co-operation.

This experience will make him acutely aware of how limited, how inadequate, how precious is this condition of his life; for in his relations with a wider society, there will be neither the sense of community nor of objective understanding. He will sometimes find, in returning to practical undertakings, some sense of community with men who are not expert in his sciences, with other scientists whose work is remote from his, and with men of action and men of art. The frontiers of sciences are separated now by long years of study, by specialized vocabularies, arts, techniques, and knowledge from the common heritage even of a most civilized society; and anyone working at the frontier of such science is in that sense a very long way from home, a long way too from the practical arts that were its matrix and origin, as indeed they were of what we today call art.

The specialization of science is an inevitable accompaniment of progress; yet is it full of dangers, and it is cruelly wasteful, since so much, that is beautiful and enlightening is cut off from most of the world. Thus it is proper to the role of the scientist that he not merely find new truth and communicate it to his fellows, but that he teach, that he try to bring the most honest and intelligible account of new knowledge to all who will try to learn. This is one reason – it is the decisive organic reason – why scientists belong in universities. It is one reason why the patronage of science by and through universities is its most proper form; for it is here, in teaching, in the association of scholars, and in the friendships of teachers and taught, of men who by profession must themselves be both teachers and taught, that the narrowness of scientific life can best be moderated, and that the analogies, insights, and harmonies of scientific discovery can find their way into the wider life of man.

In the situation of the artist today there are both analogies to and differences from that of the scientist; but it is the differences which are the most striking, and which raise the problems that touch most on the evil of our day. For the artist it is not enough that he communicate with others who are expert in his own art. Their fellowship, their understanding, and their appreciation may encourage him; but that is not the end of his work, not its nature. The artist depends on a common sensibility and culture, on a common meaning of symbols, on a community of experience and common ways of describing and interpreting it. He need not write for everyone or paint or play for everyone. But his audience must be man; it must be man, and not a specialized set of experts among his fellows. Today, that is very difficult. Often the artist has an aching sense of great loneliness, for the community to which he addresses himself is largely not there; the traditions and the culture, the symbols and the history, the myths and the common experience, which it is his function to illuminate, to harmonize, and to portray, have been dissolved in a changing world.

There is, it is true, an artificial audience maintained to moderate between the artist and the world for which he works: the audience of the professional critics, popularizers, and advertisers of art. But though, as does the popularizer and promoter of science, the critic fulfills a necessary present function and introduces some order and some communication between the artist and the world, he cannot add to the intimacy and the directness and the depth with which the artist addresses his fellow men.

To the artist's loneliness there is a complementary great and terrible barrenness in the lives of men. They are deprived of the illumination, the light and tenderness and insight of an intelligible interpretation, in contemporary terms, of the sorrows and wonders and gaieties and follies of man's life. This may be in part offset, and is, by the great growth of technical means for making the art of the past available. But these provide a record of past intimacies between art and life; even when they are applied to the writing and painting and composing of the day, they do not bridge the gulf between a society, too vast and too disordered, and the artist trying to give meaning and beauty to its parts.

In an important sense this world of ours is a new world, in which the unity of knowledge, the nature of human communities, the order of society, the order of ideas, the very notions of society and culture have changed and will not return to what they have been in the past. What is new is new not because it has never been there before, but because it has changed in quality. One thing that is new is the prevalence of newness, the changing scale and scope of change itself, so that the world alters as we walk in it, so that the years of man's life measure not some small growth or rearrangement or moderation of what he learned in childhood, but a great upheaval. What is new is that in one generation our knowledge of the natural world engulfs, upsets, and complements all knowledge of the natural world before. The techniques, among which and by which we live, multiply and ramify, so that the whole world is bound together by communication, blocked here and there by the immense synopses of political tyranny. The global quality of the world is new: our knowledge of and sympathy with remote and diverse peoples, our involvement with them in practical terms, and our commitment to them in terms of brotherhood. What is new in the world is the massive character of the dissolution and corruption of authority, in belief, in ritual, and in temporal order. Yet this is the world that we have come to live in. The very difficulties which it presents derive from growth in understanding, in skill, in power. To assail the changes that have unmoored us from the past is futile, and in a deep sense, I think, it is wicked. We need to recognize the change and learn what resources we have.

Again I will turn to the schools and, as their end and as

their center, the universities. For the problem of the scientist is in this respect not different from that of the artist or of the historian. He needs to be a part of the community, and the community can only with loss and peril be without him. Thus it is with a sense of interest and hope that we see a growing recognition that the creative artist is a proper charge on the university, and the university a proper home for him; that a composer or a poet or a playwright or painter needs the toleration, understanding, the rather local and parochial patronage that a university can give; and that this will protect him from the tyranny of man's communication and professional promotion. For here there is an honest chance that what the artist has of insight and of beauty will take root in the community, and that some intimacy and some human bonds can mark his relations with his patrons. For a university rightly and inherently is a place where the individual man can form new syntheses, where the accidents of friendship and association can open a man's eyes to a part of science or art which he had not known before, where parts of human life, remote and perhaps superficially incompatible, can find in men their harmony and their synthesis.

These then, in rough and far too general words, are some of the things we see as we walk through the villages of the arts and of the sciences and notice how thin are the paths that lead from one to another, and how little in terms of human understanding and pleasure the work of the villages comes to be shared outside.

The superhighways do not help. They are the mass media – from the loudspeakers in the deserts of Asia Minor and the cities of Communist China to the organized professional theatre of Broadway. They are the purveyors of art and science and culture for the millions upon millions – the promoters who represent the arts and sciences to humanity and who represent humanity to the arts and sciences; they are the means by which we are reminded of the famine in remote places or of war or trouble or change; they are the means by which this great earth and its peoples have become one to one another, the means by which news of discovery or honor and the stories and songs of today travel and resound throughout the world. But they are also the means by which the true human community, the man knowing man, the neighbor understanding neighbor, the school boy learning a poem, the women dancing, the individual curiosity, the individual sense of beauty are being blown dry and issueless, the means by which the passivity of the disengaged spectator presents to the man of art and science the bleak face of inhumanity.

For the truth is that this is indeed, inevitably and increasingly, an open and, inevitably and increasingly, an eclectic world. We know too much for one man to know much, we live too variously to live as one. Our histories and traditions – the very means of interpreting life – are both bonds and barriers among us. Our knowledge separates as well as it unites; our order disintegrates as well as binds; our art brings us together and sets us apart. The artist's loneliness, the scholar despairing, because no one will any longer trouble to learn what he can teach, the narrowness of the scientist – these are not unnatural insignia in this great time of change.

For what is asked of us is not easy. The openness of this world derives its character from the irreversibility of learning; what is once learned is part of human life. We cannot close our minds to discovery, we cannot stop our ears so that the voices of far-off and strange people can no longer reach them. The great cultures of the East cannot be walled off from ours by impassable seas and defects of understanding based on ignorance and unfamiliarity. Neither our integrity as men of learning nor our humanity allows that. In this open world, what is there any man may try to learn.

This is no new problem. There has always been more to know than one man could know; there have always been modes of feeling that could not move the same heart; there have always been deeply held beliefs, that could not be composed into a synthetic union. Yet never before today has the diversity, the complexity, the richness so clearly defied hierarchical order and simplification. Never before have we had to understand the complementary, mutually not compatible ways of life and recognize choice between them as the only course of freedom. Never before today has the integrity of the intimate, the detailed, the true art, the integrity of craftsmanship and preservation of the familiar, of the humourous and the beautiful stood in more massive contrast to the vastness of life, the greatness of the globe, the otherness of ways and the all-encompassing dark.

This is a world in which each of us, knowing his limitations, knowing the evils of superficiality and the terrors of fatigue, will have to cling to what is close to him, to what he knows, to what he can do, to his friends and his tradition and his love, lest he will be dissolved in a universal confusion and know nothing and love nothing. It is at the same time a world in which none of us can find hieratic prescription or general sanction for any ignorance, any insensitivity, any indifference. When a friend tells us of a new discovery we may not understand, we may not be able to listen without jeopardizing the work that is ours and closer to us; but we cannot find in a book or canon – and we should not seek – grounds for hallowing our ignorance. If a man tells us that he sees differently than we or that he finds beautiful what we find ugly, we may have to leave the room, from fatigue or trouble; but that is our weakness and our default. If we must live with a perpetual sense that the world and the men in it are greater than we and too much for us, let it be the measure of our virtue that we know this and seek no comfort. Above all let us not proclaim that the limits of our powers correspond to some special wisdom in our choice of life, of learning, or of beauty.

This balance, this perpetual, precarious impossible balance between the infinitely open and the intimate, this time – our twentieth century – has been long in coming; but is has come. It is, I think, for us and our children our only way.

This is for all men. For the artist and for the scientist there is a special problem and a special hope, for in their extraordinarily different ways, in their lives that have increasingly divergent character, there is still a sensed bond, a sensed analogy. Both the man of science and the man of art live always at the edge of mystery, surrounded by it, both always, as the measure of their creation, have had to do with harmonization of what is new with what is familiar, with the balance between novelty and synthesis, with the struggle to make partial order in total chaos. They can, in their work and in their lives, help themselves, help one another, and help all men. They can make the paths that connect the villages of arts and sciences with each other and with the world at large the multiple, varied, precious bonds of a true and world-wide community.

This cannot be an easy life. We shall have a rugged time of it to keep our minds open and to keep them deep, to keep our sense of beauty and our ability to make it, and our occasional ability to see it in places remote and strange and in our villages, in keeping open the manifold, intricate, casual paths, to keep these flourishing in a great open, windy world; but this, as I see it, is the condition of men; and in this condition we can help, because we can love, one another.[1]

1. This essay was originally the author's concluding Address in the Columbia University Bicentennial Broadcast, December 26, 1954.

Science and our Future

by

W. F. G. Swann

In the past, the life of nearly all mankind was spent in a struggle for existence. Mother Earth demanded much tribute in the form of labour as payment for the fruits which she yielded. Labour was the necessary payment of man to nature for his existence, and in turn, the potentiality of man for giving labour represented a natural element of his wealth and so a guarantee for his existence. From the dawn of history almost until the present day he lived by what the earth gave him spontaneously, and in the sweat of his brow he toiled from morn to night to collect the gift; for the gift was made in meager amount and he sought no means to expedite it. Such ingenuity as he possessed was engaged in segregating to himself as much of the gift as he could at the expense of the greater majority of his fellows who, since there was not plenty for everyone, must spend all strength in the struggle for mere existence, with little of what we call happiness, and with little apparent reason for the labour other than the perpetuation of a monotonous existence from one generation to another. What little there was in the way of scientific discovery was housed in large part in the dens of the charlatans and sought close companionship in the black arts.

And then, barely more than a century ago, a new page in the drama of history opened. The power of steam was harnessed and the time and burden of travel shrank. Soon came the era of electricity, an era in which each successive discovery added further to the comfort of mankind. More and more of the world's work was done by the forces of inanimate things rather than by the toil of the arm and hand. The seeker after truth had tasted the blood of conquest and was encouraged to enter new domains. Science spread its wings over all nature, and the search for new things was no longer a dubious occupation, a companion to witchcraft, but a legitimate and recognized ambition of the curiosity of man. As if in reward for such recognition of pure idealistic research, it turned out that investigations, started with no immediate utilitarian purpose, and without the hint of a promise of future service to mankind, yielded, in actuality, fruits in such service far beyond the wildest dreams of the investigator.

Today, we stand heirs to all this wealth of nature's resources. The labourer of today has at his disposal conveniences which no king possessed a hundred years ago. I think it would be safe to say that if King Solomon could suddenly have had installed in his house an oil furnace, a cooling system, electric light, and a telephone with the other end at the residence of the Queen of Sheba – if he could have gone careering through the streets of Jerusalem at fifty miles an hour in an automobile – he would probably have been renowned in his time for possessions to an extent far beyond even the renown recorded to his credit in Holy Writ. Today, even the humblest artisan is possessed of conveniences which, seemingly, would have outshone all the luxuries of the world of ancient times. Yet, he who possesses these things today is often an unhappy and disgruntled person, with a grievance against something or somebody as his main source of mental exhilaration.

And if in the midst of all this potentiality for happiness man is still unhappy, what is the reason for his state. What does he seek for his goal of happiness and why can he not attain it? Man is an active animal. Through the thousands of years of his history he has become accustomed to count the gains of his labour, and the gains have, for the most part, consisted in the past of accumulation of the means of existence to succour him when he could no longer labour, or better still, a means of existence without the necessity of the enforced labour of the slave. Now, as more and more of the world's work is being done by machines, we are reaching a stage in which not only is the amount of toil necessary for existence reduced, but in which the perpetuation of toil, with the greatly enhanced efficiency which the machine age has brought to it, has produced a new realm of strife, a strife between the machines, whereby the equilibrium of life becomes upset to a degree in which the little that man needs for his existence fails to reach its proper goal of distribution on account of the turmoil of activity created by the operations of inanimate things.

In the last analysis of the trend towards perpetual increase of so-called utilitarian activity beyond a certain limit, my mind turns to the thought of some great Mogul who, having gained control of the running of the affairs of the world, looks down upon our civilization and, whipping up the speed of things, while egged on by the increasing efficiency of the appliances which man has designed, comes to the conclusion that in comparison with these appliances man himself is a very inefficient animal and ought to be abolished. If I ask this Mogul what the purpose of this marvellous organization would be without man in it, I can imagine from him no reply other than one to the effect that it constitutes a beautiful, smooth-running machine which, like a picture or a symphony, is an end in itself, and that he likes to see it run. But, with man gone, there is nobody but the Mogul to enjoy it. To the fundamentally and fatalistically morbid I present this Mogul as, in all verity, a deity guaranteed to keep them lusciously miserable for the lifetime remaining to them. Under another chapter I might signify the aim of this being in the title "The Devil in Control."

If I plead with this devil to let man live, I surmise that he may object on the grounds that man may tamper with the machinery which is now in perfect running order. Here I have some sympathy with this devil. And so I make a bargain with him to the effect that man may be allowed to live provided that he will guarantee never to do anything which, in the sense of the old meaning of things, can be called useful. Man shall not be deprived of the inspiration of continuing his researches in science. He shall be allowed to continue the enrichment of the arts. He shall be kept as a kind of domestic pet of this devil, with no duties other than those concerned with amusing himself.

And so I suggest to this devil that since man has, as it were, worked himself out of a job, so that his potentiality for labour no longer guarantees his right to exist, he be pensioned off, and allowed to pursue the rest of his existence in play, confining what were formerly his utilitarian efforts to oiling the machinery.

Now, of course, I do not wish to imply that we have yet reached the stage at which the ideal I have cited is a practical one. And yet I do envisage this ideal as a limiting one to which the machine age should naturally tend. It is what the mathematician would call an "asymptotic ideal"; something which is continually approached but never actually realized. The point which I wish to emphasize, however, is that even today it may be true that many of the troubles of our economic existence lie in failure to recognize the trend toward this ideal and the necessity of a continual sensitivity to it. In the attainment of such an ideal, wealth no longer has meaning for the aims for which it exists are already attained.

However, if I take to mankind this treaty in which this devil-like potentate has acquiesced, I surmise that there will be many who will be unhappy in the thought that their future activities will lie outside of the realm of that which they have been accustomed to regard as useful. In an attempt to appraise the ultimate value of things, perhaps I may be pardoned for citing here an illustration which I have given elsewhere concerning a supposed conversation between a pure utilitarianist and an artist of the "art for art's sake" type. The conversation concerns the pictures which Michelangelo painted in the Vatican.

"Of what use are those pictures?" asks the utilitarianist. "They do nobody any good and only wasted the time of Michelangelo, who painted them."

"And what kind of creative work would you regard as of use?" asks the artist.

"Well, the development of the steam engine or the automobile," says the utilitarianist.

"But why are these of use?" asks the artist.

"Because they enable one to move about faster and get more done," says the utilitarianist.

"But why move about faster and get more done?"

"Because by doing so you create wealth for yourself and others; you save time and are enabled to enjoy more leisure," is the rejoinder.

"And what is the use of money and leisure?" asks the artist. "Is it not rather boresome to have nothing to do?"

"Oh, it is not necessary to do nothing," is the reply. "You can travel and enlarge your mind."

"But," says the artist, "what is the good of travelling? You only get seasick and very tired."

"Oh," replies the utilitarianist, "it is a wonderful experience to travel. You can go, for instance, to the Old World and visit all those places of classic renown: Paris, Venice, London."

"But," says the artist, "is that not very disturbing? I hear that many of these places are unsanitary. The food is not what you are accustomed to, and sometimes the people are not overfriendly."

"Those are but small matters," says the utilitarianist, "they are far outweighed by all of the other riches you fall heir to. You can bask in the exhilarating sun of the Alps. You can drink in the beauties of the Mediterranean. You can visit ancient Rome; and by the way, when you are there, do not fail to see those marvellous pictures which Michelangelo has painted in the Vatican."

And so I have wondered if we should be far from the truth if we should maintain the thesis that the only ultimate excuse for the existence of the things utilitarian is that they provide the means whereby we may enjoy the things non-utilitarian.

And so in the life of mankind one recognizes two types of activities, types which may crudely be described as utilitarian and those which are non-utilitarian. In the ages which have passed there has been, for the most part, no danger of saturation as regards the former. Nature claimed all the effort that man could give as the price of his existence, and the second category of effort – the non-utilitarian – was reserved for the favoured few who, by the chances of fate, had managed to acquire an exceptionally large proportion of the fruits of the labours of their fellows. As the discoveries of science have revolutionized the plans of the world's work, we have reached the stage in which the very continued effort of man in the utilitarian field can bring about lack of equilibrium of such a kind that the residue available for the individual needs, either through faulty distribution or a lack of appropriate planning, is less than it would have been if the world had been less active and if man had worked less hard. A condition, however, in which people are idle because, if they worked more, they would upset the equilibrium, is not a healthy one for the race. He who is forced to work that he may survive feels a grievance against nature, but he who is condemned to inaction lest his efforts cause trouble has an even greater grievance.

The solution of the difficulty is, I think, to be found in a proper organization of utilitarian effort to the maximum degree of efficiency in such manner that the amount of it is just sufficient and no more than sufficient for the needs of healthy existence. We must then turn the spare time of man into a non-saturable domain, a domain in which the effort of one section does not render abortive the effort of another.

We must, in fact, turn this surplus effort into the non-utilitarian field. If, in the utilitarian domain, I improve my organization in the sense that I can create a product with less and less of the utilization of manual effort, I may do somebody harm unless the increase of my efficiency is accompanied by a corresponding economic adjustment. If, however, in my spare time I play the violin and I continue to improve, it does not follow from my improvement that my neighbour, who plays the piano, will deteriorate in his performance.

In the past, we have been too accustomed to assume that support of science is justified only because of the utilitarian advantages to be expected of it. Today we are approaching the other extreme, where man is invited to keep his hands off the machinery; but if this extreme is to be accompanied by lack of provision of the means for the continuation of effort which is not accompanied by utilitarian ends, then there is much to be said for the decree of that devil to whom I introduced you earlier and who sought the complete abolition of man as an inefficient parasite upon the workings of the universe. In the old days the cry of "art for art's sake" or "science for the sake of science" was supposedly the cry of the fanatic. In the future this cry, or the cry of "something for something's sake," will be the cry of all mankind as a reason for his existence, and as an end in itself. For if, relieved of effort directed towards utilitarian ends, man becomes ashamed to do anything because of a suspicion as to its lack of usefulness, then he becomes, in all verity, the most collosal bore in the universe, and my good devil will do well to abolish him.

In the last analysis, is not happiness, in the broadest sense, the goal of mankind? It is the promised land to which science has brought us and which the future invites us to cultivate.

One trouble concerned with our existing civilization lies in the fact that we have invented so many things for our enjoyment and entertainment, and we have invented so many labour-saving devices, that the mere operation of all these devices seems to leave less time than was available to a person 150 years ago to enjoy in life the things which really give permanent enjoyment. It is a wonderful thing to listen to the radio the first time we hear it. After a time it becomes a habit, so that the machine is left to exercise its noise-making potentialities when nobody is present in the room.

All of these devices give, for the most part, only superficial pleasure and by that very token give a pleasure which soon wears out and leaves the subject with a feeling of discontent. I would suggest that lasting pleasure is only obtained when the mind is active, or when there is consciousness of development of some kind in the subject.

Earlier in these lines I have lamented the fact that man, the inheritor of wealth beyond the dreams of the kings of olden times, is often an unhappy individual, and often he is unhappy when his state is such that he is among the favoured group whom the economic battles of our times have left unscathed. Happiness itself is a strange thing. I do not believe that it is determined by the status quo of the individual, no matter how high the level of that status quo. It is determined rather by the progress of the individual from one state to another. He who, while playing the violin in the capacity of an amateur, has succeeded by his effort in surmounting some difficulty which had previously baffled him, is happier at the moment as a violinist than is Kreisler, for in this, as in all things, there is more happiness in the consciousness of improvement than in the finality of attainment. Never will there be an age in which a being of the state of development of man can expect happiness except as the result of progress through effort expended on something; and those who expect happiness from idleness in the status quo I commend to the company of their spiritual relative, the cat, whose maximum of contentment seems to be reached in a state only sufficiently different from that of slumber to admit recognition of the outside world by the maintenance of a purring sound.

The Means

(a few examples by a few scientists)

The Prospects of Genetic Progress[1]

by

HERMANN J. MULLER

Our present generation has been brought to realize more vividly than any previous one the paltry dimensions of our earth and everything upon it, in comparison with the awesome reaches of the universe at large. To many persons this perspective has seemed a forbidding one, as though a great pall had arisen to overshadow and belittle the cherished world of familiar things that our forefathers hav taught us to believe in.

However, these pessimists have failed to take sufficiently into their view one all-important aspect of the picture, that serves to illuminate and transfigure it. This lies in the conclusion, supported by many modern studies, that the natural processes of genetics have in the course of ages enabled primitive organic matter gradually to struggle upward and blossom out into the wondrous forms of us human beings and all the other living things around us. Equally significant, moreover, is the proposition, following as a corollary to the one just stated, that we humans – and we alone among all earthly creatures – have through these processes of genetic change gained the capacity rapidly to add a mighty cultural evolution on top of the stupendous biological endowment that we are heir to.

1. This essay, originally written for this book, was published earlier in "The American Scientist", Vol. 47, 551–561, in 1959, since publication of this book required longer time than was expected. It is reprinted here with kind permission of the Editor.

In terms of geological time, that is, of the time necessary for appreciable natural evolution of a genetic kind, this cultural evolution is only just beginning. Yet in this biological moment we have risen from the mastery of fire to the governance of the atom, and from expletives through speech to electronic computors. At the same time, our cultural progress has become increasingly self-enhancing. Moreover, in addition to promoting its own operations it has even reached back into the course of biological evolution itself. That is, it has acted upon the genetic processes of other organisms so as eventually to reshape these organisms drastically in adaptation to human needs.

EMPIRICALLY CONTROLLED BREEDING

True, the biological reshaping of earlier times was for the most part accomplished by means of a crude empiricism, ignorant of genetic principles, and acting one small step at a time without any realization of the magnitude of the accumulated series of steps. Yet, even so, the changes brought about within this period, most of them in less than 10,000 years, have proved to be far greater than any known to have taken place in natural evolution in an equal interval. Moreover, they have been so extraordinarily serviceable as to result in profound reorientations in the ways of life of the human groups involved.

Thus, the primitive hunting economy was raised to a much higher level not only by the development of weapons but perhaps equally by the making over of the nature of dogs so as to lead them to complement human efforts more effectively. Next, the success of an agricultural existence was enormously augmented by the remolding of primitive grains, tubers, beans, cucurbits, fiber-bearing plants, and so on, into those numerous high-yielding cultivated types that we today classify as species in their own right. And the genetic reconstruction of poultry, sheep, cattle, swine, horses, the camel family, and even carps, bees, and silkworms, has made possible further great advances, both quantitative and qualitative, in human living. In fact, cultures are often most aptly distinguished in terms of the type of remodelled organism, such as maize, wheat, rice, sheep, etc., upon which the livelihood of their peoples, their standards of living, and the size of their populations, chiefly depend.

It is evident that, if these revolutionary changes could have been wrought by such crude methods and with so little awareness of routes and goals, even though at the cost of centuries of effort, it should now be possible, with our understanding of the principles of genetic mutation, combination, and selection, to telescope into a relatively few years much more comprehensive transformations. Recent successes with the development of hybrid corn and poultry and of disease-resistant strains of many crops, give a substantial foretaste of such possibilities. These have already reduced greatly the acreage of cultivation that is necessary to support a given population. Yet in this field of conscious genetic engineering we have so far only scratched the surface.

THE METHODS NOW AVAILABLE

As the great VAVILOV demonstrated, the centers of origin of cultivated species constitute vast reservoirs of genes already selected by both nature and man for very diverse conditions and purposes. The rational exploitation of these reservoirs requires the reestablishment, in assorted situations, of copious genetic "banks" of multitudinous strains and substrains, like those VAVILOV founded but on a still more extensive scale. The potentialities of the types thus made available must then be tested out under varied conditions of climate and cultivation, both in their present forms and in many of the innumerable combinations obtainable by intercrossing and selection. This is an enormous, global task, that calls for widespread cooperation of international scope.

It should be recognized from the start that this kind of work is long-term and ever-continuing. It seldom yields the quick and easy results falsely promised by the devotees of the naive doctrine of inheritance of acquired characters, who after gaining power allowed much of the fruit of the work of geneticists to be lost. As in the far more protracted experiments of nature, although in lesser degree, the great majority of the genetic trials can give only negative results. Nevertheless, the relatively few successes can open up permanent and expanding opportunities. They thereby yield immeasurable recompense in return for the expenditures.

While this work of making the most of what is already to be had is going on, there is also much to be gained by seeking out the individual variations that are continually arising within the strains presently in use, by testing them out and incorporating those that prove useful into ever more serviceable combinations. Beyond this, there is the actual induction of new mutations by means of radiation and chemical mutagens.

In considering the induction of mutations, it should be borne in mind that the great majority (ordinarily, well over 99%) of induced mutations, as of spontaneous ones, are of a detrimental kind, but that mutations which have already existed in a population for a long time represent a more or less selected residue from which the detrimental types have tended, in proportion to their degree of detriment and the time elapsed, to be eliminated. Moreover, it would be unrealistic to bank on the dim and distant hope, unsupported by critical analysis of the situation, that it may, even if some centuries hence, be found possible to induce mutations of diverse desired types at will by specific treatments. We must, for practical purposes, therefore assume that among induced mutations an even smaller proportion will usually prove useful than among mutations already present in populations. This being the case, the profitability of inducing mutations, in comparison with that of discovering suitable spontaneous ones, varies directly with the expendability of the individual organisms of the given species, with the ease of breeding them, with the difficulty of culling already existing populations for mutations contained in them, and with the difficulty of transferring specified genes from their stock of origin into the strain in which it is desired to have them. By all these criteria smaller organisms, and more especially microorganisms, constitute the material in which the induction of mutations can most advantageously be practiced.

OBJECTIVES TO BE AIMED AT

The job of remodelling the genetic constitution of organisms is a never ending one as needs and conditions change and as the innovations in the organisms themselves open new routes to their progress. So, for example, the use of more effective insecticides, fungicides, and fertilizers allows more of the metabolic effort of the plant to be concentrated upon growth itself. Similarly, artificial aids and protection allow an increasing fraction of that growth to be concentrated in that portion – whether it be seed, fiber, tuber, fruit or sap – which in the given organism is of special use to man. Thus, as our non-genetic techniques of raising and tending our organisms evolve, correlative genetic changes become not superfluous but advantageous. It therefore seems likely, in view both of our own inventiveness and of the almost unlimited genetic plasticity of organisms, that as their artificially directed evolution continues they will depart ever further from their present norms until they become quite unrecognizable, even as happened in their natural evolution but inordinately faster.

When such work becomes more advanced, it should become feasible to make blue prints for an ever larger number of generations ahead, just as in some of the fruit fly experiments of as long as two decades ago designs for genetic synthesis covering more than forty successive generations of precisely ordered crossings were successfully carried through. At present, however, we are in the stage of little more than feeling our way along in the improvement of types of economic importance and it would be rash to predict what only 10 years might hold in store for such work on annual forms.

It should also be remembered that, although primitive man brought so many species under cultivation and must have tried out far more than those that he finally succeeded with, we with our longer-range breeding methods and our more analytical techniques for testing and utilizing organisms may find many still wild species to be promising candidates for conversion into cultivated forms. Some of these will be useful for the food, drugs or industrial products they can yield. Others will be valuable for services of a less direct kind, such as promoting the fertility of the soil, preventing erosion or drought, facilitating the turnover of materials for the organisms of more direct importance, combatting pests and parasites, and, in general, assisting in the maintenance of ecological conditions favorable for the immediately useful types or (as in the case of shade trees) favorable for man himself. Here a rational union of the ecological and genetic attacks appears to present rich possibilities. Such developments call for the pooling of much detailed familiarity with local types, conditions, and problems along with knowledge of general principles and advanced techniques. In this field it is evident that the most effective efforts involve international collaboration.

Among the most promising of the organisms for future exploitation by man with the aid of genetics are those of microscopic dimensions. Yeasts and bacteria have been unwittingly employed by man for many thousands of years but only recently have these and other microorganisms been knowingly cultivated and improved upon. The five or more fold stepping up of the yield of penicillin by the judicious application of radiation to the mold *Penicillium* for the induction of successive mutations having this effect is a case in point. Not only laboratory, factory, and hydroponically bred organisms but also those bred at large, in soils, in fresh water situations and even in marine waters, present opportunities here, for the production of food, food accessories and drugs, and industrially useful materials, such as oils.

In this connection, nearly everyone nowadays has heard of the experiments with green algae, notably *Chlorella*, which seem to afford the possibility of supplying many times the yield of food per acre that higher plants, with their excess of inedible structural material, can offer us. It is not so generally known, that, as Dean Burk has recently shown, a special "thermal" strain of *Chlorella*, adapted to growth at relatively high temperatures, gives several times the yield that ordinary *Chlorella* is capable of. With the application of genetic methods to such organisms they could be molded to fit our requirements still better under the special artificially contrived conditions that we could make available to them, and diverse strains could be adapted for different purposes and for different situations. By such means wide stretches of our planet now unproductive may be increasingly subjugated to supply human needs.

Some advocates of the chemical approach might interrupt at this point to say that long before any such union of genetics, ecology, industry and food processing as is here in question has come about, photosynthetic and chemosynthetic reactions will have been mastered in the laboratory, and put into mass operation, that will free men from their dependence on living organisms. This may well be true. Certainly, our present means of transportation and haulage by inanimate machines is already for most purposes superior to that by draft animals. Similarly, in the making of special organic substances, such as many drugs, hormones, and antibiotics, that form but a small part of the organisms containing them or that have evolved relatively recently in special groups of organisms, it is likely that organic chemistry, by the conversion of lesss pecialized organic compounds, will soon prove more effective for us than biosynthesis and extraction.

However, the production of foodstuffs in general from inorganic materials involves an incomparably more intricate series of operations than has either transportation or the production of a given end-product by the conversion of organic precursors. For aeons natural selection has been working to increase the efficiency of organisms in carrying out this great series of syntheses. As a part of this work they manufacture, maintain and multiply their own superb organizations, in endless cycles, and only a minimum of tending on our part is needed, as compared with the services required of us for the replacement and repair of wholly artificial mechanisms. It therefore seems unlikely that men will in the "foreseeable future," that is, for some hundreds of years to come, at least, be able to surpass in large scale operations the potential efficiency of biological growth. At any rate, we must for a long time to come be prepared to exploit all available possibilities for supplying our material needs. In doing so we shall find that the world of living things, judiciously dealt with by a combination of genetic methods and artificial appliances, offers us enormous opportunities of the kind we are seeking.

GENETIC CHANGE IN EARLY MAN

It would be a strange incongruity if mankind instituted extensive alterations in the genetic constitution of his companion organisms in the interests of an ampler and better life for himself, while leaving his own biological basis entirely to the mercy of natural forces or of whatever genetic currents his present artificial ways of living unintentionally subjected him to. Surely his paramount obligation, as regards applications of genetics, is to himself; not however under the delusion that he is already perfect in any respect but in the knowledge that he too has plenty of room for further progress. However, before undertaking to move forward consciously it is necessary for him to realize what direction was taken by his genetic evolution in the past, what factors decided that direction, and to what extent his present situation may have entailed changes in the direction or in the factors. It is also imperative for him to reach a solid conclusion concerning what direction he should consider "forward."

Studies of the remains of early men have made it increasingly evident that their most distinctive characteristic, that which enabled them so far to outdistance all other animals, was their capacity for cultural evolution. This is a complex capacity, requiring not only a modicum of intelligence (not necessarily much higher at its inception than that possessed by present apes) but also a social disposition that takes delight in cooperating and communicating. Important accessories were manipulating proclivities, that led to the use of fire, tools, etc., and vocalizing and symbolizing proclivities, that facilitated communication.

We need not here attempt to trace the development in apes of the preparatory stages of these faculties. Nor can we detail how men's transition to an erect ground-dwelling life, surrounded by both predators and potential victims, was conducive to an intensification of both defensive and aggressive group behavior, mediated by their hands, and thus forced human beings to act increasingly in concert both to protect themselves and to overcome their prey. This situation resulted in a natural selection that put a premium on intelligence both of the manual, thing-conscious type and of the type involving understanding of and communication with other persons. This selection favored at the same time the innate drives that led to the exercise of these faculties, and the disposition that derived satisfaction from exercising them in the service of others of the immediate group.

As these selective pressures resulted in the multiplication of the mutant genes that happened to be conducive to intelligence and cooperative behavior an ever better genetic groundwork was laid for the acquirement, dissemination, handing down, and consequent accummulation of the lessons learned through the experience of many men in many generations, and of the innovations in techniques and mores based upon these lessons: in other words, for cultural evolution. Reciprocally, as cultural evolution developed, the conditions must for a long time have undergone an intensification that favored the survival of the individuals and groups who were more intelligent, more skillful, more cooperative, and better at communication. That is, genetic evolution and cultural evolution must have reenforced one another in a kind of zig-zagging fashion. Thereby, along with the progress of techniques and mores, the genetic bases of intelligence, of the communicative propensities, and of the social impulses generally, became rapidly enhanced, so as to give that appearance of a discontinuity in evolution which is so striking a feature of man's emergence.

The genetic bases even of some features of men's physical structure became changed by natural selection as a result of the new conditions resulting from their social evolution. For example, the socially evolved use of weapons in hunting and fighting, and of fire, knives, scrapers and pounders in the preparation of food, replaced the earlier natural selection for powerful jaws and teeth with conditions that allowed and probably even favored their reduction. And the adoption of clothing and other artificial protection from cold and rain allowed the advantages of relative hairlessness (greater opportunity for cleanliness and for eradication of ectoparasites) to take precedence, in selection, over the advantages of a native coat of hair. Again, when men's advancing cultures made it possible for them to live in colder climates, a number of other bodily and physiological changes were favored by the types of natural selection thereupon ensuing. Thus, in varied ways men's present genetically determined constitution bears the unconscious imprint of the artificial ways of life that he himself developed.

GENETIC PROCESSES IN MODERN MAN

With the further progress of culture, however, along the lines laid down by men's advancing techniques and group coordination in coping with their inanimate, human, and other biological environment, the conditions governing the natural selection of genetic traits among men have changed greatly. With the growth and the progressive merging of social groups and the concomitant reduction in the numbers of groups, there has been an inevitable reduction in the efficacy of that *inter*-group selection which, by favoring the more cooperative and more skillful groups had tended to enhance genetically based social traits as well as intelligence. At the same time, the heightened efficacy of *intra*-group cooperation has lessened the competition for survival and reproduction among individuals and among families of the same group. Those who through physical, intellectual or character defects are less well able to fend for themselves or to raise a family are increasingly supported by means of social aids to a degree that may even allow them, if they will, to leave more children than the others. Inevitably, then, the increases of the last several centuries in the size of human populations and in men's successes in their contests with outer nature must have been accompanied by a slackening of their genetic advancement and perhaps even by a genetic decline in some important respects.

The advanced technologies of the present day and the greater efficiency of social organization in ministering to need must be having the effect of making these anti-evolutionary tendencies much stronger. Genetic studies make it very probable that in technically advanced countries far more mutations, the great majority of them detrimental to health, mentality, or character, are arising in each generation than the number of genetically handicapped persons who are failing to survive or to reproduce. This situation spells a genetic retrogression that, if continued through a persistance of the same conditions, could not ultimately be compensated for by any conceivable advances in medicine, education, automation, or other cultural methods. Thus we are at present allowing our very successes to dig away the foundations from under everything most valuable in our own natures. The more advanced the peoples, the more is this the case.

Another circumstance affecting the genetics of modern man that merits our objective attention here is the recent reversal of the tendency of human groups to become genetically differentiated from one another. In earlier times the differences in conditions of life between different regions and the difficulties in travelling from one of these regions to another undoubtedly led to the selection of some special characteristics peculiar to and helpful specifically in the given regions. Examples are the darker skin that serves for protection against stronger ultraviolet, the narrowed eyes that reduce the threat of snowblindness, and the small stature that facilitates penetration through jungles. There is no reason to think that these essentially superficial characteristics connoted any parallel differences in the more basic human faculties previously discussed, that were developed as a result of the advantages accruing from intelligent cooperation against the forces of nature in general, but they did lead people of each group to emphasize their distinctivenesses.

Now, however, these special characteristics are losing their value, with the development of man-made expedients for meeting the special situations. These expedients are in effect replacing the natural environments with ever more artificial ones. At the same time, our generalized modern culture is diffusing ever more widely, rapidly and deeply, and is increasingly bringing to all peoples alike not only its techniques but its ways of thinking, mores, ideals, and standards of appreciation. It is also promoting political mergers and economic cooperation between peoples. And along with all this cultural homogenization there is also an increasing physical movement and interbreeding that is progressively, as yet mainly at the edges, blurring out the lines between the age-old genetic pools. With the accentuation of all these factors by the progress of technology and education mankind, barring a return to barbarism, will undoubtedly come to form one world community within which local differences of a genetic nature have largely lost whatever importance they may once have had.

This course of events is a very different one from that usually obtaining for successful species, which tend to split and split again into divergent groups, among which selection operates. Similarly, within each group, there has in man, unlike the successful groups of the past, been a tendency to obliterate the lines between the small semi-isolated subgroups that provided useful experiments in natural selection. We cannot say that this tendency to merge is bad, for it is a condition of human progress as we must think of progress. However, it as well as the other peculiarities of the genetic processes of modern man, previously cited, must be taken seriously into account in the consideration of future policies affecting human genetics. For when trial and error are removed, foresight must be substituted.

PROSPECTS OF FUTURE GENETIC PROGRESS IN MAN

In any such consideration of policies and prospects there is one not strictly genetic fact regarding human reproduction today that must not be overlooked. This is the fact that modern medicine combined with all our other artificial aids to living is so reducing the death rate as to result – unless there is a compensatory reduction in birth-rate much more drastic than any now occurring – in serious global over-population very soon. By no advances that we could conceivably make in the next 500 years in the production of food and other materials could we decently provide for the world population of some 15 trillion (more than 5000 times the present world population) that would theoretically be in existence if only the present rate of increase of a doubling every 40 years – an increase that applies to the present United States population and is not so very much higher than that in the world as a whole today – were maintained.

The slowing down of population growth that will undoubtedly prevent the attainment of this calculated plethora of people can come about only by the resumption of an increased death rate, brought about by the failure of civilization to achieve human betterment, or else by an adequate voluntary restriction of births. In the past such voluntary restriction has only developed among peoples who attained a high standard of living. There are some reckless optimists who think that this will happen again. However, it is very doubtful whether such a living standard can be attained by the populations that are at a low level of technology and grossly overcrowded already, unless the means and motivations for planned parenthood are brought to them with little delay. In other words, birth restriction should be initiated even while the standard of living is low, or it may never be able to achieve an adequate and stable rise. At the same time, enormous efforts should be put forth to effect the rise as rapidly as possible.

The voluntary restriction of births that will have to be adopted if civilization is to succeed implies a recognition of men's responsibility toward their children and descendants. It constitutes a break with the hoary tradition of having as many children as possible to honor oneself and one's ancestors. It opens the door to the recognition by modern men and women everywhere of their obligation to bequeath to the next generation the best conditions possible. With the spread of education, men will come to realize that not least in their ultimate importance, among such conditions, are the genetic ones. They will therefore develop the desire to do their bit in leaving humanity somewhat better off, even genetically, than it was in their own day.

The growing social conscience of men, developing along with their cultural progress in cooperation and understanding, will cause increasing numbers to regard the having of children as a service to mankind, not to be undertaken for purely personal vainglory. This reorientation can lead them to look upon the production of children who are likely to suffer from more than the average share of genetic defects as an act to be avoided while, on the contrary, it should be felt a special honor to produce children who are likely to be especially fortunate in their genetic endowment. This redirection of motivation can in itself turn the scales from genetic decline to genetic progress. It involves a way of looking at things that must not be imposed, but must represent an outgrowth of men's natural seeking for betterment. But it can be materially aided by wise policies in education, economics, and law, that facilitate the course of action that would follow from such motivation.

It is, however, naive to use such words as "betterment" unless one has some concept of what one means by "good." Yet, despite minor diversities in the ideals of different major cultures, they are in fundamental agreement in attaching especially high value to service to one's fellows, that is, to cooperative behavior, and to wisdom. As we have seen, these are the very qualities that are genetically as well as culturally most characteristic of man, and it is they above all others that have brought him to his present high estate as compared with other animals. At the same time it is universally recognized that even in man the degree of their development still leaves much to be desired. So far as the genetic side of this development is concerned, grounds have been cited above for inferring that, after human groups became larger and fewer, progress in these directions must have slackened, so that men were left inwardly stunted. But it is still in the power of civilized men to remedy this situation, if only they will recognize it and act realistically upon it.

The task here confronting humanity is that of guiding our progress in genetic respects so as to allow it once again to parallel our cultural progress. Here the word "our" implies a feeling of unity of the individual with the species as a whole. This attitude of responsibility to all humanity is the very antithesis of that of the racists who not so long ago brought the world to the brink of ruin by their monstrous perversions of both genetic and cultural perspectives. Concentrating upon the fundamental human values regarding which all peoples can agree, men of modern outlook will seek to strengthen these values in every way possible, and to reduce the stress too often laid on superficialities. Given a peaceful world, joined in a universal cultural cross-fertilization, this is a logical development.

Acting on the same principle, good parents today seek to strengthen these same values by cultural means, in the process of educating their children. The same standards are needed in their attitude toward genetic matters.

As in all human activities, the rise of techniques can often act as a lever to implement a change in social practices and attitudes. So, for example, in the control of population the working out of substances that would readily and safely prevent overpopulation might be decisive. Similarly, in the sphere of positively planned parenthood, there is still much room for finding practicable ways for controlling the production of reproductive cells, for storing them, and for transferring them, that may bring radical possibilities within the reach of those who take these matters seriously.

Despite the progress that man makes, he finds many

phases of his transitions painful, and is often reluctant to move. Yet he does move eventually. And as he learns to control more powerful forces, no matter what their nature, he must also learn to apply them wisely in the light of his newer, wider knowledge. In this way he may at times proceed beyond the horizon, but he will be enabled to rise to heights hitherto undreamed of.

Men would indeed be ignoble if they, Narcissus-like, worshipped their present selves as the acmes of perfection, and reserved their efforts to bring about genetic betterment for their cattle, their corn, and the yeast that gives them beer. But not all men will continue to maintain such smugness of attitude. And those who look higher will find that, increasingly, they can put their ideals into corporeal form, and help to create men worthy of the great new material opportunities that they have opened up. And for such men, in their turn, still further advancement, cultural and genetic, will always be the major aims.

Science, Scientists and World Policy

by

HAROLD D. LASSWELL

An unavoidable consequence of innovation in science and technology is the rearranging of power relations. The balancing process sometimes operates so smoothly that no crises of coercion occur as Nation-States change their relations to one another or the whole structure of the world arena undergoes extensive modification. It is, however, too much to assume that the dynamic equilibrium of world affairs is set up to avoid friction at all times.

Great waves of war and revolution have sometimes followed in the wake of innovations in the technology of warfare. We can relate some of the invasions from Inner Asia with innovations in the bow and arrow, or in cavalry tactics.

We know what happened when European civilization eventually welded gunpowder, metallurgy, and the internal combustion engine into a lethal combination.

But political structures are tough and have been capable of withstanding and even dominating the applications of science. Consider the enormous growth of population that has occurred in modern Europe, and the cumulative curve of invention that helped launch and sustain the industrial revolution. It is noteworthy that despite tremendous innovations of production (and destruction) the Nation-State system of Western Europe became an identifiable structure as soon as England, France, Spain, Austria, Sweden,

Russia, Prussia and the Low Countries grew to be among the principal entities in the world arena. Despite the vast scientific and technological efflorescence of recent centuries it was not until after World War II that the Great Power system began to give way with some rapidity to a bipolar pattern.

The tenacity of the Great Power system is not, however, the most significant evidence of the durability of political institutions. The crucial factor is the *expectation of violence* itself, the assumption that whether we like it or not, many conflicts are going to be settled by recourse to large-scale and organized violence. *Even today the political elites of the world do not expect to be as well off by making the sacrifices required to change the situation as they are by* allowing it to continue. The key problem of political science in this domain is to discover the factors, short of physical conquest, that will alter these expectations. The problem of statecraft is to devise and execute policies that realize upon all available potentials for voluntary unification.

I shall not present a thorough analysis of the factors that conjoin to keep a divided world alive despite the impressive potentials of modern science and technology for destruction on a global scale. It may be enough to recall the fact that the officials of every independent Nation-State keep in power because it is expected that they will maintain the "security" of their State by the use of organized violence if necessary. As an indication of how deep-rooted the expectation of violence has become one may cite the fact that no one seriously challenges the legal "right of self-defense." There are doctrines, of course, that forbid "aggression" and impose an obligation to come to the assistance of a Nation-State that is deemed (by an appropriate authority) to be a target of aggression. But all this is further confirmation of the ubiquity of the expectation of violence and the acceptance of organized coercion.[1]

1. Concerning the present plight of the world community as a legal entity the following treaties are especially outspoken: WALTER SCHIFFER, The Legal Community of Mankind, New York, Columbia University Press, 1954; CHARLES DE VISSCHER, Theory and Reality in Public International Law, tr. by P. E. Corbett, Princeton, Princeton University Press, 1957; MYRES S. MCDOUGAL and Associates. Studies in World Public Order, New Haven, Yale University Press, 1960.

What factors explain why scientists and engineers, despite the world view that frequently prevails among them, continue to act as the servants of the politics of a devided globe? It is evident that the generalizations of science are universal. It is equally evident that the applications of science are, in principle, universal. But in fact every application is localized at first. Hence the "paradox," if you will: *The universal is introduced parochially*. If after a long series of developments the patterns initiated at a point of origin diffuse and multiply until they nearly succeed in covering the globe, we can properly speak of universality. When we examine the process in detail we find that the moment-by-moment, locality-by-locality sequence of introduction enables an innovation to be absorbed with *minimum damage* to the structure of interests that prevails at the centers of origin. This almost surely carries the further implication that minimum damage is done elsewhere to the alignment of vested and sentimental interests as the innovation diffuses.

The latter point – the occurrence of minimum damage during further spread – follows from the automatic sequence by which a threat is defended against. Consider the classical analysis of power balancing: Assume that State *A* gets bigger, richer and better armed than its neighbors; neighbor *B* joins neighbor *C* in order to deter neighbor *A* from attacking them and enlarging its domain further as a result. This analysis is unobjectionable as far as it goes, but it fails to describe the situation as a whole, and ignores important responses that are likely to be made by *B* and *C* concurrently with the diplomatic acts that are mentioned. The ruling elites of *B* and *C* will, in all probability, focus attention upon *A* to discover why *A* has become a potent threat. A typical discovery is, for example, that *A* is employing new weapons, or that *A* is encouraging the growth of a native steel industry by means of subsidies and tariffs. The typical response of *B* or *C* is to do the same thing. We speak of this as *restriction of Power A by partial incorporation* of the patterns that are expected by others to account for *A's* strength (*Total incorporation* would be the amalgamation of *B* with *A*). The outcome of the tactic of partial incorporation is that the positions of the ruling elites in *B* and *C* are kept intact while scientific and technological innovations – in this case new weapons and industrialization – are encouraged.

It would take us too far afield to examine the complications that appear when these relations are subjected to further examination. The principal point that concerns us here is that the spread of science and technology does not necessarily – or typically – bring scientists or technologists into power. They may, of course, contribute more individuals with scientific training to the White House or the Senate (or to equivalent top decision spots in other nations). But the individuals who get these posts are *ex*-scientists and *ex*-engineers. Anyone who makes a transition from the career of a specialist in science to become a politician must rise or fall according to the usual criteria that register success or failure in politics. For instance, he must continue to carry conviction that he is devoted to national security. Hence he will find it necessary to keep alive the expectation of violence in the world by fortifying the position that his Nation-State is able to play in the world power process.

As indicated before, we recognize the fact that the practice of science produces more than a few men and women who long to use the methods and results of science for the universal benefit of mankind. They think in all-inclusive terms and recoil from any exploitation of knowledge for the benefit of those who apply it first, and who perpetuate the dangerous cleavages that divide the globe. They are imaginative enough to see the remarkable opportunities that are now within the reach of mankind.

Under today's conditions these universal minds feel remarkably ineffectual. How can they possibly move the Nations toward a cooperative world of knowledge, friendship and abundance? A disturbing insight is that the customary tactic of enlightenment – outspoken disclosure of universal propositions – does not promise to be politically effective. To utter a universal principle is not to perform a universal act; on the contrary, it is parochial, limited in time and space. It is a particular case of the general statement formulated above in saying that in politics at least all innovations have parochial points of origin.

What, if anything, can be done by men of universal vision and good will under these circumstances? The question can receive an intelligible answer, and one that provides at least a modicum of policy guidance. The problem is to de-parochialize the impact of desirable innovations. The reply would appear to be that a special strategy is required. The challenge is to *cultivate a strategy of parallel action at representative places over the globe*. All nations and all cultures are necessarily included within the scope of such a program.

On reflection it is apparent that during the early phases at least the strategy requires tactics at the centers and sub-centers of introduction that evoke the support, not the hostility, of local elites. This implies that local elites must be led to accept the probability of net gain rather than net loss for themselves by joining the movement.

An inference is that the agenda of the operation should be composed of long-term undertakings of common concern to mankind until an institution wins enough acceptance to enable it to turn to the clarification of more immediate problems. There is no dearth of long-range issues. Experimental embryologists are bringing us close to the time when it will be practical politics to consider the treatment to be given to intelligent forms which are different and in some ways, no doubt, superior to man. Specialists on machines are engaged in planning and constructing automata whose functions are ever closer to those of living systems.[2]

2. Elsewhere I have raised the question when we should extend the provisions of the Universal Declaration of Human Rights to these non-human forms. "The Political Science of Science: An Inquiry into the Possible Reconciliation of Mastery and Freedom," *Amer. Political Sci. Rev.*, L (1956) 961–979. Reprinted in *The Sci. Monthly*, 84 (1957) 34–44.

In an era of space travel we can look forward to the opportunity of experimenting with new biological and institutional models in habitats isolated from one another in the galaxies.

If the intelligence function of governmental and private organizations is to become more effectively attuned to the tempo of the epoch of science and technology, new agencies must be brought into existence which enable a sample of the ablest minds of the Earth to devote themselves intensively and often to the consideration of problems that touch upon the destiny of man. As I have hinted, not the least of these challenges is that of mobilizing all our knowledge, experience, judgement and imagination to accomplish the *rational planning and preparation of man's successor*. It may be that this will prove to be the noblest work of human history.

The Significance of Border Sciences for the Future of Mankind

by

S. W. Tromp

PREFACE

In September 1957 the author was invited by Dr. Hugo Boyko to prepare an essay for the book "Science and the Future of Man," to be published as a first step towards the creation of a "Universal Academy of Art and Science." This International Academy would transcend national frontiers, both spiritual and geographical, and act as a forum of humanity. Despite the great honour bestowed upon him by this request, the author was most reluctant to accept because in his opinion far more competent scientists with longer experience in research and teaching might have been asked instead.

However, after careful consideration he accepted the invitation on account of the very specific subject he was asked to discuss: "The Significance of Border Sciences for the Future of Mankind."

An explorer by profession I have always been attracted more to the unknown realms of science, which require careful balancing along the steep ravines of human knowledge, than to well trodden paths, which ensure a feeling of safety for those adhering to them. However, it is my personal conviction that progress in the development of mankind has been achieved not so much along those established roads of scientific knowledge as along more hazardous trails. Still, it should be realized that the consolidation of the newly acquired knowledge requires a team of men specially interested in the levelling and cultivation of the newly discovered mountains of promise.

The idea of a Universal Academy of Sciences appealed to me because "as one who has lived as a geologist with the people of other lands, his affection for his own country and his own science undergoes a change in perspective. Instead of admiring the accomplishments as selfish things to be confined within its borders they are viewed in the light of the advantages they may offer to those outside, who are not so fortunately situated. This is true internationalism, the political philosophy which stresses the solidarity and mutual dependence of all nations and offers a foundation for international peace." [1]

Geology as a border science has affected humanity so much, both in its fundamental concepts and its material welfare, that I always felt an urge to spread its concepts to other scientific disciplines.

Geology, like astronomy, leads us to the borderland of the unlimited precipices of time, as Pierre Termier, the famous French geologist, used to say. But it gives us more than astronomy, because it teaches us that nothing on earth is eternal, that everything changes, both matter and mind. We geologists feel daily the instability of the best organized systems in nature, the fragility of the most solid concepts of human mind. In other words, we are continuously aware that the universe in all its appearances is a function of time and no barriers of development, however strong and unconquerable they may seem at this moment can resist the pressure of human mind if the will prevails to overcome these barriers.

Young [2] in his book "The Medici" wrote the following

1. Linn M. Farish, geologist, in "The true Strength of America". N. Dakota, 17 June 1941.
2. Col. G. F. Young: The Medici. London, John Murray, 1911.

warning to the present generation: "In the fifth century storm upon storm out of the dark swept away in a great deluge of barbarism all the civilisation of the western half of the Roman Empire. From the Atlantic to Constantinople, and from the Rhine and Danube to the deserts of Africa, all that learned and cultivated, all that was artistic and beautiful, was overwhelmed in an avalanche of ruin in which the triumphs of architecture, literature, arts and sciences were involved in one general destruction. After a night of thick darkness, at length in the 12th, 13th and 14th century the re-civilisation of the west began in Italy with men like NICCOLO PISANO, the father of modern art, DANTE ALLEGHIERI, the immortal poet, GIOTTO DI BONDONE, the father of modern painting and PETRARCH, the father of modern learning. But as yet there was none with power to make these efforts produce their full fruit and to spread the knowledge of them throughout the world. And then, in the city which had produced three of these men, arose a family, who with the power of wealth and with a great love for these things, lifted learning from its grave and gave art the encouragement to advance to its highest achievements."

In the 20th century, when new attacks are threatening to destroy the fundamental concepts of mankind, we see among a group of scientists the growth of a love for, and a desire to preserve the knowledge obtained in the past, and with it a desire to spread this knowledge for the welfare of mankind. This group is trying to build a Universal Academy of Sciences where the vital problems of mankind can be discussed objectively and scientifically and plans for exploration in the future can be reviewed.

Just as the grandeur of the concepts of the human mind is not due to the individual cells of the brain, but to the interaction of groups of cells, so the greatest achievements in the future of science will result from the interaction of existing and recently developed branches of science. It is this interaction which creates the true border sciences, one of the most recent being Bioclimatology and Biometeorology. But before we can enter deeper into their significance a more distinct definition is required of what we actually mean by border sciences, a term barely defined even in the largest encyclopaedia.

I. INTRODUCTION

A. DEFINITION OF BORDER SCIENCES

The word science in its broadest sense means learning or knowledge, from the latin word "scientia" (latin scire – to learn or to know). Therefore, in principle, it can be used in connection with any qualifying adjective which indicates a certain branch of learning. In general usage, however, a more restricted meaning has been adopted. As a result, science is usually defined as "purposefully acquired, systematically ordered knowledge of natural phenomena and of the relations between them."

At the time of ARISTOTLE (350 B.C.) only knowledge based on stingent proof and a small number of axioms, as in mathematics, was considered to be pure science. Gradually, through the ages a wider concept developed, particularly after the French philosopher AUGUSTE COMTE (abt. 1800) had developed his philosophical concept of "positivism." According to COMTE the task of science is mainly the discovery of statistical laws and rules, irrespective of the explanation of observed facts.

When Paleolithic man was faced with the apparent irregularity of sequence and connection between observed phenomena, he may have been inclined to believe that these apparently capricious events were due to the intervention of some unseen being of a nature essentially similar to his own.

In view of the fact that in younger prehistoric periods

certain monuments were oriented in such a way as to suggest a certain amount of astronomical observation, it is probable that the purely mythological view of primitive man formed the basis of one of the oldest sciences: *Astronomy.*

Whereas primitive man considered disease to be caused by some malignant demon, in Greek times a more rational thought developed and later formed the basis of *Biological and medical sciences.*

During much of the first half of the 19th century it was generally believed, that the known forces on earth, in the atmosphere and the earth's crust, were insufficient to explain observed geological processes of the past. It was mainly due to Sir CHARLES LYELL (1797–1875), an outstanding English geologist, that the *Concept of actualism* (previously expressed by JAMES HUTTON in 1785) was introduced about 1830. This formed the basis of all succeeding geological sciences. Although it is not denied that certain geological processes may have taken place with greater intensity in earlier periods of earth's history, considerable evidence has been collected, indicating that for at least 2000 million years no fundamental differences have existed between the type of forces acting and shaping the earth today and those in the past.

Another important concept in geology was the recognition that fossils were remnants of animals and plants which had been living on earth millions of years previously. LEONARDO DA VINCI and the Veronesian doctor FRACASTORO assumed, as long ago as 1517, that fossil prints represented organisms. But even in 1726, when SCHEUCHZER discovered near the Lake of Constanz the skeleton of a salamander, almost a meter in length, he assumed that it had belonged to a man who had been a witness of the deluge ("*Homo diluvii tristis testis*"). It was by CAMPER and CUVIER that this skeleton was first recognized as that of a giant salamander.

The development of the various concepts which furthered the growth of geological science gave sufficient support to Paleontology and General Biology for the *Theory of evolution,* another outstanding concept of human knowledge mainly developed by CHARLES DARWIN (1809–1882), to be generally accepted as a fundamental pillar of human knowledge.

During the 19th and 20th centuries several branches of science grew from this group of concepts, which have been classified differently, according either to subject of research, or to problems, methods applied, etc.

These sciences are sometimes classified into four main groups: the Norm – or Standard-Sciences (arithmetic, geometry, etc.), Natural-Sciences (Physics, mechanics, chemistry, astronomy etc.), Vital-Sciences (biology, medicine, etc.) and Mental-Sciences (Sociology, Jurisprudence, etc.). Whereas the Natural Sciences are objective in their basic concept but subjective in the interpretation and validity of their conclusions, the Norm-Sciences are subjective in their basic concept, but objective in the validity of their conclusions. For example, a straight line without dimensions (an object of geometry) does not exist in reality, it exists only in our subjective mind.

Sciences have also been classified into Exact Sciences, Descriptive Sciences, Theoretical and Applied Sciences, etc. It was mainly in the later years of the first half of the 20th century that a new group of sciences developed, the so-called Border Sciences, one of the oldest being the Geological Sciences as indicated above.

Border Sciences comprise those branches of science which interconnect the fringes of well-established basic sciences (either norm-, natural-, vital- or mental sciences) forming new independent sciences. They also comprise those types of fundamental research which penetrate into completely unknown realms of human knowledge, until recently considered the domain of vague, unrealistic quasi-scientists and unfortunately often the hunting-ground of unscientific charlatans.

B. TENTATIVE CLASSIFICATION OF THE PRINCIPAL BORDER SCIENCES

Some of the most important border sciences can be classified as follows:

1. Established Border Sciences
   - A) Geological Sciences
   - B) Psycho-physics
     - (1) Physical embryology
     - (2) Physical neurology
     - (3) Geo-ecology
       - (a) General Geo-ecology
       - (b) Medical Geography and Geographical Pathology
       - (c) Bioclimatology and Biometeorology
     - (4) Biorhythmics
   - C) Cybernetics

2. Non-established Border Sciences
   - A) Astronautics
   - B) Supersensorics
     - (1) In Man
       - (a) Paragnosy (telepathy, clairvoyance)
       - (b) Stigmatization
       - (c) Hypnosis, trance conditions and yogi phenomena
     - (2) In animals
       - (a) Direction finding of birds
       - (b) Homing instinct of salmon, eel and shad

Each of these branches of Border Sciences can be defined as follows:

Whereas *Geological sciences* are concerned particularly with the study of the history and development of both the inorganic and organic part of the earth (and of the earth's crust in particular), *psycho-physics* is a modern concept for a group of border sciences which study the fundamental psycho-chemical properties of the web of life and its interrelationships with the inorganic and organic world surrounding it.

Psychophysics comprises several branches of border sciences:

Physical embryology, the study of the physico-chemical, but particularly the purely physical aspects of the fundamental problems of life in its embryonic stages; *Physical neurology*, the study of the physical mechanism of nerve conduction and brain processes in general; and *Geo-ecology*, comprising the study of the interaction between environment and living organism. This interaction determines for a considerable part the conditions of life, behaviour and geographical distribution of plants, animals and man (*General geo-ecology*), and also the geographical distribution of diseases (*Medical geography*) and the differences in clinical symptoms, severity and development of these diseases in different parts of the world (*Geographical pathology*).

The environmental factors affecting the living organism are determined by four principal groups of inorganic forces: the lithosphere (earthcrust), the hydrosphere (rivers, lakes, oceans and underground water), the atmosphere and the extraterrestrial or cosmic sphere, particularly those parts of it which lie in the neighbourhood of the earth. This depends greatly on the physical conditions of the sun and the changes in its activity.

These four domains of the inorganic world have determined the type and distribution of living organisms both in the past and in the present. They comprise the so-called biosphere which, in itself, forms a fifth group of forces affecting the individual living organism.

Whereas the forces of the lithosphere and hydrosphere are studied in the geological sciences and those of the biosphere in biological and medical sciences, the effect of the atmosphere and nearby cosmic events on the living organism are mainly studied in a relatively new border science, *Bioclimatology* and *Biometeorology*, which will be described later extensively in the following sections.

The study of the living processes in plants, animals and man have shown us the existence of certain fundamental rhythmical phenomena in nature, the study of which has grown in recent years into another independent border science: *Biorhythmics*.

Another fascinating border science of recent years is called *Cybernetics* (from the Greek cubernetes = steersman), the study of the direction and control of certain distance mechanism in the inorganic and living world. It comprises the "Control and Communication Theories" and the study of the so-called *Feed-back mechanisms* [3] and the processes involved in "*Memory*" both in the mechanical and living world.

Although the general idea of Cybernetics was developed in principle by C. MAXWELL (1868) it has been formulated more specifically about 1943 by N. WIENER (Prof. of Mathematics at the Massachusetts Inst. of Technology at Cambridge, U.S.A.) and Dr. A. ROSENBLUETH (Instituto Nacional de Cardiología, México), assisted by a large number of scientists from various disciplines of science: physiology, sociology, anthropology, biology, etc.

Dr. ROSENBLUETH always insisted that "a proper exploration of the blank spaces on the map of science could be made only by a team of scientists." He had dreamed for years of an "Institution of independent scientists, working together in one of these backwoods of sciences, not as subordinates of some great executive officer, but joined by the desire, indeed by the spiritual necessity, to understand the region as a whole, and to lend one another the strength of that understanding."

3. "*Feed-Back*" is the mechanism in which the result of a certain process is automatically signalled back and therefore has a regulating effect on this mechanism (e.g. thermostat in an oven, certain muscular movements, etc.).

Whereas the previous review of border sciences deals with "Established Border Sciences" there are a number of less established or even non-established Border Sciences which in my opinion may, in a not too far distant future, develop into new independent branches of Border Sciences, e.g. *Astronautics* and *Supersensorics.*

Astronautics studies the problems involved in the transport both of living and of non-living objects from the earth's crust into the universe (i.e. to other planets or satellites) and the study of conditions under which living organisms could live in the outside space.

This science is extremely young and inexperienced. The first milestone was passed on October 4, 1957, when scientists of the USSR launched the first 84 kg artifical moon, "Sputnik I" to a height of 900 km. This was followed on January 1958 by the 13 kg "Explorer", launched by U.S.A. scientists to an elevation of 1700 km. These artifical celestial bodies, moving around the earth at the immense speed of almost 30,000 km/hr, represent the first victory of the human mind in conquest of outer space.

Supersensorics (by others defined as extra-sensorics) represent the study of certain phenomena shown by living organisms, the registration of which seems to take place by means of physiological or other mechanisms, unknown at present in human physiology. Part of these phenomena are only observed in animals and, although apparently missing in man, they can be explained at least partly, by the known laws of physics. However, other supersensory phenomena have been carefully studied in animals the explanation of which is entirely lacking.

The study of this group of phenomena was primarily the work of charlatans until recently, when these problems began to be studied by scientists of good repute. The problem of supersensorics has now reached a stage at which extensive scientific research seems to be warranted.

C. GENERAL SIGNIFICANCE AND UNIVERSAL CHARACTER OF BORDER-SCIENCES

In chapter II four promising new Border-Sciences will be discussed in greater detail. This discussion will demonstrate more clearly the significance of Border-Sciences in general.

The fact that a Border-Science, by definition, represents the interconnection of the fringes of well-established basic sciences (see p. 88) into new independent sciences, clearly demonstrates their universal character. It is also evident that such extremely complex branches of human knowledge as these Border-Sciences can only be developed by a great many experts in various disciplines of science, and unless a truly universal team spirit can be developed no results can be expected.

In chapter II we have briefly indicated the significance of these Border-Sciences for the future of mankind. Parts of these sciences are not sufficiently established yet, for their real significance remains to be demonstrated. It is for this reason that we review in this section the significance of one of the oldest and best established of the Border-Sciences for the development and future of mankind, i.e. the Geological Sciences.

Geological Sciences have been applied to different problems of mankind, of which the most important ones can be tentatively classified into four main groups:

1. PROBLEMS ARISING FROM NATURAL CATASTROPHES; such as earthquakes, volcanic eruptions, floods, etc.

It is well-known that certain places on earth have been devastated again and again over many centuries as a result of heavy earthquakes originating along the same regional faultlines in the earthcrust. For example, the city of Erzincan in Turkey has been destroyed 26 times during the last 900 years, causing thousands of casualties. Similar examples could be given from Japan and other seismic areas.

In recent years the frequencies and causes of earthquakes have been studied more scientifically. In many instances the geologist has been able to suggest better locations for rebuilding destroyed villages. New types of building construction have been discovered which can resist even big earthquakes. By scientifically studying the history of volcanoes it is often possible to predict approaching eruptions and the prevailing direction of the devastating lava and mudstreams ejected. In certain areas too, energy from volcanic steam has been utilized for industrial purposes.

2. PROBLEMS ASSOCIATED WITH THE STRUGGLE OF MAN FOR HIS PRIMARY NECESSITIES OF LIVING: For his modern way of life man needs a great variety of raw materials, both biological (food, textiles, etc.) and geological (various metals, precious stones, radioactive minerals, etc.). The distribution of biological raw materials is determined both by climate and the geological conditions of the soil. Geological raw materials are needed for the construction and decoration of living quarters of man. Problems due to underproduction or lack of water in arid regions can only be solved with the assistance of hydrologists and geologically trained engineers. Modern electrical methods enable us to determine the location of underground reservoirs of water in desert regions. Dam constructions or the building of underground reservoirs in arid regions enable us to store water during the rainy season and to irrigate and cultivate large areas, which would otherwise support a much smaller population.

3. PROBLEMS ASSOCIATED WITH THE ACTIVITIES OF MAN FOR THE IMPROVEMENT OF LIVING CONDITIONS AND FOR THE INCREASE OF HIS POWER: Geological studies are required for large tunnel projects through mountains and under rivers and seas, to foresee the technical problems likely to be encountered. Railroad constructions, harbour works and many other

engineering problems often need the assistance of the geologist to prevent the subsoil from sliding, to estimate the reserves of construction materials, etc.

Man needs, above all, large quantities of energy both for transport of himself and of his industrial and agricultural products, and for heating and lighting purposes. The discovery of enormous oil and coal reserves on earth faciliated the development of airtransport which has changed completely intercommunication between far-distant population groups. This is largely a result of the development of the Border Science of Geology. In recent years the discovery of large quantities of radioactive minerals has enabled the development of atomic energy, another powerful tool of modern man.

4. PROBLEMS RELATED TO RELIGIOUS AND PHILOSOPHICAL PROBLEMS OF LIFE: On pp. 84 and 87 we indicated that the development of geology, and especially of its subscience Palaeontology, has given an important impetus to the understanding of the concept of time and the continuous evolution of the universe. Geology and Astronomy have probably contributed more to the understanding of the fundamental problems of life than have any other sciences.

D. CAUSES OF SLOW PROGRESS

In chapter II various reasons for the slow progress in the Border Sciences will be discussed in greater detail. As an introduction some general remarks can be made.

As mentioned in the previous section, Border Sciences require both the National and International cooperation of many experts in the various disciplines of science. Apart from personal factors cooperation is often hampered by national differences. Although international cooperation is making rapid progress, particularly in science, considerably more is required in these extremely complex and difficult border sciences.

Another important problem is the fact that each science has its own language which often makes it difficult for a research worker in one discipline to grasp the problems of others. In addition, lack of mental flexibility often prevents scientific compromise in definition and nomenclature.

Furthermore, each individual working in a particular field of science, has his own "pet-projects." Unless he has a very broad field of interest, he dislikes being forced to scatter his energy by cooperating in complex team-projects which require great adaptation and flexibility both in mind and character. It is not only unwillingness to cooperate, but more often inability resulting from his psychological pattern which prevents him from becoming a good Border-Scientist.

Although innate character to a great extent determines the working field of a scientist, in my opinion a drastic change in educational systems is required to overcome this problem. By teaching children the details of several specific sciences and by stressing the interwoven relationships between them, future scientists may be trained who, despite problems of personality, may be valuable tools in the future development of the Border-Sciences.

II. REVIEW OF SOME OF THE PRINCIPAL BORDER-SCIENCES

On p. 89ff a brief review was given of a number of important Border-Sciences, four of which will be discussed more extensively: Biorhythmics, Supersensorics, Medical Geography and Bioclimatology and Biometeorology.

A. BIORHYTHMICS

The scientific study of biological rhythms, which in this essay has been called briefly *Biorhythmics*, is a comparatively new branch of science, which received a major impulse after the creation of the International Society for the Investigation of Biological Rhythms [4] about 20 years ago, the first international conference being held in 1937 in Ronneby, Sweden.

As all living substance, either the body as a whole or its components are constantly moving and as external or internal resistances usually prevent unlimited movements, most biological movements, after reaching a certain limit, have to be reversed. When this process repeats itself with more or less constant time intervals, the phenomenon is described as *Biological rhythm*, either endogenous or exogenous.

Endogenous biological rhythms can be observed only if organisms are cut off completely from all external stimuli. The frequency and amplitude of the various observed endogenous biological rhythms differ greatly. Considerable changes in these rhythms may occur due to the interaction of external physical rhythms, such as rhythmic variations in light, temperature and humidity of the air, rhythmic fluctuations of the barometric pressure, fluctuations in the electric field of the atmosphere, etc.

In view of the great variety in periodicities, both in the inorganic and organic world, many scientists in various basic sciences are deeply interested in the mechanism and fundamental causes of biological rhythms, for biorhythmics touches many branches of sciences: biology, physiology, chemistry, geophysics, mathematics, etc. It is therefore a Border-Science in the true sense.

Despite a vast amount of research carried out during the last 20 years and the introduction of modern methods of statistical analysis, neither the exact location nor the ana-

4. Its present, very active, Secretary-General is Mr. A. SOLLBERGER, Solnavägen 1, Stockholm 60, Sweden.

tomical and physiological composition of the biological rhythm centres in the living organisms are known. As these rhythms are closely connected with the fundamental nature of life, biorhythmics is a promising Border-Science of the future.

It has been shown by GERRITZEN (the Netherlands), MENZEL (Germany) and others that human diuresis has a 24 hour rhythm with maximum excretion around 2 p.m. and minimum around 2 a.m. This rhythm applies both to the excretion of water and to chloride and urea excretion by the human body. When the experiment is carried out in various parts of the world, this rhythm is found to be determined by local sun-time. Artificial changes in the daily light and dark rhythm of the environment can cause a reversal of the original rhythm.

Rapid airtravel over large distances is responsible for serious disturbances in this natural rhythm, and may even lead to disease. After the Vienna Philharmonic Orchestra travelled to Tokyo by air it took the members four days to become fully adapted. Similar experience were learned from European athletes at the Melbourne Olympic Games. Even more serious consequences can be expected in interspatial travel as planned by "Astronautics."

MOLLERSTROM (Sweden) and DENNEMARK (Germany) were able to demonstrate, independently, that the hour of the day at which various drugs are administered greatly effects the results of the therapy depending on the time-phase of the endogenous rhythm.

Several psychiatrists assume that external stimulation during inhibitory phases of the human nervous system may be responsible for many of the contemporary psychosomatic disorders. Disturbances of the day-night rhythms of the autonomous nervous system may be responsible, according to various scientists, for peculiar experiences during sleep. Many of the so-called *Weather-sensitivity phenomena*, to be discussed later, may depend on similar disturbances in the endogenous adaptation rhythm or other physiological rhythms.

KLEITMANN, ENGELMANN, GIFFORD and other psychologists in the U.S.A. could demonstrate that the adaptation of the infant's autonomous endogenous rhythm to the 24 hour activity pattern of the mother creates a sleep-wakefulness rhythm in children long before the 3rd month of life. GIFFORD (Boston) stated in 1957 during the congress of Biological Rhythm that "although the highest functions of time-perception are established in later childhood, it is possible that the quality of these early experiences (rhythm adaptations) with time and external reality influences the adult's attitude toward time, his capacity to estimate duration and orientation, his tolerance for frustration and delay, his need for punctuality or freedom from restriction and his ability to adapt or depart from fixed schedules of activity."

Important rhythms have also been reported from both the plant and animal world, the occurrence of endogenous rhythms in plants having been known for a very long time. Sir NIGEL BALL (London) recently has demonstrated a 24 hour rhythm in the growth of coleoptiles of seedlings of the Oat (*Avena Sativa*) due to lightdark cycles in the environment. This rhythm could be retarded by lack of oxygen. He also demonstrated that the time-keeping mechanism is not confined to the tip of the coleoptiles.

CLOUDSLEY-THOMPSON (London) has pointed out that in most animals there is a rhythmic alternation of activity, during which feeding, mating and dispersal takes place, with periods of physiological recuperation, the activity usually being linked with rhythm of daylight and darkness. Rhythms of diurnal and nocturnal activity are common and, in the case of terrestrial arthropods, often related to fluctuating light intensity or variations in temperature and humidity and affected by the water-balance of the animals.

In the case of insects a close parallel has been observed between the rhythm of biting activity of certain East African mosquitoes and the bimodal flight activity of the Trichoptera.

STEPHENS (Minneapolis) has shown the influence of temperature on the 24 hour rhythm of the movement of the melanophore pigment in the fiddler Crab, *Uca pugnax*, a light-controlled rhythm previously established by KALMUS (London). The phases of induced rhythms could be shifted by sudden changes in temperature, provided these exceeded certain threshold values.

General problems like the daily or seasonal time concept, very marked both in plants and in animals, and the observation that many people are able to wake up at prefixed hours, are also probably related to certain endogenous and exogenous biological rhythms.

The above examples, a spectrum of the various implications of the theory of biological rhythm, clearly demonstrate the importance of this new Border Science for the future of mankind. The problems involved are extremely complicated and unless scientists of various disciplines of science join hands, we shall never be able to penetrate into the deeper causes of the rhythmic activity of the living organism.

B. SUPERSENSORICS

Supersensory phenomena, as defined on p. 92, have been observed both in animals and in man. Of the many reported observations a few can stand critical scientific tests despite the fact that these observations have been made many times by a large number of observers. The processes involved and the conditions under which they have to be observed facilitate fraud. Furthermore, even in well-controlled experiments it is difficult to collect sufficient evidence for a statistical analysis or to reproduce the results at any given time for a group of unbiased observers. It is for this reason that we have selected a number of phenomena in which the available evidence seems to warrant extensive future research by a team of scientists consisting of physiologists, neurologists, psychologists, geophysicists, etc.

Of the various reported *Supersensoric phenomena in man* which seem to be worth studying I should like to mention the following ones: *Paragnostic phenomena* (from the Greek para – next and gnosis – insight, i.e. observations made without the aid of the well-known human sense organs) and in particular the reported studies in telepathy and clairvoyance; *Stigmatization phenomena* (i.e. appearance in males and females of usually non-infectious bleeding wounds on hands, feet or breast, little affected by medicine, appearing often with regular intervals on certain religious days, and mainly occurring in very religious Roman Catholics; after the bleeding has stopped no scars can be found); *Hypnosis* and *Trance conditions* (peculiar sleep conditions as a result of certain external psychic influences, during which the person does not wake up to noises, the whole condition being characterized by reflexes different from ordinary sleep; and according to various research workers also differing in encephalographic pattern); *Yogi phenomena* (comprising methods, requiring intensive mental training, developed in India probably around 1500 B.C., enabling a person to control extreme physiological conditions, such as cold, hunger, thirst, and purposely lowering the whole metabolic process of the body, and apparently facilitating paragnostic observations).

Of the *Supersensory phenomena in animals* the following seem to be of particular interest for future research: direction finding of birds and the homing instinct of salmon, eel and shad.[5]

5. Other supersensory phenomena in animals, recently explained by physics, are the sensitivity of bees to polarized light and the sensitivity of bees and other insects to supersonic waves.

(1) *The study of paragnostic phenomena*

For thousands of years man has believed in the existence of unknown forces in the world surrounding him. This has been based partly on mystical belief and various religious concepts, partly on spontaneous experiences and, in more recent times, on scientific experimental research. This experimental work has arisen from a vast hinterland of spontaneous events which have been described as "paranormal phenomena" or "extra-sensory phenomena" (RHINE). The term extra-sensory phenomena more or less implies that all these observations take place without the aid of our sensory organs, whereas no evidence for this assumption exists. However, since these experiences may be related to other physiological mechanisms, unknown to us at present, it seems better to speak of *Supersensory phenomena*, i.e. sensory registration with a sensitivity surpassing that of the known sense organs in man. The study of most of the so-called paragnostic phenomena can be described as investigations into the apparent transference of ideas, sensations and mental images from one mind to another in the present, past or future.

Two important groups of phenomena have been described: *Telepathy* (a name introduced in 1882 by F. W. H. MYERS, a famous classical scholar and inspector of schools) and *Clairvoyance*. Both terms have a very poor reputation amongst scientists because they have been so often connected with charlatans and parapsychological "cranks."

SOAL, Senior Lecturer in pure mathematics at Queen Mary College of the University of London, one of the leading experimental workers in this field in W. Europe, gave the following definitions of these phenomena: "If a present mental pattern of a person wholly or in part corresponds to a past, present or future mental pattern of another person (who may be dead or living) and the correspondence cannot be accounted for by ordinary physiological sense-perception or by inference based on sense-perception or by chance coincidence, the phenomenon is called *Telepathy*. However, if a person experiences a present mental pattern which corresponds wholly or in part with sensory aspects of a past, present or future physical object or event, in such a way that the observed correspondence cannot be accounted for by sense-perception or inference based on normal sense-perception or by chance coincidence, we are used to describe this phenomenon as *Clairvoyance*."

Around 1930 it was felt more and more that unless rigidly controlled experiments could confirm the reality, or the great probability of various reported phenomena, no progress in this new field of research would be possible. The great resistance of orthodox science however prevented and still prevents the necessary scientific studies from being carried out by large research teams, as in the case for example in modern atomic research.

What have been the reasons for the resistance?

1. Orthodox scientists are often less unbiased and less open-minded than one would expect. Alexis Carrel ("Man the Unknown," 1935) rightly pointed out that "our mind has a natural tendency to reject the things that do not fit into the frame of the scientific and philosophical beliefs of our time. After all scientists are only men. They are saturated with the prejudices of their environment and of their epoch. They willingly believe that facts that cannot be explained by current theories do not exist." "Evident facts having an unorthodox appearance are suppressed. By reason of these difficulties the inventory of the things which could lead us to a better understanding of the human being has been left incomplete." In other words it is the mental condition of man which is usually more important for the infiltration of new ideas than the facts themselves.

2. The interest shown by charlatans and "cranks" in these subjects makes a scientist reluctant to enter this field of research.

3. The acceptance of the phenomenon of clairvoyance of future events, so-called "precognition," requires a fundamental and revolutionary change in the basic concepts of natural sciences, physics in particular, overthrowing several fundamental pillars of knowledge and creating a feeling of mental unrest and instability which most scientists cannot endure.

4. It has been very difficult to supply sufficient evidence to satisfy most present day scientists. In other words, facts should be made highly probable with mathematical statistics, a concept greatly neglected in the past, although in recent years highly overrated.

SOAL rightly pointed out that "cases of apparent thought-transference, of a presumed observation of future events in dreams or in a physical state of high nervous tension and awareness of what is happening to friends or relatives at a distance, without the normal means of communication, have been reported in ancient as well as in modern times, among primitive and civilised peoples, both religious and non-religious groups of mankind. To attempt to apply modern statistics to such spontaneous cases usually fails for lack of precise figures giving the expected probability."

In July 1955 a symposium was organized by the Society for Psychical Research in London, together with the Parapsychology Foundation of New York City, at Newnham College, University of Cambridge (England). This provided an opportunity for an exchange of views between scientists interested in Supersensorics. Prof. MURPHY, well-known American psychologist and Director of Research of the Menninger Foundation (Topeka, Kansas), Prof. STRATTON (Cambridge), Prof. BROAD (Cambridge), Prof. PRICE (Oxford), Prof. HART (Dept. of Sociology, Duke Univ., U.S.A.), Dr. HENRY MARGENAU (Sloans Physics Lab., Yale Univ.) and several other leading European and American scientists were able to meet and discuss fundamental problems of supersensorics and the reasons for slow progress. During this conference MAR-

GENAU pointed out correctly that scientists working in this field may be inclined to overrate the competence of wholly empirical material as a means for convincing, heaping fact upon fact without theoretical concepts to explain these observations. "Full credibility involves 1) immediate experiences or reports of them, 2) certain well-connected theoretical concepts, and 3) rules of correspondence between them. The two latter points must be provided before the need for accepting experiences as real will be universally felt," which does not mean that the observations are not true if these points cannot be provided.

Considerable statistical evidence for the existence of paragnostic phenomena has been gathered during the last 30 years particularly through the work of Prof. RHINE and his co-workers at Duke University (USA), Prof. SOAL (London University), Prof. HEYMANS (Prof. of Psychology at Groningen, the Netherlands) and VAN BUSSCHBACH (School Inspector in the Netherlands). These four types of research were carried out independently in different parts of the world and confirmed, with a high degree of probability, the existence of paragnostic phenomena. However, due to reasons given above, various scientists have tried to belittle the results obtained and have not hesitated to accuse them of fraud. However, a sufficiently large number of well-known scientists have been able to check their work and none of them seems to doubt the truthfulness of the observations reported.

In most of these experiments the so-called *Card calling test* is used. This was developed about 1928 by Prof. FISCHER and Miss INA JEPHSON in London.[6] The test employs so-called *Zener cards*, a pack of 25 cards of five groups of symbols: crosses, squares, stars, circles and waves, five cards of each symbol. By pure chance-guessing in a series of 25 trials one has an average chance of five hits only. Mathematical statistics permits us to determine, provided any form of fraud or

6. For details see BETTY M. HUMPHREY: Handbook of tests in Parapsychology.

ordinary psychological sense perception is excluded[7], the degree of probability that such card guesses (surpassing the chance figure 5) are due to pure chance only.

RHINE, PRATT and WOODRUFF demonstrated in 1939 by a series of 96700 card tests, carried out under rigidly controlled conditions at Duke University with 66 different percipients, that a surplus in guesses was obtained representing a critical ratio of 7.8, in other words a possibility that this result could be obtained by chance only in 1 to 10^{14} cases. A comparison between those 96700 cards and a group of cards turned at random, without using a percipient, gave a critical ratio of 0.8 only. Similar experiments by SOAL in London and by HEYMANS in Groningen (the Netherlands)[8] indicated probabilities of even more than 1 to 10^{30}. In other words it seems difficult to explain these results by pure chance only.

A recent series of scientific experiments has been carried out since 1951 in Dutch schools by VAN BUSSCHBACH.[9] Using modified Zener cards and the class teacher (who could not

7. For example by placing the *Agent*, who is presumed to initiate a telepathic transmission, and the *Percipient*, the person who endeavours to receive the mental message, in different rooms far apart.

8. SOAL and GOLDNEY carried out similar experiments during 1941 and 1942, at Queen Mary College, University of London, using pictures of animals. In a series of 3946 pictures with the percipient Shackleton a critical ratio for surplus guessing was obtained of 13.2. In other words a result to be obtained by chance only in 1 to 10^{35} cases. A series of 17000 guesses with the percipient Mrs. Stewart even gave a critical ratio of 52.

About 1921, at the Psychological Institute of the University of Groningen (Netherlands) HEYMANS, assisted by BRUGMANS and WEINBERG, carried out carefully controlled draught-board guessing experiments, in which the percipient, van Dam (a student in Physics), obtained a surplus in "good" guesses which can be explained by chance only in 1 to 10^{30}.

9. The first series of experiments made in Amsterdam with pupils of 10–12 years of age and the teacher as agent consisted of 20,190 trials. A significant critical ratio of good guesses was obtained of 2.79. Similar experiments in the city of Utrecht consisting of 26,880 trials gave a critical ratio of 2.73. Both series together give a critical ratio of 4.07. The most interesting result was, however, that similar extensive tests with older pupils, or tests with young pupils but a stranger as agent, gave only chance results. In 1956 VAN BUSSCHBACH received an invitation from the Parapsychology Lab. at Duke Univ. to conduct similar investigations in American schools. After 36,160 trials with 5th and 6th grade pupils a positive deviation was found with a critical ratio of 2.70, a result almost identical to that obtained in Holland. Again 20,160 trials with 7th and 8th grade pupils or a stranger as agent produced results almost according to chance.

be seen by his pupils) as agent, VAN BUSSCHBACH tested the success with which pupils in a class could acquire knowledge from their teacher by supersensory means. It was found that only young children (10–12 years of age) produced statistically significant results. In the case of older children no positive results were obtained, nor if a child or stranger were used as agent with a group of young children. His experiments were repeated in the USA and his results confirmed.

During 1956 similar experiments were carried out in the USA by ANDERSON and WHITE on the influence of the teacher-pupil attitude. These experiments (and similar tests carried out by BETTY HUMPHREY and others in previous years) seem to suggest that the positive attitude of percipient and agent improves the results, whereas a negative attitude causes considerable negative critical ratios. If these observations are confirmed they will clearly show the enormous difficulties to be encountered in this type of research because the observer may affect the results obtained in a way similar to a thermal experiment in Physics in which the observer is getting too close to the measured object.

The results obtained by these various research workers in different parts of the world make it difficult to deny the existence of some kind of supersensory communication between men. Unless we assume, as some critics do, that all these scientists have been practising fraud systematically, we have to accept the existence of a group of unknown phenomena, whose existence is supported by a vast number of spontaneous cases described in recent years by various serious research workers.

The greatest stumbling block for disbelievers in supersensorics is the phenomenon of *Precognition*. SOAL and others were able to demonstrate statistically, that the percipient often guesses not the card at which the agent is looking but the succeeding one, at that moment unknown to the agent. Well-established spontaneous cases reported in recent years also suggest in certain people the existence of a supersensory faculty, i.e. the capacity to experience events before they have taken place.

If future events are accessible to us, it implies that the future is already predetermined. In a similar way, a passenger in a train can watch the scenery of the present and remember what has passed before. But he lacks the capacity to look ahead, although the future scenery is already in existence.

It seems that the philosophical consequence of precognition, in other words the doctrine of predestination, forms one of the greatest mental obstacles both for certain religious groups and for people who believe in absolute free will and in freedom of choice for the human mind.

Another difficulty in the acceptance of precognition is the consequence that the effect can precede the cause. In card-calling experiments the percipient is apparently guided by events in the future. Something in the future is governing the percipient's behaviour in the present. Many theories, like those of the British philosopher BROAD and of the Dutch scientist KOOY, have been proposed in an attempt to explain those difficulties. They involve modern space-time theories using various dimensions. Recent developments in nuclear physics may help to shed light on these hypotheses which are still unsatisfactory.

(2) *Supersensorics in animals*

It is surprising that the same scientists, who deny the existence of any supersensory capacity in man, accept biological observations on animals suggesting e.g. a peculiar gift in birds to find their home thousands of miles away, even if they have to cross the ocean without any landmarks. Despite the many theories advanced in the last fifty years to explain this direction-finding capacity in birds, no satisfactory explanation has been given yet.

Even less comprehensible is the homing instinct of the Salmon, Eel and Shad. NIERSTRASZ (1916) demonstrated by tagging salmons (*Salmo salar*), which live in small brooks in the centre of the Netherlands, that after spending three years in the Atlantic Ocean they returned to the same spots in those brooks in the Netherlands. Similar experiments were carried out in the USA (SHEER and others, 1939) where newly born hatched salmons were removed from their birthplace to other rivers. After few years they returned, not to these latter rivers but to the original brooks in which they were hatched. SCHMIDT, Director of the Royal Danish Commission for Sea Research, was able to demonstrate (between 1903 and 1922) that the full-grown eel (*Anguilla anguilla*) of approx. 1 m length, migrates in autumn from the rivers of Scandinavia, W. Europe and the Mediterranean area to the Saragossa Sea, N. of Puerto Rico and S. of the Bermudas (3000–4000 miles from their home) and breed there at a great depth. The females drop their eggs which are fertilized by males who die afterwards. From the eggs the young eels, the leptocephali, develop. After three years they reach the coasts of Europe again. The same happens to eels living in the southern part of the USA, but the European type of leptocephalus never migrates to the American coast or vice versa.

Extensive studies in the USA by LEIM, BORODIN, BARNEY and GREYLEY in 1948, and by HOLLIS and HAMMER in 1951 have demonstrated similar almost unbelievable migrations amongst shads. The young shad, which spends the first few months of its life in fresh water basins of N. America near the Atlantic Ocean, moves in autumn to unknown parts of the Atlantic Ocean. Experiments with tagged fishes have shown that the shads return, usually after 5–7 years, to the same fresh water basins in which they spent the first months of their lives.

These examples of very astonishing migrations, which could easily be extended by others, are difficult to understand without accepting certain supersensory sensitivities in the animal world, which may comply with the laws of a future branch of physics, "*Psycho-physics.*"

In this chapter more facts are given than in other parts of the essay, because most scientists seem to be ignorant of them; and without this knowledge the study of supersensory phenomena does not seem to be a very realistic science.

Although the study of supersensory phenomena still belongs to the non-established Border Sciences, there seems to be little doubt that this new branch may one day grow into a vast new science opening vistas of knowledge not even dreamt of in the present atomic age.

C. GEO-ECOLOGY

(1) *Medical geography:*

Medical Geography involves the study of the geographical distribution of diseases and the fundamental causes of the interaction between the environment and living organisms and their conditions of health in the different parts of the world.

The differences observed in the structure and external appearances of living organisms seem to be entirely, or at least largely, determined by the influence of the Lithosphere, Hydrosphere, Atmosphere and Cosmic (extra-terrestrial) sphere. This influence could be a direct one, but may also be indirect through food (animal – or plant food) consumed. Differences in food or climate (determined either geographically or topographically) may change even the anatomical and physiological characteristics of populations, both animal and human. Differences in climate and soil and in useful raw materials available in or on the earth crust may affect social habits, such as differences in housing, hygienic conditions, clothing, etc. Complex groups of such factors affect marital habits, and so on. Similar environmental differences have affected, particularly in previous centuries, methods of heating, lighting, road construction and means of transportation.

In recent years the discovery of so-called trace-elements in the soil has taught us the far-reaching effects of slight deficiencies or surplusses on plants, and indirectly on man and animals consuming them. Cattle in one region may be strong, healthy and active; the same breed in another area having a certain trace-element deficiency in the soil, but with the same climatic conditions, may be weak or slow. Thus the agricultural methods and food conditions of peasants living in such an area are affected. The same may apply to the mental capacity of people of the same race living in different parts of the world.

Complex environmental factors, affected by the geological history of a particular region during hundreds of million of years, may even determine the origin of beliefs or religions in some parts of the world.

The study of this complex geo-ecological web of life has become a very important tool in recent years in the study of the diseases of man.

Diseases can be studied in laboratories or clinics, but more and more it is realized that several complex diseases, such as cancer, must be also approached in a different way. We should start with a field study and try to establish beyond doubt whether two areas really differ in mortality or morbidity from a certain disease. Age group corrections should naturally be made. In addition medical and hospital facilities and training of physicians should be comparable, before it is decided that observed differences are real. In other words, we should be certain that differences in degree of accuracy of diagnosis are not alone responsible for the observed differences.

Once such regional differences have been established beyond doubt, a field team composed of experts should study these different deathrates in order to discover the actual reasons for the observed differences. This empirical approach can be of inestimable value, in the study of disease. Results can only be obtained, however, if a true team-spirit exists amongst scientists; and this may explain the relatively small progress made in this new Border Science: *Medical geography*.

The significance of Medical Geography for the future of mankind is gradually being realized. In fifty years or perhaps even sooner it may play an important part alongside the orthodox sciences.

(2) *Bioclimatology and Biometeorology*

The fourth Border Science that I should like to discuss more in detail is the science of Bioclimatology and Biometeorology. This was defined in 1956 by the "International Society of Bioclimatology and Biometeorology" as "the study of the direct and indirect interrelations between the geo-physical and geo-chemical environment of the atmosphere and living organisms, plants, animals and man, the term "environment" being broadly conceived and including micro-, macro- and cosmic environments and the diverse physical and chemical factors comprising these environments."

The great influence of the atmospheric environment on man is known to everybody who has been forced to be active on a hot summer day and to those who have lived in tropical climates. People living in the Swiss Alps, Austria or Bavaria are well acquainted with a group of peculiar symptoms described as "foehn-disease," which seem to be related to specific weather conditions, known as "foehn."

Despite a great number of subjective observations, it is extremely difficult to prove in many instances that such experiences are really due to specific weather conditions and not merely to coincidence. In those cases in which a weather-disease relationship has been established it is often not known through which physiological processes these weather conditions are reflected in the body. In some instances the influences seem to involve a direct cause- and effect relationship; in others a more complicated indirect relationship seems to exist. This is common in the case of animals where the indirect influences of climate and weather on soil and plants may affect physiological processes of animals living on those plants.

Two kinds of studies are being made in the field of Bioclimatology: so-called "empirical" and "experimental studies." *Empirical studies* (from the Greek empeiria – experiences) comprise observations of facts or events and the knowledge resulting from them without a preconceived idea or theory, whereas in the case of *Experimental studies* (from the Latin experiri – to try) observations of facts or events are made during a trial with the purpose of testing a special hypothesis, theory or assumption.

Bioclimatology can be classified therefore into two main groups depending on the methods of Research.

1. EMPIRICAL BIOCLIMATOLOGY:

In this type of approach observations on certain physiological or pathological phenomena in man, animals or plants, caused or triggered by atmospheric agents, are collected on a statistical basis, without any preconceived idea or theory. Usually there are no clear-cut, quantitative relations between the atmospheric agent and the observed biological effect.

In one group of such studies the effect of more or less known atmospheric agents is being studied. These are either specific meteorological factors (temperature, humidity, etc.) or groups of such factors, air pollutants or aerosols. In such studies the effects are often basically reproduceable.

Other studies involve the effects of either little known or unsuspected atmospheric agents on certain biological phenomena, the results being based on statistical data and often difficult to reproduce.

In recent years new methods have developed from this

group of studies which are described as Experimental Bioclimatology.

2. Experimental bioclimatology:

In this type of research observations on exactly measurable changes in man, animals or plants are collected under reproduceable, controlled experimental conditions, both in the laboratory and in the field. Such conditions are the result of measurable environmental factors, the effect of which is understandable from the physical, chemical and (or) biological viewpoint and usually enables us to predict the qualitative and quantitative aspects of responses to those particular environmental conditions. The purpose of these observations is usually to test a special theory, hypothesis or assumption.

In order to understand the wide scope of bioclimatology as a Border Science and its significance to living organisms, man in particular, we must consider not the different methods of research but the various branches of Bioclimatology and their significance for various aspects of life.

In the case of *Phytological bioclimatology* the influence of climate and of various meteorological factors on the development and distribution of plants is being studied for general phytological, agricultural and forestry purposes. In experimental laboratories artificial climates, which enable us to study the effect of specific meteorological factors on certain plants, are created.

These studies enable the bioclimatologist to determine the best periods for sowing and harvesting and the species which is best adapted to a specific regional climate.

A special aspect of Phytological Bioclimatology is *Bioclimatological phenology* (founded by Linnaeus in 1751 in his "Philosophia Botanica"). It is the study of periodic phenomena in the development of organisms. In the case of plants, the periodicity is caused by seasonal variations. In practice in various parts of an area dates are collected on which a certain type of plant or tree reaches a specific stage of development, e.g. first budding, first appearance of flowers or of certain pollen or spores, first ripening of wheat, etc. Such data are plotted on a map and then connected by curves, indicating regions with equal development. This may give us information about the best areas for growing certain plants in a country, expected dates of harvesting, etc.

A new branch of Phytological Bioclimatology has been developed in recent years by BOYKO (Israel). It is known as *Ecological climatography*. The ecological climatologist defines climate on the basis of plant and animal associations of a region, a valuable tool for underdeveloped areas where there is a lack or shortage of accurate meteorological data.

Another important branch of Bioclimatology is *Zoological bioclimatology* with its two main sections, *Entomological* and *Veterinary bioclimatology*. The entomological bioclimatologist studies the influence of climate and weather on insects and other terrestrial Arthropoda, the effect on their physiological processes, development, diseases and geographical distribution. It is evident that the study of this branch of bioclimatology has far-reaching practical applications if we only think of the yearly damage caused by locust swarms. Veterinary Bioclimatology is a more recent branch of Zoological Bioclimatology which studies both quantitatively and qualitatively the effect of climate and weather on the anatomical and physiological characteristics of domestic and farm animals and birds, and on animal products such as eggs, wool, milk, etc.

The oldest and probably most extensively studied branch of Bioclimatology, even known to the ancient Greeks, is *Human bioclimatology*. Four main sections of this subject have been developed in recent years:

Physiological human bioclimatology comprises the study of the influence of specific single or groups of meteorological components and of different climates (mountain-, marine-, forest-, tropical climates, etc.) and of their seasonal variations, on the various physiological processes of normal healthy man. It also involves investigation of their effect on race and body structure of man, his capacity to become adapted to extreme climatic conditions, etc. The methods applied belong mainly to Experimental Bioclimatology, using special climatic chambers in which various conditions of temperature, humidity, etc. can be changed at will.

A second section of Human Bioclimatology is known as *Social bioclimatology*. In this branch the influence of climate and weather on the social habits of man in general is studied. In a more specific way the use of favourable climatological factors for the treatment of large population groups as preventive or curative measures, and the various social implications in the field of organization of climatic health stations, social insurance, etc. are studied. The Social Bioclimatologist also studies the influence of climate and weather on the mental processes of man (*Psychological bioclimatology*) and on his aesthetic expression (*Aestheto-bioclimatology*). He is also interested in the deeper climatic causes (either direct or indirect) of the origin, distribution and disappearance of past civilizations (*Archaeological bioclimatology*).

A third section of Human Bioclimatology is known as *Pathological bioclimatology*. Here the influence of climate and weather on the various physiological and pathological phenomena associated with the diseases of man, both their frequency, intensity and geographical distribution are studied. The effect of air pollution, either organic (pollen and spores) or inorganic particles or chemical substances, the latter notorious for their devastating effects during "smog," are also investigated. In recent years the great importance of Aerosols[10] in biological processes has also been realized. Finally, various therapeutic effects of climates are being

10. Aerosols are gaseous, liquid or solid aggregates, with diameters of 1/1000 to 10μ and often with either positive or negative electrical charges, which float in the air and are able to penetrate deeply into the lungs of man and animals.

studied. These branches of the subject are more specifically known as Thalassotherapy (sea climate therapy), Heliotherapy, Aerosol- and Ionotherapy, etc. Man is gradually beginning to realize that he is not living as an independent subject, unaffected by his environment, but that he is continuously influenced by the atmosphere surrounding him, both by its favourable and by its detrimental influences.

The fourth main section of Human Bioclimatology is *Urban bioclimatology*. This is the study of micro-climates in houses and cities and their influence on the health of man. Methods are being developed for eliminating unfavourable influences and for increasing favourable biological effects in certain types of architectural construction and in town planning. It is often not sufficiently realized that in the regional planning of a city, the spaces between buildings, their height and the creation of large parks whose vegetation affects the amount of solar energy and ionization of the air, etc. present important biometeorological problems. In addition the type of heating and chimneys used and the location of industries in relation to the prevailing direction of wind govern the local micro-climates and the health of large population groups. Closely related to this problem is the study of the best locations and construction methods for sanatoria from the point of view of climato-therapy.

Another interesting branch of Bioclimatology is known as *Cosmic bioclimatology*. This is the study of the effect of extraterrestrial influences on biological processes. It is well-known that variations in the activity of the sun affect the meteorological conditions of the outer parts of the atmosphere. These in turn influence weather conditions at the lower levels in which we are living. Such long-range indirect effects may seriously influence economic conditions in an area through abnormal rainfall, snow, heat, cold, or drought spoiling harvests and often killing animals in the open fields.

Recent studies by PICCARDI (Professor of Physical Chemistry in Florence, Italy) suggest a possible direct effect by unknown cosmic agents on physico-chemical processes, both inorganic and organic. If these studies can be confirmed an important new field of research will be opened up.

The fifth main branch of bioclimatology is *Palaeo-bioclimatology*. It involves the study of the influence of climatic conditions in the past on the development, evolution and geographical distribution of living organisms. Recent developments in the border Science Geology, the improvement of methods of dating geological periods (in particular those using various radioactive methods), the introduction of Palynology and other related sciences have enabled us to analyse the type of climate prevailing during the different geological periods in various parts of the world. In many instances the flora and fauna during these periods are also known so it has been possible to draw some interesting bioclimatological conclusions, often with far-reaching philosophical consequences.

These various aspects of Bioclimatology and Biometeorology, originally studied by individual research workers in different countries have been coordinated recently through the creation of the "International Society of Bioclimatology and Biometeorology," [11] comprising 500 members from 44 countries. The members represent many scientific disciplines and come from countries with widely differing political systems. The friendly relations between the members of this organization clearly demonstrate how a border science, perhaps more than any basic science, is able to unite people of good will all over the world, irrespective of race, creed or political conviction.

11. Founded 1 January 1956. Secretariate Hofbrouckerlaan 54, Oegstgeest (Leiden), The Netherlands.

III. SUGGESTIONS FOR THE CREATION OF A UNIVERSAL ACADEMY OF BORDER SCIENCES

In the previous chapters a review has been given of the various problems studied in four new Border Sciences. The solution of these requires the cooperation of many scientists trained in different disciplines. Although by correspondence and regular international contacts the necessary cooperation between scientists can be furthered, it is doubtful whether real progress can be made in a complex Border Science unless an international team of scientists actually works together in the same research institute. In the field of atomic research we have a good example of international cooperation in International Research Institutes. Similar Institutes should be created in future for the Border Sciences.

Of the various Border Sciences the international team spirit seems to be most strongly developed in the field of Bioclimatology. Therefore, if funds could be raised for a Universal Academy of Border Sciences, a Universal Centre for the Study of Bioclimatology and Biometeorology in its various aspects should first be created as a *Faculty of bioclimatology and biometeorology* in the future Academy. The experience obtained in such a truly International Centre could be applied to the creation of other Universal Centres for the Study of Border Sciences. Although it seems preferable that the different "Faculties" of a Universal Academy of Border Sciences should be located in the same area, this does not seem to be an essential requirement.

In the previous chapters I have tried to review the significance of a number of Border Sciences, both established and non-established, for the future of mankind. I fully realize that there is a long way to go before the ideas expressed can be realized. On the other hand, it is the first time in the history of mankind that many scientists in the world have become fully aware of the urgent need for universal cooperation. Let us therefore be confident and believe in the creed of the geologists that "the Universe in all its appearances is a function of time and no barriers of development, however strong and unconquerable they may seem at this moment, can resist the pressure of human mind if the will prevails to overcome these barriers."

The Human Significance of Natural Resources

(with special reference to man's cultural resources)

by

RICHARD M. FIELD

All human beings are animals and therefore depend on the material, natural resources which constitute their environment. Human beings should not try to conquer their environment but learn to live in harmony with it. Whether the earth was created for man or with man, they are inter-dependent correlated expressions of life, and it is either man's God-given or man's inevitable responsibility to explore, develop and distribute the earth's material, natural resources for the benefit rather than the ultimate impoverishment of himself and his fellow-men.

Probably most organized warfare since the dawn of civilization has been because of the unequal geographic distribution of material, natural resources, beginning with the areas for food collecting or hunting by the smallest groups of humanlike beings hundreds of thousands of years ago.

Because history is cyclic, as well as progressive, we are now in one of the most tempestuous cycles in the history of mankind. This is due to that particular branch of man's activities which we call science, and its powers for war as well as for peace. If man wishes to avoid the most devastating war of all time scientists and statesmen must coöperate so that the future rôle of science will be increasingly social in that science and human affairs have become inseparable.

Popular science may no longer be defined only in terms of

the marvels of inventions and new gadgets; popular science must also include the relation of science to society, and the sincere attempt by scientists to see that this information is available not only to a few favored individuals or groups, but also to all elements of society through whose coöperative efforts their developed environments have been created. As HUGO BOYKO says in one of his communications (July, 1957); "So we shall have to find ways to stabilize the equilibrium of our Society, and the ways to this aim cannot be sought through egotism or through terrorism. The sole power lies in our own (the scientists) hands and has to be brought about by trying to amalgamate science with humanitarism. Therefore new ways of teaching have to be found in all and every ways and branches of science; teaching not only of knowledge but also of responsibility."

All living things have their responsibilities, chief of which is re-creation (reproduction of species). This is just as true of plants and animals as it is of man; but man's responsibility is greater than that of all other living things because of his greater mind, thought, reason and conscience. A conscientious person may be defined as one whose moral sense *within himself* determines whether he considers his own conduct right or wrong. This constitutes the spirit and soul of man. Consequently, for thousands of years, man has prayed for a mysterious, extraneous power to help him live with the least trouble and the most happiness. All the great philosophers and prophets have advised man that he cannot be happy without trouble. That he cannot have a clear conscience and consequent peace of mind without some suffering. Therefore, I believe that each man's religion is his greatest *natural* resource; and that although it is superphysical it is not super-natural. How can any man claim to be an atheist unless he is so conceited that he believes only in himself? To quote from Sir RICHARD TUTE in his essay "The Loom of a Plan": "Every thing is super-physical, and remains super-physical after it has acquired the additional attribute of being perceptible. You and I are super-physical here and now. When death supervenes we will continue to be what we are, while disappearing from the physical stage. What we will encounter when we come face to face with the naked forces of four dimensional reality is unknown to us, except in mystic reports" ... This statement should appeal to all scientists, no matter what their theology, because it was written by a lawer, scientist, and devout Anglican.

Because human beings are the greatest of all natural resources, all the factors which constitute the complex interrelation of the material, cultural and spiritual activities of human beings should be considered as natural resources; and because no human being lives only to survive, we must assume that *the joy of living must overcome the fear of living*. The mere act of living depends on the fundamental physical factors which affect all human beings, such as climate, topography, water, plants, animals, and minerals, including air and soils.

Therefore, the *physical* welfare of all human beings requires the exploration, development and distribution of the world's geographically varied *material resources. The joy of living* requires the exploration, development and distribution of the world's geographically varied *cultural and spiritual resources.*

It would be a very useful step forward in mutual understanding of peoples, if we could achieve a thorough survey of all natural resources, namely not only of the material resources but also of the cultural and spiritual resources of all peoples.

In this sense the following classification of Natural resources was used at the International Conference on Science and Human Welfare, Washington, D.C., 1956.

MATERIAL RESOURCES

I. ORGANISMS.

Ia. *Plants:*

1. Food plants (cereals, vegetables, fruits, sugar plants, spices, beverage plants, etc.)

2. Fodder plants (grasses, leaves, fruits etc.)
3. Fibers (textile plants, paper plants, etc.)
4. Forest products (for Wood, Cork, Tanning materials, etc.)
5. Latex plants (for Rubber, Gums, Resins, etc.)
6. Plants for Essential oils (perfume plants)
7. Fats and Waxes.
8. Medicinal plants.
9. Plants for Fumitories (Tobacco, etc.)
   Masticatories, (Cola, etc.), Narcotics (Opium, Hemp, etc.)
10. Various plant raw materials (e.g. vegetable ivory for buttons, palm leaves for roofs, starch for industry, lichens for Agar agar, fungi and bacteria for inoculation, fermentation, and so on).

Ib. *Animals:* Many raw materials are to be found in the animal world.
1. from food to hormones used in medicine.
2. from furs and leather to ivory and pearls, strings for musical instruments, hairs for the brushes for the painter or for hygrometers for the Meteorologist, etc., etc.

II. FUELS:

Such as peat, coal, natural gas and petroleum. It should also be noted, however, that power resources include wind, water and solar radiation, as well as fuels. Although atomic power depends, to a certain extent, on several types of minerals this source of power should not be considered except as a special problem from the destructive as well as the constructive point of view.

III. USEFUL MINERALS:

1. Soils (Complex sediments composed of minerals and mineral salts, and certain amounts of living and decayed organisms).
2. Ceramics (Aluminium silicates which are used in the manufacture of china, tiles, bricks, etc).
3. Fertilizers (Rock phosphates, Chile saltpetre, etc.)
4. Refractories and Insulators (Asbestos, Graphite, Mica etc.)
5. Chemical Compounds (Numerous mineral salts used in the chemical industries.)
6. Abrasives (Diamond, Corundum, Garnet, etc.)
7. Structural (base) Metals (Iron, Copper, Lead, Zinc, etc.)
8. Ferro-alloys (Manganese, Tungsten, Chromium, Lead, Zinc, etc.)
9. Precious (noble) Metals (Gold, Silver, Platinum, etc. These are also termed the monetary metals).

IV. STRUCTURAL (MINERAL) MATERIALS:

1. Building Stones (Such as Granite, Sandstone, Limestone, Gypsum, Marble, Slate, etc.)

2. Sands and Gravels (Detrital and fragmental aggregates, naturally derived from various types of rocks.)
3. Natural Cements.

CULTURAL RESOURCES

I. RHYTHMIC.
1. Music. Instrumental and vocal.
   a. Individual. b. Group
2. Dance.
   a. Individual b. Group.
3. Historical.
4. National.
5. International

II. GRAPHIC
1. Pictures. Picture-writing, Symbols.
2. Sculpture. Mobile, architectural
3. Etching and Engraving.
4. Printing and Lithography.
5. Historical.
6. National.
7. International.

III. ARCHITECTURE
1. Religious structures
2. Domestic structures.
3. Business structures.
4. Historical.
5. National.
6. International.

IV. DRAMA
1. Folklore.
2. Theatre.
3. Historical.
4. National.
5. International.

V. REPRODUCTIVE.
1. Cinema and Television.
2. Phonographic and Telephonic
3. Historical.
4. National.
5. International.

TECHNICAL RESOURCES

I. SCIENTIFIC
1. Literature
2. Organizations.
3. Laboratories.
4. Field work.
5. Schools.
6. Societies.
7. Historical.
8. National.
9. International.

II. ENGINEERING.
1. Mapping. Topographic:
   a. ground. b. aerial.
   c. geological. d. geophysical.
2. Construction.
   a. Roads, Railroads. b. Airfields.
   c. Bridges, Tunnels, Aqueducts.
   d. Vehicles. e. Airplanes.
3. Historical.
4. National.
5. International.

W. F. G. SWANN correlates the experience of the scientist and the artist. He recognizes the awe with which all scientists and artists view the "cleverness" of the Universe, the "potentiality" for "happiness" in "living things as part of the experience of beauty as the whole worth-while purpose of living beings." Although his essay concerns music, he points out three truths for all the arts: 1) As one seeks for the stimuli which are responsible for exaltation, he finds great simplicity ... as the forbear of grandeur. 2) In general, beauty may be divided into two types, that which represents an immediate appeal to him that beholds it, and which emerges only in the light of understanding ... sometimes it embraces both. 3) In seeking perfection in such an art as music ... the goal must be divided into two categories; perfection of concept, and perfection of realization on the instrument or instruments on which the music is played.

JOAN FIELD, Chairman of the A.I.G.N.R. Dramatic Council sums up these thoughts with evidence of theatre and folklore as experience, thereby having "happiness potential" for a majority of – not all – people at all times in history. The analysis of any classic play or folk-story reveals a simple basis character-situation which has universal appeal. This situation inevitably concerns one of the "moments of exaltation" in which a human being has a positive realization of beauty in his relationship to others, thereby giving the viewer or listener, whether in a group or "solo" experience, a sense of being "part of the structure." In other words he finds entertainment in being drawn into the universal experience of the story's character; he escapes into a larger world and finds a larger self.

Folklore, being close to nature and based on elementary values, can be successfully presented through any of the handicrafts or the performed or graphic arts, but perhaps the theatre is the most challenging of media for the presentation of folklore, for it offers the interpretive play wright, composer, director, designer or choreographer the widest possible combination of effects in the complexity of the selection required to eliminate non-essentials and point up the main line of action and related elements.

In our day, the Japanese Kabuki theatre, American musical plays such as "South Pacific" or "Fanny," JOHN GIRAUDOUX's fantasy "Ondine," are all examples of complex theatrical production based on simple fables or folk stories. Any style can be used to reach out and touch the heart of the onlooker, making him one with all. "And so, if we pray for anything, pray that ye may find senses to which all nature's beauties bring response, for then shall ye be angels. Then shall ye have attained the pinnacle of what may have been the intent of the Universe, the creation of the realm in which happiness may grow to full maturity."

The theatre's primary purpose is recreation for groups of people, whether through creative participation or as members of the audience. It is the common sharing of experience which makes the theatre especially rewarding, therefore the primary "natural resources" necessary for theatrical production are people. Any group is potential "theatre-material." Specialists such as playwrights, talented performers, composers or designers, develop in certain places individually for reasons which seem to be beyond control, but the finished theatrical product usually flowers and finds recognition and wide usefulness in centers of concentrated population and relatively advanced culture: the great cities of the world.

A survey of the "theatrical wealth" of the countries of the world should have two branches: 1) The listing of production groups or centers of each nationality which offer the finest entertainment for its own people as for people of other nations. 2) The listing of all known groups or centers in each nation which emphasizes creative theatre work of any kind: a) commercial, b) educational, c) community, and d) social welfare and therapeutic. Of particular interest because of their universal appeal are the four fields of the theatre: 1) The use and development of theatre methods. 2) The growth of the creative individual through improvisation. 3) Children's theatre, and 4) Folk-drama. Through existing organizations such as ANTA or other national theatres and regional groups throughout the countries of the world, a survey might be made of the resources already developed in these fields, and any special contributions which these groups are making.

Needless to say the desire for theatre (although painfully unencouraged in some places) is common to all people, and the potential resources of theatre are world-wide. Children do not need to be encouraged to "play house," they only need to be discouraged from stopping when they think the child in them is childish.

The border between imaginative play and art in general, poetic vision and science is not as sharp as many people believe. They all are ways to the joy of life and many bridges bring them together.

A short poem and a few additional lines may serve as example:

Ode to the Grand Canyon of the Colorado River

What makes the lingering night so cling to thee?
Thou vast, profound, primeval hiding-place
Of ancient secrets, – gray and ghostly gulf
Cleft in the green of this high forest land,
And crowded in the dark with giant forms.

Now, far beyond all language and all art
In thy wild splendor, Canyon marvellous,
The secret of the stillness lies unveiled
In wordless worship: This is holy ground;
Thou art no grave, no prison, but a shrine,
Garden of Temples filled with Silent Praise
If God were blind thy beauty could not be.

Thus sang the poet HENRY VAN DYKE as he watched the many splendors of this great canyon gradually develop under the rays of the rising sun. Here are line-color marvellously compounded in grand structural simplicity, which delights the eye of the engineer and the architect as well as that of the poet and the painter. Probably in no other region of the world is the structure of so vast a scene so clearly displayed. Even those who have had no geological training cannot fail to notice that this great canyon, a mile deep and ten miles wide, has exposed to view a great series of horizontal formations which, on each side of the narrow inner gorge, have been still further dissected into spires and castellated blocks of many sizes and shapes. To the geologist, the canyon looses nothing of its beauty under his analytical attack. To his trained eye, the architectural splendor has a glorious history, which he traces by the most delicate use of line and color, combined with the techniques of petrology and structure. He too paints a picture, both scientific and spiritual, which rivals the Semitic conception in Genesis, or the later emotional and artistic song of the poet. If the canyon is the work of God, then it is through His agents that it has been wrought. Surely there can be no better place for the wedding of science and religion than before such a splendid spectacle as this chasm, which exposes the history of the earth down to the oldest known rocks. So might a geologist add two more lines to the final hymn of praise:

If God were blind thy beauty *might* not be
So to compel the searching eyes of man
And thus reveal the history of His work.

Summarizing we may say that science and art are functioning, or should function, as parallel ways to the same goal, to achieve joy in living for all, and that means, to real progress in human welfare. Organizational links of these two roads can be and should therefore be found.

It was for this reason that apart from all other Institutions, Organizations, and Personalities also the International

Union of Geodesy and Geophysics, through its committees on the social Value of the Earth Sciences, during the XIth Assembly of the I.U.G.G., held at Toronto, Ontario, Canada, September 3–14, 1957, unanimously approved the suggestion for a "World Academy of *Arts* and Sciences, as P. B. SEARS expressed it:

> *"On behalf of free and cordial collaboration*
> *among scientific men of all nations*
> *at a time when the power of modern technology*
> *is being employed out of all proportion*
> *to the exploitation, rather than to the nurture*
> *of man's environment."*

Resource Planning: A Problem in Communication[1]

by

PIERRE DANSEREAU

The leading authorities on gamesmanship recommend that scientists who find themselves intimidated by confreres in another field of knowledge extend an immediate invitation to visit their own bailiwick. By no devious route that is what I intend to do: my area of investigation is ecology, and where it emerges on the social plane it has some bearing on resource utilization, an area of human activity now potentially dominated by physicists. Furthermore, in alluding to communication in my title, I do not have in mind the transport of iron ore from the Ungava or long-distance telephone calls, but the difficulties of exchanging information and achieving verbal and working co-ordination. The incentives and the duties of the academic community are very great in this respect.

Before I venture the opinion that the universities do not show enough awareness of the problems of resource planning, I feel I must draw a brief historical sketch of the sciences that are involved therein and outline some of the pioneering plans that have been put into effect in the past ten years in a few institutions.

1. Yale Conservation Studies, Vol. 6, pp. 3–6 (1957). Reprinted by kind permission of the Editor.

PIERRE DANSEREAU

THE MEANING OF CONSERVATION

A key word, at this point, is conservation. Much has been said about the conservative mind by royalists, republicans, liberals, socialists, progressives, reactionaries and revolutionaries. It is not inappropriate, in fact, that scientific conservation received some of its early impetus from political conservatives who are traditionally dedicated to a cult of the national patrimony. But it is hardly less in keeping with the liberal and the socialist doctrines to have stressed the pre-eminence of public ownership where resources are concerned. In other words, the good state of the land has long been everybody's business, from the right to the left, and back.

Lest the scope of my topic be obscured by this statement, let me define conservation as a *wise utilization of natural resources.* Such a definition poses three questions:

(1) What is a *natural resource*? It is a mineral, plant, or animal which occurs in the spontaneous state, such as water, soil, iron, coal, lumber, fish.

(2) How can it be *utilized*? It may be used indirectly for power or irrigation (water), nutrition of crops (soil), recreation (water, forest), or directly for industry (copper, timber) or food (blueberries, ducks).

(3) What is *wisdom* in this case? Surely this is more difficult to answer. The only reasonable reply is that good stewardship is proportionate to enlightened planning for the future. This suggests the further question of immediate objectives, inasmuch as natural resources are not all renewable and that some justification must be made for exhaustive tapping.

It seems to me, that public opinion and the recommendations of scientists who have variously led and followed it have undergone four phases, which I would call: legislative, biological, ecological, and sociological.

Legislative phase. At the beginning of the century protection afforded to wild plants and animals was largely decreed by law and was focussed almost entirely on rare species. Birds of paradise were saved but not the Arctic penguin or the dodo bird. Such rulings did not concern themselves with soil and water, for instance.

Biological phase. As detailed inventories of flora and fauna were made, a more scientific approach was initiated. Naturalists demanded freedom of certain areas from disturbance so that individual plants and animals could be studied. Others requested protection of large populations of trees and birds, as a sort of capital investment. This did not save the passenger pigeon, although it halted the decline of the buffalo and the caribou.

Ecological phase. Presently, however, with the extinction of many beautiful or valuable plants and animals, and because of a rising consciousness of the interrelatedness of living beings, the claim was made that no efficient protection of individual species was possible if the habitat as a whole were not free from interference, direct or indirect. For instance, the continued integrity of the landscape became expedient when it was realized that forested banks maintained high water levels and cool temperatures in Canadian streams and allowed the salmon to spawn: spruce and fir protection was the condition for a normal cycle in the fish.

Sociological phase. The far-reaching effects of flooding, fires, the introduction of pests soon made it evident that a scientific approach was not enough. It did not always provide a satisfactory answer, and it did not begin to meet the social, political, economic, and occasionally religious aspects of the utilization of natural resources. It was not possible to quarantine the chestnut blight and the Dutch elm disease. The antagonisms of hydraulic power and agriculture, of lumbering and game management came into the open, and conservationists began to strike at the social and economic systems. But reactionary politicians were long reluctant to impose burning of corn stalks that harbored the dreaded corn-borer, and relict stands of timber were ruthlessly lumbered. The complicity of the ignorant and the mighty resulted in indiscriminate farming off of resources without concern for the upsets of natural balances.

Conservation has meant various things at various times, and has involved many kinds of thinking and campaigning in the course of its development. Some of the classic figures are THEODORE ROOSEVELT, his heroic mustaches aquiver, bringing peace to the African and Brazilian wilderness, and that group of determined ladies brandishing their umbrellas on Trafalgar Square to prevent the murder of offending pigeons. Even sturdier battles were fought in varous legislatures to stop irresponsible licensing of streams and forests to private interests. Above all, the press and the universities, especially in their departments of forestry, have carried the torch and have finally destroyed the myth of inexhaustibility. As a result, great works of conservation like those in the Tennessee or the Fraser Valleys in North America have been a concentration ground for the testing and application of a new-found knowledge.

RESOURCE UTILIZATION PROBLEMS

The harnessing of the natural resources of the world is now being viewed in a new light and a joint attack is being made upon the question as a whole, which is nothing less than man's survival. The conflicting forces are: increasing human populations and decreasing resources. The favored solutions are: limitation of births, technological increase of renewable resources, halting of waste, and economic readjustment of distribution. On all counts, at this time, there are apparent deadlocks: religious and cultural opposition of birth control, resistance to industrialization of production, and disparity in standard of living. In the minds of many who have written on this subject, the hope of making progress on all fronts is so dim that humanity is doomed to a terrible regression, unless generalized atomic bombing be indeed considered a feature in the self-regulating process of population-resource balance.

We must therefore ask ourselves what we actually know about *population*, about *resources*, and about the management of human *societies*. Do we really know enough to point to a scientific solution? Furthermore, what use are we making of the knowledge that we do possess? And finally, are these different kinds of knowledge being co-ordinated as they must in order to fit the problem at hand?

I would like to give an optimistic answer to these three questions, and I am somewhat encouraged to do so by the fact that a small number of our fellow scientists now seem able to read the problem in its full complexity and no longer incline to a single solution.

Population. We know much less about humans than we do about the fruit fly and the corn plant. But our knowledge of the interplay of heredity and environment, as it affects man in health and disease is now considerable. The mapping of anatomical and physiological features has progressed a great deal, and many valuable statistical analyses of birth and death rates in different environments are available. The causes of fertility and sterility are now better known, and so are means of increasing and decreasing them. Although no valid understanding of these biological functions can bc achieved without a thorough grounding in physiology and genetics, it does not follow that a pertinent social interpretation can be drawn by the methods of natural science alone. Life cycle figures do not speak for themselves outside the ethnical, cultural, religious and economic context of human societies.

Resources. The world inventory of water, minerals, soils, plants and animals is, or course, not complete, not even qualitatively. And where quantitative surveys have been made, our grasp of the complex interrelationships that permit renewal (at certain rates and times) is not yet very firm. Although, on the one hand, one may be impatient with the optimistic technologists who predict indefinite progress in harnessing new or untapped resources, on the other hand, it is hard for some of us to go along with the negative pronouncements of those who say that saturation is in view. There is cause for alarm in the large-scale ravages of soil erosion, the apparently irreversible destruction of many forests, the drying up of water courses and lowering of water tables, the virtual extinction of valuable trees and animals, and the complete exhaustion locally of coal or oil. For all of these, technology may or may not produce adequate substitutes, and our future way of life may or may not make the same demands. Much more ecological research is needed which should be focussed on natural balance in the landscape. All existing ecosystems [2] can be exploited and even harnessed much more efficiently when we have measured the forces that hold them together.

Society. If our knowledge of population and resources is incomplete and insecure in many ways, how much narrower is our view of human societies. The precision which bears on the mechanics of hereditary transmission, or on the life-cycles of domesticated plants and animals has been usefully carried over to anthropology, and much has been learned which has dispelled some time-honored beliefs of man about himself. But social psychology, history, economics, and political science must of all necessity handle more delicate tools. So many of the "facts" in the sciences of man are values that cannot be tested to provide truly experimental answers.

I cannot pretend, with the means at my command, to delineate in its entirety the population-resource problem. I can only outline the requisites to a proper understanding, the

2. Ecologists have coined this term which deserves recognition in every man's vocabulary: it refers to the interacting whole which comprises the substratum together with the living population which it supports: thus, a lake, a bog, a dune, a forest.

lines of a valid perspective. I would like to follow this by pointing to the functions in the university which can best serve the interest of such a concern.

EDUCATION FOR RESOURCE PLANNING

Whether the scope is local or world-wide, resource-planning must draw from many sources. And since it is impossible for one man to be equally well-versed in genetics, forestry, pedology, anthropology and economics, some kind of team-work has to be undertaken. And yet the mere addition of specialties does not engender a synthesis. The latter has two basic requirements, in my mind: a solid grounding in at least one field and an early awareness and general understanding of the principles and basic facts in other fields. A plea for "generalists" instead of specialists should not lead us so far astray as to renounce technical competence in at least one discipline for each worker. There probably is no such thing as "general culture", unless it is an aggregation of various kinds of knowledge around a solid nucleus in one field.

It would seem to me, therefore, that a programme of education for conservation practices, for land-use planning, and for natural resource utilization should of all necessity have its point of departure in somewhat specialized training. In the past, this initial step has almost always been taken in forestry, agronomy, engineering, zoology or botany. At present, it seems just as valid to begin in geography, economics, or political science. In either case, it is expedient not only to rise above the initial field of concentration and to apply its data and principles to the problems of resource utilization, but also to dig right back into other fields, at the elementary level if necessary. For instance, a student who has come up from economics can be required to take forestry or hydrology courses, to attend a regional geography or an ecology seminar. A good deal of such preliminary acquisition of knowledge will provide an ample background for the specific attack upon problems of resource utilization.

Such plans have been in effect since 1950 in two American universities, Michigan and Yale. It is not as important to look into the administrative structure that supports these studies, as to note the pre-eminence of a programme system over a rigid departmental curriculum. Guidance of students in the early stages of their development and orientation towards a well-integrated course can give a totally different meaning even to their undergraduate years.

COMMUNICATION TROUBLES

The problems of natural resource utilization can neither be posed nor solved by one discipline alone. Therefore an efficient understanding of them awaits a better communication between the natural scientists and the social scientists and the emergence of a larger number of men capable of encompassing both aspects and of acting upon this improved knowledge. Maybe this can be done by mature men in prominent places in government, public administration, industry, business, and the liberal professions. But I should have more hope of its being achieved in the microcosm of the university campus, where representatives of all fields are available to each other, if they will just learn to take advantage of their opportunities.

Communication trouble does not stop here, in the inner circle of our academic milieu. No matter how rationally we organize our data and map out our knowledge, no matter how well agreed we are on ways and means, we still face the task of providing the people with an intelligible and relevant plan. The campus must be an open forum where adult education groups as well as youth organizations feel at home. The natural and social scientists who have together elaborated these plans are also bound to go out into the economic and social world and make their views known. Let us destroy no ivory towers; in fact we need more of them, for the peculiar alchemy of creative thinking is a secret process that does not function well in the open. But let us not be so vulnerable to difficulties of social reality as to shrink before the task of fighting for a more enlightened planning of natural resource utilization, if we are convinced that we bear some of the light in our own hands.

This thrusts great responsibilities upon us as educators. On this subject, more than on many others, our capacity for objective thinking will be strongly tested. We are committed to teaching the truth. We are supposed to be living examples of lucid thinking. As free men we may subscribe to some religious or political dogma, but as teachers we may do no violence to fact. A Catholic historian is not bound to justify the Inquisition, a fundamentalist geologist is not bound to deny the accuracy of Carbon-14 datings.

With respect to the dynamics of human population, the test is a severe one: there are few topics upon which doctrinal issues impinge more strongly, few which invite more academic evasions and rationalizations of one kind or another. It is all too easy to invoke a commodious ignorance of the actual level or potential of resources and to trust blindly in technological progress. This is the worst way in which our true mission can be by-passed, and eventually also the least efficient way of serving the very dogmas which we adhere to as individuals: a breach with one truth is a breach with all and every one of them. If our religious and political orthodoxies are aspects of truth or compendia of human wisdom, they should welcome the confrontation.

I can draw no simple conclusion and I am sure you expect none. In blueprinting a plan for natural resource administration, many difficulties are involved. Some are semantic and some are technical but most of them can be overcome. The main area of the contest is in the now broadly overlapping fields of the natural and social sciences. It seems to me that we, on university campuses, would be well advised to direct much of our energy to the development of mutual understanding and to the elaboration of joint programmes that would instill new life and a new hope for the solution of problems that require an open mind and a dedicated effort.

LA PLANIFICATION DES RESSOURCES: UN PROBLEME DE COMMUNICATION

par

PIERRE DANSEREAU

Le mot *conservation* a connu une évolution qui reflète la préoccupation croîssante de la société au sujet de ses ressources naturelles, et particulièrement au sujet de celles qui ne sont pas renouvelables. On peut dire qu'une première phase (*biologique*) s'est accomplie par des inventaires détaillés de plantes et d'animaux, et surtout de ceux qui étaient menacés; qu'une seconde (*écologique*) a cherché à placer ces êtres vivants dans leur cadre naturel, l'habitat qu'il fallait alors protéger tout entier; et que nous sommes entrés depuis peu dans une troisième (*sociologique*) qui tient compte davantage des structures sociales, économiques, politiques et religieuses et de leurs exigences.

Pour bien poser les problèmes d'utilisation de nos ressources nous devons puiser dans nos connaissances concernant la *population*, les *ressources* elles-mêmes et la *société*. Ces trois termes nous sont inégalement connus. Les données de l'anthropologie et de la sociologie ne se présentent pas à nous avec la même précision que celles de l'hydrologie, de la botanique ou de la physiologie. Nous disposons encore moins d'un personnel qualifié pour faire la synthèse de deux ou plusieurs de ces disciplines. Quelques pas ont toutefois été faits par des universités où l'on a mis au point des programmes d'études auxquels on accède désormais aussi bien à partir de la sociologie ou de l'économique que de la foresterie, de l'écologie ou de la zoologie, voies traditionnelles. Ce curriculum nouveau exige d'ailleurs que les économistes se plient à la biologie et à la géologie et que les naturalistes s'instruisent en sociologie.

Ainsi l'armée montante de ces "conservateurs" nouveau-genre, de ces administrateurs des ressources humaines et naturelles, nous aide présentement à rompre certaines barrières: les difficultés de communication entre les disciplines scientifiques et sociologiques d'une part et entre les diverses classes sociales d'autre part.

Food Supply and Increase of Population

by

M. J. Sirks

The statement, that in many countries there is a large excess of food-production and food-supply, while in other parts of the world the great masses of the people suffer from an almost permanent scarcity of food, periodically leading to starvation, looks like carrying coals to Newcastle, or like we in this country say, like carrying water to the sea. There is no doubt whatever that a regular and sufficient supply of food is one of the primary conditions of life, not to say the most fundamental one. There is no doubt whatever that starvation is one of the most cruel and merciless processes, by which life is menaced, that death by starvation is the hardest fate human beings can meet. Those of us who live in one of the privileged countries, look upon a good breakfast, a loaded table at lunch or dinner as phenomena of the same regularity as sunrise or sunset, they not only consider a quantitatively and qualitatively good feeding one of the claims to which every-one is entitled, but they accept a well stocked pantry as a matter of course. In quite exceptional cases, our Western populations are put up against a serious food-shortage, or even against starvation: the last months of World War II have taught the urban population in the Western part of this country the gravity of a situation in which foodsupply has been decreased to the extremely low level of 600 calories a day. But we all know that this situation in other parts of the world is not an exception at all, we all know it and we all shall be conscious of the fact that in many other countries a large majority of people do not receive the amount of food, which is taken for the minimum necessary for a worthy living of human beings. And for those who are not yet fully aware of this extremely alarming fact, a study of books like that of the WOYTINSKI's and that of Sir JOHN RUSSELL may serve as an eye-opener.

We all have to face this very big problem squarely; not only because those who suffer from under-nourishment are human beings, our fellow-men and by this it is our moral duty to help as much as we can, but also because there is a serious danger in this situation that hunger fetches the wolf out of the wood, that hunger demoralizes the people, sets going the unreasonable elements within a population, and by that causes an explosion of the large masses, which by their state of mind destroy by sheer force what has been achieved and acquired during long years for the profit of the people's welfare.

To all appearance this situation of a shortage of food in large parts of the world has taken a turn for the worse since the last World War. I may quote two conclusions from RUSSELL's alarming book: "The quantities of food produced during the last ten or fifteen years have changed but little while the population has been steadily increasing" (p. 329). And: "The net result of all these changes is that the countries of Asia, already ill-fed before the war, are on a still lower dietary now, but while in the aggregate they used to produce the whole of their food supply and even have margins for export they now no longer do so but have become dependent on America and Australia for the reduced amount of food they are getting" (p. 352).

The urgency of this very big problem of food supply has not decreased in the least; this problem is a problem for today, for tomorrow, for the near or a more remote future.

The problem for today is one for the economist: to find a

better way of international exchange of food materials for other merchandise available for export in the food-lacking countries. Such an exchange, however, demands that in these countries where deficiency of food continuously threatens the peoples welfare, materials for exchange shall be available and as long as this requirement is not satisfied, a real exchange remains a wishful day-dream, which like most dreams, is empty. A remedy for the present situation can be obtained only by a one-sided relief-action on an extensive and large scale, and therefore asks for so much understanding from both sides that I am afraid that the most competent and the most altruistic economist will be unable to find an efficient and immediate solution for this lack of equilibrium between different parts of the world.

The problem for tomorrow belongs to the domain of the biologist, more especially to that of the plantbreeder and the animal breeder. In many of the Western countries varieties and strains of cultivated plants, of cattle, of fowl are available which are much better producing than the rather primitive races in the food-lacking countries. These improved races have been obtained by a long year program of hybridization and selection and they are available now for immediate use. It seems to be a task for the biologist to pick out those strains which are suited to be grown and raised in those destitute countries and to introduce them there for further cultivation and for improving the production rate of the indigenous agriculture. It is a difficult problem which needs some time of experiment, but which in my opinion can be solved before long by international cooperation.

There are various problems for the near future which aim at developing agriculture and agricultural methods all over the world, most especially in the socalled less developed countries.

The first and most obvious one is a subject of technical education. In many of those countries methods and equipment for agricultural practice are still primitive and not at all efficient. Modern technics has been developed since a number of years and by that it is a task for educational technicians to teach the agricultural labourer in those countries how to handle these modern machinery and to adapt these tools to the needs of the native farmers. This task shall be performed with the greatest care: it is quite easy to import large stocks of modern implements into these countries, but it takes much time and patience to teach the farmers how to use them and how to keep them in repairs. Education is a matter of time and forbearance, a very simple thesis, which by advanced people, even in highest politics, is too frequently forgotten, which rouses the teachers indignation and disappointment, the pupils unconcern and apathy.

The second problem for the near future is that of extension of agricultural areas. This problem shall be committed to the charge of a cooperative team of soil scientists and biologists. It has a bearing in all opportunities of extension of foodproducing areas, of opening up those large parts of the world, which still are out of cultivation, which still do not produce any foodsubstances at all, though they are well qualified to do so. This is not only a question for less developed regions, but for the most advanced countries as well. I should like to mention one or two special cases only: those who have seen the province of Drenthe in this country fourty years ago and now again, or the new polders, reclaimed from the former Zuiderzee, will understand how even in prosperous countries still many possibilities are present like sleeping beauties, to be wakened by an enterprising conqueror.

A counterpart to this opening up new and thus far untapped resources of foodproduction is becoming more and more important in recent years: the prevention of erosion and as its results barrenness of large areas which for long years have contributed a great deal to the worlds foodsupply. This problem also belongs to soilstudies in its widest sense; it speaks in favour of modern agricultural science that not only extension of agricultural areas shall be tried, but that also intensification and preservation of agricultural standards is considered a factor of utmost importance.

A third way in which the near future may contribute to the worlds foodproduction is that of breeding and selecting indigenous plants and animals and raising their yield and productivity. In those less developed countries races of cultivated plants and of farmanimals mostly are as primitive as agricultural technics; plantbreeding and animal breeding are sciences which for these primitive crops and live-stock promise to be of as much value as they have proven in countries of Western Europe and the United States. But this plantbreeding and animal breeding again takes some time for development and so its results cannot be expected tomorrow, but after a lapse of years only.

All this looks promising and hopeful for the near or more remote future; those masses of people who are suffering from undernourishment may find some comfort in the knowledge that the present scientists are aware of their duty to do as much as possible for a change for the better in the worlds foodsituation. However, the extremely serious and continual warning by Sir JOHN RUSSELL in his book, shall be permanently kept in mind: "No scheme, however attractive, should be attempted until the basic knowledge has been acquired by properly conducted experiments" (p. 130) and: "The general rule is that planning easily outruns achievement in agriculture" (p. 315) and so on.

There is more: modern science of nutrition has learned to admit the value of foodquality. We know now that not so much quantity of food is a matter that counts, but that before all quality in its scientific meaning, like digestibility, caloric values and contents of vitamins, are of the greatest importance for human wellbeing. Years ago, in the middle of the twenties, when visiting the United States, I had my breakfast in one of New Yorks Childs Lunchrooms and I was quite astonished to see, in what part at that time already, science took a place on the menu-card. For each dish the contents of vitamins was mentioned in three grades: a large V for many vitamins, a small one for little contents of this valuable substance and no v at all when the food did not contain any vitamins at all. Two numbers were added: one for the total value of calories of the dish, and one for the number of protein calories. One may doubt if the general guest of such a lunchroom will be impressed with the real drift of this information, but for those who are inclined to a scientific outlook, such an advice probably is not quite useless. And for those visitors, who prefer a more philosophical contemplation of life, the same firm gave this lesson: "Everything springs from the egg; it is the world's cradle" runs a Hindoo legend. On the measureless waters Brahm placed a great golden egg, in which were locked Wisdom and Power and of these the world was made. Advice on the menucard: "To those in search of wisdom and power the egg is still recommended, for it is rich in food iron which now enriches the brain and strengthens the body." Once again: the great majority of the customers of such a lunchroom will leave the matters there, while they are not to be bothered by that, but the attempt to give some advice in the choice of food, in dietetics, certainly deserved our appreciation.

There is still more: in the modern world one of the slogans, most in use, is the cry for industrialization. We have reached the point already, that in every drugstore you can obtain a few cents tablets containing the type of vitamin or a combination of vitamins you think to need on behalf of your metabolism, of your good health. Nutrition is a chemical process: the human body needs a number of chemical substances by which it is enabled to perform its physiological functions. In this line it seems quite conceivable that our foodproducers some day will succeed in preparing a tablet in which all elements, necessary for one man for one day, are present; the right contents of foodsubstances, of vitamins, the right production of calories. Theoretically there is no limit to foodproduction for everybody in the world, provided that science develops methods for an artificial making-up of the right mixture of the foodstuffs we want.

In this way the scientific needs of nurture are fully satisfied. But quality is more than a scientifically calculated mixture of elements; there are qualities of taste, qualities of individual choice, qualities of religious precepts. By that the constitution of our food is not only a scientific problem of metabolism; it has become a problem of psychology as well. Equalization of foodsupply in a scientific way is a serious mistake; though there is some truth in the statement of the nineteenth century german philosophers, like FEUERBACH, who said "Der Mensch ist was er isst," "Man is what he eats," there is also a good deal of psychological fallacy in this superficial and purely materialistic view. Certainly, hunger is the best sauce, or like we in this country say "hunger sweetens raw beans," but the problem of foodsupply reaches more than taking off the edge of hunger; foodsupply shall not lower the demands of a truly human life. Human beings are no robots; they have a body which is composed of chemical substances, but they have something more; they possess a spiritual character of no less importance. It is true, this side of human life may be latent and undeveloped in numbers of human beings, but nobody will deny that the aborigines of Australia and the pygmies of Africa do belong to the biological species, which we still call Homo sapiens, the wise man, and because of that they are entitled to be considered human beings in the full sense of the word. It is one of the mistakes of our present time, that we make a pretence of considering human psychology one of the most important sciences, but that we omit its conclusions in problems of foodsupply. Foodsupply is not only a problem for economy or physiology, it is also a problem with many psychological faces.

There is no end to industrial developments. It requires no

stretch of imagination to picture a future in which almost every side of human life will be favoured by new tools, new machinery, new inventions. If we believe what is told to us all about the possible prospects of industrialization, we can fancy a future in which so to say every square metre of the worlds surface, not in use for industrial purposes, will be available as a shelter for one human being, who receives his food in the form of an all-containing pill and the water he needs in a measured bottle.

And so it would appear that there is an effective solution for the problem of foodsupply, not only for the near or more remote future, but also for years and centuries to come. Increase of the worlds population seems no longer matter of concern. There will be room for everybody, there will be a sufficient foodproduction to feed every individual no matter where, in what country. Our technicians will see to that, and the economists will find the suitable ways of a fair distribution.

However, when we consider the problem of food supply and the increase of population not only from the one-sided and limited viewpoint of the technician and of the economist but with the broader outlook of a human being in the full sense of the word, we are seized with fear of this industrial way of thinking.

It is true, we all are impressed by the many ways in which modern industry has contributed to human welfare. We all are thankful for her numerous gifts. We all enjoy the comfort of our homes with its many tools produced by industrial technics. We greatly appreciate the variety of conveniences for our daily life, born from industrial activities. We all accept gratefully the services of railways and airplanes. In our so-called civilized countries we all hope that these blessings in a not too remote future will be available for everyone all over the world. But notwithstanding that we keep modern industry in high esteem, we shall not shut our eyes to the dangers of its development. Wise men have warned frequently against the levelling down of man as a human being caused by the recent developments of the industrial way of thinking. I may quote here a few lines from the Nobel prize winner ALEXIS CARREL in his admirable book "Man, the unknown." He says: "Man should be the standard of everything. In fact, he is a stranger in the world he has created. He has been unable to organize this world for the good of himself, because he did not understand his own nature. The enormous progress of the sciences of the inanimate things as compared to the advance of those of the living beings is one of the most tragic events in the history of humanity. The environment we have constructed by means of our intellect and our inventions is not adjusted to our size, not to our shape. It fits us badly. We feel unhappy in its surroundings. We degenerate morally and mentally. The very groups and nations, where the industrial developments have reached the pinnacle, become most weakened. They return to barbarism with a fatal speed."

We all, who have lived for five years in the prison of a country, occupied by enemy forces, have gained some experience of the effects of this barbarism. And all those who have passed through the hell of war, have learned the same tragic lesson. But this barbarism not only expresses itself in wartime. I may remind of the fatal accidents which occurred in recent years in various countries, where crazy demonstrations of the speed of cars before a public in search of sensation, led to the death of numerous people. Such demonstrations are the symptom of a mentality, poisoned by a diseased worship of technical power; they are not only crazy, but they come very near to crime.

This holds good not only for industrial developments in engineering; the same danger of levelling down threatens the production of foodsubstances as well. Human beings are no automatons, no robots. They need more than nourishment alone. The more technical our food, the more mechanical man will become.

But even if we accept such a change in our way of nutrition, if we allow our technicians to deprive us from a part of our joy of living, if we submit to the worlds crazy adoration for industrialization, even then a second danger comes to the fore. The scheme propagandized by our food industrialists engenders the thought that an unlimited increase of population all over the world should be considered a blessing for mankind. Here again: human beings are no robots, they cannot be packed like herrings in a barrel.

We have the disposal of a rich collection of statistical data concerning the increase of the worlds population. I do not intend to discuss these data in detail. A few figures will show the far reaching facts.

The worlds population in millions three hundred years ago was about 540, two hundred years ago 730, one hundred years ago 1170 and now more than 2600 millions. The annual increase in these three centuries in percentages of the population was 0.29, 0.51 and 1.20.

The population of a so-called well-developed country with a high standard of living, like the Netherlands, has increased from 3 millions in 1850 to 5 millions in 1900 and to 11 millions in 1956.

The population of a less developed country like China has increased in the last fifty years from 360 millions to 460 millions, that of India from 235 to 357 millions, that of Japan from 44 to 85 millions.

Those are bare facts. Statisticians have snowed us under with collections of data, and with studies of the background of this population-pressure. There is a great diversity of demographic causes of this enormous increase, different for different countries. Large birthrate, decrease of deathrate, improved hygiene have all contributed to this almost morbid growth. The most spectacular phenomenon in figures is perhaps the increase of life expectation; in this country one hundred years ago 40% of new born reached the age of 50 years and 5% the age of 80 years; now these figures are 90 and 35.

There are numberless people who consider these facts symptoms of a healthy and robust existence. Quantity should be the ideal to be pursued. There is however a reverse.

We have respected with warmest admiration the strenuous efforts by the United States to improve the conditions of living for the crowded population of Porto Rico, to further hygienic measures, to apply modern medicine, to advance public health, to raise the level of education, to put science into service of the people. We may rejoice the results obtained, the fact that mortality has been reduced half, that the population of one million in 1900 has increased to two millions in 1943. But with a heavy heart we state that this population is growing three percent every year, that in 1960 the population has surpassed 3 millions, in 1970 possibly 4 millions. For this means that the density of population, now already 245 per square kilometer, within twenty years will rise to 500, that the area of cultivable ground, at present only 1300 square meters will be dwindled to 650. A number which tells its own tale by comparison with the extensive agriculture in the United States, where 10.000 square metres of cultivated land is available for one man, or with our own country with its dense population and its very intensive agriculture, where 2500 square metres of agricultural fields is available a head. Compare these numbers with Porto Rico with its careless and unkempt agriculture, where only 1300 square metres are available.

In the American periodical Journal of Heredity in 1947 attention has been drawn to this terrifying situation. Since 1934 committee after committee has studied the consequences of this population growth and proposed radical measures. Harrowing descriptions of the situation told the truth, but no improvement has been obtained. Stimulation of emigration since 1946 was undone by the overspill of birthfrequency over mortality. Porto Rico is a small island, but its situation may be considered a lesson for all those who think the quantity of a population the standard of well-being. A hard and serious lesson.

For such an increase is observed not only in Porto Rico, but also in many States of Central America and Asia and in a few countries of Europe. An annual increase of more than two per cent leads to a population density which becomes fatal for the population itself and for the human race as well. A population of one million with a growth rate of 3 percent annually after fifty years will have reached the size of 4 millions, after hundred years 16 millions. An increase of only two per cent rises the population from one million today to 3 millions within 50 years, to 7 millions one hundred years hence.

Three ways may lead out of this deathly strangling labyrinth:

Common opinion tells us that the problem is rather easy to solve. The quantitative character of the worlds population, as well for its various countries, is generally considered one of the most important problems for the economist. Food-supply is regarded its central question. Technical, industrialized food production and distribution indeed may seem to be the determining weapon in the fight against hunger for everyone on the earths surface. It is true, for the time being we have not yet reached this equilibrium between foodsupply and population growth, but if we believe what we are told by many industrial economists, we are on the right way. Many agricultural projects have been set up for improving foodproduction in so-called less developed countries, but as soon as these projects, successful as they may be, will have resulted into doubling the foodsupply, the population has grown threefold. I quote from an interesting article by KARL SAX on population problems of Central America (p. 163): "The experience of the Rockefeller Foundation indicates the need of a completely balanced program. For many years a public health program had been conducted in Mexico. The public health program was very effective and the population grew rapidly, even though dietary standards were low. The Foundation saw little virtues in preventing death from disease if the people were to die more slowly from starvation and malnutrition. In 1943, the Foundation established an agricultural project, in cooperation with the Mexican government, to increase food production. This project, too, was very successful, but the population grew faster."

Besides, it should not be our only aim to save the population of these less developed countries from starvation, but also to improve their living standards and the number of calories they receive. Here again SAX may be quoted concerning Mexico: "During the past ten years, beginning in 1943 when the agricultural program was initiated, the population increased about 30 per cent. As a result the advances in agriculture have been absorbed by rapid population growth and the diet of the common man has shown little improvement."

Population problems, complex as they are, have three different aspects. One is that of the quantity of the worlds population, the second one that of the conditions to which these populations are subjected, their way of living, their standards, and the third problem lies in the quality of the population itself.

The first problem, that of the quantity may possibly be solved by our technical economists, but even if they reach their aim, the population problem is not solved at all. The present trend of considering food supply the only medicine for the world miseries is a monstrum, a quack medicine, a stunning substance, not a remedy at all. This is clearly recognised by the Indian Health Survey, as stated in its report published in 1946: "We feel, however, that such measures can constitute only a temporary expedient, because a limit to economic productivity will be reached sooner or later, and uncontrolled growth of population must, as far as we can see, outstrip the production capacity of the country."

The first way out, food supply alone, either by improving

agricultural production as such, or even by preparing a fantastic concentrated industrial foodsubstance in pills, takes into account only the quantitative side of the population. It will never lead to improvement of the conditions of living for all human beings. It will lock in the entire mankind in one large prison, without any possibility for recreation or free exercise. It will lead to a population pressure, to a density of population, which is rightly characterized by KARL SAX, professor at Harvard University, in the title of his fascinating, but alarming book "Standing room only." The economists view in my opinion is an extremely narrow one; the solution presented very dangerous and fatal for the human race.

The second way which is thought to prevent overpopulation is that of emigration. Many people consider emigration an efficacious remedy of all troubles caused by a too high population density. Many and ponderous doubts however may be advanced against this optimistic suggestion. One hundred seventy years ago BENJAMIN FRANKLIN has said this: "In my piece on population, I have proved, I think, that emigration does not diminish but multiplies a nation. You will not have fewer at home for those that go abroad." The experience of our own nation since the last war has led to the same conclusion: in ten years about 250,000 individuals from the Netherlands have emigrated, while the normal increase of the population in this period has been six times this number.

In his clever book "Hungry people and empty lands," Dr. CHANDRASEKHAR, the Director of the Indian Institute for Population Studies, defends the thesis that the population of Southern and Eastern Asia cannot be confined to its present geographical limits, as long as there are empty spaces around the world. It is true, there are countries in which the population is far too large for an existence worthy of human beings, and there are countries where empty spaces are available which by reasonable opening up could give room to large numbers of people, but I think Dr. CHANDRASEKHAR overrates these possibilities, certainly in the long run. In his foreword to this book WILLIAM VOGT gives a serious warning: "Much of the "Empty" land Dr. CHANDRASEKHAR would use as a home for surplus people is as undependable as a pair of paper shoes: expose it to the rain and it melts away. As other students of the tropics have also pointed out, we simply do not know to use most tropical soils without destroying them. The empty lands are not nearly so empty as some of us wish they were."

Besides, emigration has two important drawbacks for the people staying at home; it harms the quality of the remaining population in a serious way. Those who are willing to emigrate belong to a type of character, which is of great value for the nations prosperity; they are energetic and enterprising, they have got the nerve to accept the difficulties, presented by a change of environment, to adapt to new conditions of life. They certainly belong to the better part of the population. And secondly they are young, anyhow under a certain age, and by their leaving the remaining population is ageing artificially. It seems to me that this danger for a nations existence is generally overlooked by those who propagate emigration as an effective way out from the maze of overpopulation. Emigration counteracts the increase of population in a small scale temporarily only, not for years to come, while it also is injurious to the populations quality.

The third way, which may lead to a solution of the problem of overpopulation is that of birth control. In our Western countries this process is regarded as most delicate and sensitive, out of reach of governments measure. Limitation of the family number is left entirely to the desire and the sense of responsibility of the individual. On the contrary, in many countries government-measures by means of family-allowances stimulate the number of children and by that an uncontrolled increase of population. Clerical parties support these governmental efforts and the clergy propagates the cult of large families. These government-measures however involve a great danger. For birth control is applied mainly by those who have enough mental ability to see and to value the impending dangers of overpopulation. This means that on the whole those families with a larger intellectual capacity and more social responsibility have a smaller number of children than have those who are less intelligent and more careless. Here we meet the very serious problem of the differential birth-rate, which is strongly linked to that of the increase of population in so-called civilized countries. Already in 1934 LORIMER and OSBORN in their Dynamics of Population have pointed to a decrease of national intelligence caused by this differential birth-rate. And in 1946 the President of the Royal Commission on Population in Great Britain, Sir CYRIL BURT has said: "In a little over fifty years the number of pupils of "scholarship" ability would be approximately halved and the number of feeble-minded doubled." This danger of "genetical erosion" threatens all countries with a high standard of development when the family numbers are stimulated without any attention to the inherited quality of the members of these families.

For the less-developed countries the danger of stimulating family numbers lies in a somewhat different direction. I may quote here one of the best friends of the Chinese people, GERALD WINFIELD: "All the proposed steps toward industrialisation and increased agricultural productivity, all the processes necessary to enable China to play her logical role in a world community, all plans for her progress, are and will be futile unless her population growth can be controlled. Existing misery and poverty can be permanently eliminated only when there are fewer, healthier people, with longer life expectancy and greater economic security. The future welfare of the Chinese people is more dependent on the prevention of births than on the prevention of deaths." Or a quotation from an article by A. A. BUZZATTI-TRAVERSO (Science and Freedom, N. 2, April 1955, p. 24): "The obvious facts of the case were actually admitted at the September meeting of the National People's Congress of Red China, when the Deputy SHAO LI-TZE declared: "It is a good thing to have a large population but in an environment beset with difficulties it appears that there should be a limit set". I will not say more on this extremely difficult, but also extremely grave and serious subject. I may only say that blindly stimulating family numbers all over the world on grounds of national or party political motives is an unsound procedure. Here again I may ask attention for the book by KARL SAX, "Standing room only."

To sum up:

Promoting foodproduction and foodsupply is highly necessary for today and the near future, but this method is quite unsatisfactory to prevent all troubles of population increase in the long run.

Emigration is a temporary means of relief for overpopulated countries but its results will never lead to reducing the population of such a country to its desirable size.

Stimulating family sizes under present world conditions is a grave mistake; the counterpart, reasonable birth control the only way out on behalf of the well-being of mankind.

Increase of population asks for action, for radical measures, but these measures shall be supported by well-founded and sober reason, not by sentimental bias.

LITERATURE

BURT, CYRIL, 1946. Intelligence and fertility; the effect of the differential birth rate on inborn mental characteristics. London Cassel and Company. Occas. Papers on Eugenics 2, 1946, Sec. ed. 1952: 44pp.

CARREL, A., 1935. L'homme, cet inconnu. Paris, Plon, 1935: 400 pp.

CHANDRASEKHAR, S., 1954. Hungry people and empty lands. London, Allen and Unwin, 1954: 306 pp.

LORIMER, F. and F. OSBORN, 1934. Dynamics of population. New York, Mac Millan, 1934.

OSBORN, F., 1951. Preface to eugenics. Rev. Ed., New York, Harper Bros. 1951: 333 pp.
RUSSELL, E. J., 1954. World population and world food supplies. London, Allen and Unwin, 1954: 513 pp.
SAX, K., 1954. Population problems of Central America. Ceiba, a scientific journal issued by the Escuela agricola panamericana, 4: 153–164, 1954.
SAX, K., 1955. Standing Room Only, the Challenge of Overpopulation. Boston, Beacon Press, 1955: 206 pp.
WINFIELD, G., 1950. China: the Land and the people. Rev. ed., New York, Sloane, 1950.
WOYTINSKI, W. S., and E. S., 1953. World Population and production. Trends and outlook. New York, The twentieth Century fund, 1953: 1268 pp.

Quelques voies probables de développement des nouvelles techniques en agronomie[1]

par

P. Chouard

Avec tous les risques d'erreur que comporte fatalement une telle initiative, je voudrais essayer de dégager les tendances actuelles du progrès technique en agronomie, de décrire, par anticipation, quelques unes des techniques qui entreront d'ici cinq à vingt ans dans la pratique. Par là, je me propose d'attirer l'attention des techniciens agronomes sur certains aspects de la Recherche Scientifique, et de les porter à s'en tenir informés pour en assurer le plus tôt possible la transposition agricole ou horticole.

RÉSISTANCE À LA SÉCHERESSE

L'eau étant le premier des facteurs limitants la croissance des plantes, son utilisation présente une importance capitale, et nous pouvons nous attendre ici à de nouveaux progrès. Par exemple, nous commençons à savoir ou à soupçonner qu'un emploi judicieux d'oligo-éléments tels que le cuivre, ou des traitements infligés aux graines avant le semis, peuvent

1. Cet article contient la substance d'une conference faite au Comité parlementaire pour les Sciences et les Techniques (Bull. No. 2, 24 février 1955) et à la Confédération Internationale des Ingénieurs et Techniciens de l'Agriculture. A cet article l'auteur a ajouté mention des découvertes récentes et des tendances nouvelles, en vue du rapide progrès dans ces dernières années en nombre des branches scientifiques liées à l'agriculture.

peut-être améliorer la résistance ultérieure des plantes à la sécheresse. Si de telles découvertes se confirment et se précisent, il sera possible de faire reculer plus ou moins la limite des terres arides; les plantes cultivées pourront gagner sur les territoires où, jusqu'ici, la pluviosité était insuffisante; ou bien le rendement de l'eau disponible dans les terres déjà cultivées sera amélioré et la production accrue.

On peut citer ici les perspectives d'emploi plus économique de l'eau (par exemple par des cultures sur le sable des déserts irrigué par dessous en solutions nutritives), et d'approvisionnement des deserts en eaux dessalées par divers procédés, etc.[2]

FUMURE FOLIAIRE

La fumure foliaire nous offre des perspectives peut-être plus immediates. On sait en effet depuis longtemps que les plantes peuvent absorber les matières fertilisantes, non seulement par la voie normale des racines, mais, dans une certaine mesure, par la voie anormale des surfaces foliaires et même des écorces. Mais cette connaissance physiologique n'a fait que depuis peu l'objet de recherches systématiques et de tentatives d'application. Cependant, les expériences faites

2. Note de l'Editeur: A ce propos on peut peut-être signaler les résultats des recherches suivantes, à cause de leur probable importance mondiale:

Depuis 1949, en Israel, H. et E. BOYKO ont prouvé avec succès qu'il est possible d'irriguer des plantes économiquement importantes par des eaux très saumâtres et même avec de l'eau de mer à concentration océanique.

Il y a plus: Cette méthode est particulièrement indiquée pour rendre productives les vastes zones sablonneuses des bords de la mer et des déserts, ainsi que les terrains graveleux.

Ces expériences ont combiné l'approche géophysique avec celui de l'écologie végétale, et elles ont été récemment verifiées par des expériences semblables en Suède et en Espagne.

Cette méthode s'est ainsi montrée valable pour le profil climatique tout entier, depuis le chaud désert d'Eilat et la sémi-aride plaine méditerranéenne d'Israel et la chaleur temperée d'Espagne jusqu'à la Suède fraiche et humide. En Suède on a même pu utiliser des terrains argileux, grâce aux pluies plus fréquentes et aux températures plus basses.

Ces expériences ouvrent des nouvelles lignes de recherche en plusieures directions, et nous montrent comme on pourra peut-être un jour ajouter aux terrains actuellement cultivés d'autres grandes extensions comparables à un vaste continent

dans divers pays commencent à montrer qu'il est possible, d'une manière économique et efficace, de suppléer par cette voie à certaines insuffisances de la pénétration des engrais par les racines, notamment dans les cas de certains sols trop pauvres ou trop difficilement fertilisables. Ainsi, le phosphore si souvent immobilisé par le calcaire dans le sol, peut, de la sorte, pénétrer plus facilement chez les plantes; l'azote peut être introduit sous forme de sels minéraux ou, souvent mieux, d'urée; dans un tel cas, ou dans l'emploi de carbonates ou de bicarbonates, c'est même un peu l'équivalent d'une fumure carbonique, non point gazeuse mais soluble, que l'on distribue de la sorte sur les plantes. Des améliorations sensibles de rendement ont déjà été observées dans quelques cas. Et si l'expérience se généralise et aboutit à une mise au point, il sera, sans doute, possible de l'appliquer dans les cultures en sols squelettiques, en combinaison avec l'apport d'eau ce qui constituerait une sorte de rénovation des principes de la culture "sans sol" et peut-être permettrait de doter d'une fertilité réelle des territoires réputés incultivables comme ceux de certaines zones au pourtour du Sahara. Je tiens à souligner la marge d'incertitude qui cerne une telle perspective, mais aussi l'importance qui s'attache aux essais qui pourraient être entrepris dans ce sens.

* * *

En ce qui concerne les applications de la génétique, nous avons encore devant nous des progrès importants et dont on peut déjà déceler l'orientation:

RACES RÉSISTANTES AUX MALADIES

La production de races génétiquement résistantes aux maladies ne cesse de progresser: chaque année on découvre, par recherches dans les pays d'origine des plantes cultivées ou l'on crée par hybridation, des races nouvelles résistantes à l'une ou l'autre des maladies ou des parasites. Par exemple, il n'est pas exclus de penser qu'un jour nous disposerions de pommes de terre sur lesquelles le Doryphore ne saurait pas se multiplier, ni le Mildiou s'établir, ou même qui seraient résistantes à certains types de virus.

HYBRIDES "HÉTÉROSIS"

D'autre part, le succès enregistré chez les maïs dans l'accroissement de la production par l'emploi d'hybrides de première génération, autrement dit par "hétérosis," se retrouve peu à peu chez d'autres plantes: il y a peu d'années, les Américains ont découvert une race d'oignons chez laquel le pollen est incapable d'assurer l'auto-fécondation; ils ont pu transmettre cette auto-stérilité à n'importe quelle race ou espèce d'oignons. A partir de ces races auto-stériles il est facile d'assurer la fécondation par une autre race ou variété normale et d'obtenir de la sorte, à l'échelle commerciale, des graines hybrides de première génération qui sont capables de redonner le type d'oignon qu'on désire, mais avec une vigueur accrue et une productivité augmentée de l'ordre de 30%. Récemment il vient d'être fait de même pour le ricin et l'étude de tels hybrides est actuellement en cours. On peut penser qu'une telle méthode d'amélioration pourra s'étendre à bon nombre d'espèces et qu'une marge importante d'accroissement de production est contenue en puissance dans un tel processus.

MUTATIONS PROVOQUÉES

On doit mentionner aussi la façon de plus en plus précise avec laquelle nous savons maintenant appliquer sur les plantes des rayonnements divers, depuis les rayons X jusqu'aux flux de neutrons. Par de tels moyens, nous créons dans la plante des accidents génétiques d'où il nait un grand nombre de mutations, c'est-à-dire de races ou de variétés nouvelles. La plupart ne sont que des monstruosités. Mais l'analyse systématique des effets de tels agents mutagènes a permis de montrer que certaines mutations utiles pour nos besoins peuvent être obtenues de temps en temps et isolées par un effort attentif et méthodique de sélection; de sorte que, là encore, un champ certainement important et imprévisible d'amélioration nous est ouvert. L'emploi des agents chimiques mutagènes se développera au moins autant que celui des rayonnements mutagènes.

PLANTES INDEMNÉS DE VIRUS

Dans la voie de la phyto-pathologie, les progrès possibles sont considérables et on peut indiquer quelques-uns des chemins par lesquels ils parviennent. Par exemple, dans l'étude des virus, nous commençons à savoir que des applications ménagées de température chaude permettent, dans certains cas, de détruire le virus dans l'intérieur de la plante sans tuer celle-ci. Ou bien, grâce à une découverte française faite à l'Institut National de la Recherche Agronomique, il a été montré que les points végétatifs de beaucoup de plantes ne contiennent pas le virus qui a envahi tous les autres organes du végétal; et grâce à une technique délicate de prélèvement et de culture des extrémités des tiges, il a été possible de régénérer, dans l'état absolument exempt de virus des variétés de pommes de terre ou de dahlias, que l'on croyait totalement perdues parce que entièrement contaminées par les virus. Cette méthode pourra sans doute s'étendre.

CHIMIOTHÉRAPIE CONTRE LES PARASITES

Mais c'est surtout dans le domaine de la chimiothérapie que des découvertes imprévisibles vont se faire dans des délais les plus proches; chaque année, chaque semaine même, apporte l'annonce de la découverte de produits nouveaux, qui jouissent de propriétés extrêmement puissantes dans la destruction des parasites: bactéries, champignons, insectes, etc. Comme je l'ai dit plus haut ces produits, à coté de leurs vertus, présentent souvent des dangers graves, soit parce qu'ils sont toxiques pour l'homme, soit parce qu'ils détruisent, en même temps que les parasites, certains des facteurs de l'équilibre faunistique et floristique. Mais si ce sont des armes à double tranchant, cependant il est hautement probable que leur connaissance approfondie, leur emploi judicieux, ménagé et convenablement diversifié, permettra une lutte de plus en plus spectaculaire contre les parasites qui détruisent encore une fraction si importante de beaucoup de nos récoltes.

NOUVEAUX EMPLOIS DES HORMONES

La physiologie moderne nous ouvre enfin les perspectives les plus surprenantes, celles sur lesquelles portent à la fois le doute qui s'attache à toute anticipation, et l'enthousiasme qui s'allie à toute suggestion nouvelle.

On peut indiquer, par exemple, qu'en matière d'emploi des hormones végétales, notamment des auxines, à coté des découvertes classiques, d'autres peut-être interviendront dans l'agriculture: Je viens de lire, dans un périodique agronomique de Californie, deux résultats expérimentaux assez significatifs: dans l'un une pulvérisation à 33 parties par million de 2, 4, 5 – T, substance connue comme un puissant débroussaillant est capable, à une telle dilution, de provoquer une précocité considérable et une régularité remarquable de fructification chez certains arbres fruitiers à noyaux; ce qui peut notamment modifier les conditions d'écoulement de ces fruits à faible durée de conservation. D'autre part une application à 15 parties par milliard de 2, 4 – D, le célèbre agent herbicide, s'est montrée capable de stimuler puissamment la croissance de boutures d'Avocatier avec une sensibilité telle que 5 parties par milliard en plus se montrent déjà toxiques, 5 parties par milliard en moins ne donnent qu'un résultat très faiblement amélioré par rapport au témoin. De telles indications signifient que les progrès dans la connaissance de ces substances stimulantes capables d'agir à des doses aussi petites, peuvent apporter d'un jour à l'autre des bouleversements importants dans les techniques agricoles de production, mais en exigeant des précautions de plus en plus délicates dans leur emploi.

LE PHYTOTRON ET LES PROGRÈS DE LA PHYSIOLOGIE DE LA CROISSANCE ET DU DÉVELOPPEMENT

La physiologie de la croissance et du développement est encore dans ses premiers balbutiements. Par elle, nous savons déjà l'existence d'un certain nombre de mécanismes régulateurs de la croissance et du développement, tels que la vernalisation et le photopériodisme: autrement dit nous savons que certaines plantes sont dotées d'un système physico-chimique par lequel elles se trouvent empêchées indéfiniment de fleurir tant qu'elle n'ont pas subi une période appropriée de température froide: c'est la vernalisation. D'autres sont dotées d'un autre mécanisme physico-chimique par lequel elles se trouvent indéfiniment empêchées de fleurir, ou au contraire immédiatement poussées à fleurir, selon que la durée quotidienne d'éclairement qu'elles reçoivent est augmentée ou réduite de quelques minutes en plus ou en moins; ce sont les mécanismes du photo-périodisme. Chez d'autres ce sont les alternances quotidiennes de quelques degrés de température qui constituent une condition absolue de survie, tandis qu'une température constante entraine soit la mort, soit la chute rapide des boutons floraux ou des fruits; et ce sont là des mécanismes qui relèvent du thermopériodisme à rythme quotidien.

Pour étudier ces mécanismes régulateurs, il a été institué un appareillage compliqué auquel le nom de "phytotron" a été donné, par analogie avec le cyclotron bien connu des physiciens et de tous les lecteurs de la grande presse: de même que le cyclotron permet, en accélerant des particules atomiques, d'analyser l'intimité de la mécanique de l'atome, de même le phytotron, en accélérant ou en ralentissant certains des processus de la vie de la plante, permet d'analyser les mécanismes intimes qui contrôlent sa croissance et son développement. De même que le cyclotron est un appareil coûteux mais qui permet des découvertes hautement rentables dans le domaine atomique, de même le phytotron est un appareil coûteux qui a déjà permis des découvertes importantes dans les applications et qui en procurera certainement beaucoup d'autres dans l'avenir.

Ce dispositif n'est en réalité autre chose qu'un ensemble complexe de serres et de locaux complètement conditionnés, où l'on est entièrement maître de tous les facteurs physiques et chimiques de l'ambiance, soit pour les maintenir constants, soit pour les faire varier à tous moments et à volonté. Dans de telles enceintes, des plantes ou même des animaux de toutes sortes, peuvent être élevés de façon prolongée, l'intimité des mécanismes qui se manifestent peut être analysée par les techniques modernes de l'emploi des isotopes, de la chromatographie, ou autres. Il n'existe à l'heure actuelle qu'un seul phytotron complet et important, celui que le Dr. F. WENT a réalisé, après une quinzaine d'années d'études, au California Institute of Technology, à Pasadena. Un grand équipement analogue existe à Moscou. D'autres sont en projet à Madison, à Canberra, etc.

Un appareil plus réduit existe à l'Université de Liège chez le professeur BOUILLENNE. Un autre, le premier en Europe du type complet, est actuellement en cours de construction à Gif-sur-Yvette, sous ma direction et à l'initiative du Centre National Français de la Recherche Scientifique.

Par les études qui se développent, et se développeront avec

de tels dispositifs, non seulement les mécanismes régulateurs que je citais plus haut ont déjà été découverts et analysés, non seulement les propriétés des diverses espèces et variétés de plantes, vis-à-vis de ces mécanismes, ont été déterminées expérimentalement, et les aptitudes culturales de ces plantes définies très rapidement, de telle sorte que l'expérience agronomique se trouve considérablement abrégée. Mais encore, nous pouvons espérer acquérir une maîtrise plus ou moins complète de la précocité du développement, de son orientation, du maintien des fleurs ou des fruits sur les plantes, de leur maturation, de la rapidité de germination, etc..., autrement dit acquérir la maîtrise des facteurs les plus importants pour la conduite des opérations culturales. Certes, ce n'est pas pour demain que nous posséderons la totalité de ces connaissances; mais, pièce par pièce, elles tombent déjà entre nos mains; le progrès dans cette voie peut être auguré de la manière la plus favorable.

RECHERCHES SUR LA PHOTOSYNTHÈSE ET CONSIDÉRATIONS SUR LA PORTÉE DES EMPLOIS DE L'ÉNERGIE SOLAIRE

Enfin je ne puis manquer de mettre ici en place les importantes perspectives que nous donne l'étude de la photosynthèse, le procédé naturel par lequel les plantes vertes sont capables de retenir l'énergie lumineuse venue du soleil, sous forme de lumière et de la transformer pour aboutir à la synthèse des matières organiques, sucres, protéines, etc... à partir des éléments minéraux, le gaz carbonique de l'atmosphère et les aliments minéraux dissous dans les liquides du sol. A elle seule, l'étude de la photosynthèse mériterait tout un exposé, et l'on peut trouver dans les publications récentes tous les éclaircissements nécessaires sur ce point.

Ce qu'il importe de souligner, c'est que l'énergie reçue de la lumière solaire présente des particularités que l'on néglige souvent de considérer; d'une part, c'est une énergie extraordinairement dispersée, nous pourrions dire "à bas potentiel," c'est-à-dire tout le contraire des sources d'énergie fortement concentrée, à haut potentiel, qui sont d'ordinaire utilisées dans l'industrie. La lumière reçue du soleil à la surface de la terre représente, en effet, approximativement, 1,4 petite calorie par cm^2 et par minute, autrement dit c'est à peu près l'équivalent d'une puissance d'un kilowatt par m^2. Ce chiffre est déjà appréciable, mais il paraît bien petit au regard des centaines de mille de kilowatts qui sont couramment produits par les grandes chutes captées pour l'énergie hydro-électrique ou par les grandes centrales thermiques. Mais par contre l'énergie radiante émise par le soleil est reçue sur toute la surface de la terre; et sur des surfaces aussi immenses, elle représente un total prodigieux, à côté duquel les autres sources d'énergie sont insignifiantes. C'est ainsi que si l'on exprime en calories l'énergie reçue du soleil sur l'ensemble de la surface de la France, on peut calculer qu'elle représente environ 500 à 1.000 fois l'équivalent énergétique du total du charbon, du pétrole, et des sources hydro-électriques qui sont actuellement utilisées en France.

La plus grande partie de cette énergie reçue du soleil est dissipée sous forme de chaleur; une fraction infime est retenue par le tapis vert des plantes sauvages et cultivées; en Europe on peut estimer à environ 1 pour 1.000 la moyenne générale de ce qui est ainsi retenu par l'action photosynthétique des plantes. Cette fraction est cependant elle-même d'une grandeur considérable puisqu'elle est, en énergie, équivalente, pour la France, aux 70 millions de tonnes de charbon qui y sont consommées par an.

Depuis un siècle et demi que le processus de la photosynthèse a été découvert, son analyse détaillée progresse pas à pas; mais c'est seulement au cours des quinze dernières années que les découvertes dans ce domaine ont soudain subi une grande accélération; grâce à la combinaison de l'analyse chromatographique et de l'emploi des éléments marqués, il a été possible de déterminer les premiers produits de la photosynthèse et d'analyser de mieux en mieux le mécanisme intime de cet extraordinaire enchaînement de réactions, les conditions de réalisation de la photosynthèse, quelles sont les modifications subies par les pigments, le rôle capital de la teneur en gaz carbonique, de la température, de l'hydratation, de l'état du cytoplasme et des éléments minéraux qui sont présents dans la cellule vivante. Les journaux ont annoncé récemment les derniers progrès accomplis en Amérique dans l'isolement de la photosynthèse hors du complexe de la cellule végétale: l'anglais ROBIN HILL, avait déjà réussi, en 1937, à faire fonctionner une partie de la photosynthèse c'est-à-dire la photolyse de l'eau, sa décomposition en oxygène et hydrogène utilisables pour d'autres réactions, par des grains isolés de la matière verte des plantes, les chloroplastes. L'américain ARNON a réussi à pousser plus loin l'activité des chloroplastes isolés qui se sont montré capables de réduire le gaz carbonique et de faire ainsi la synthèse de l'amidon et des sucres. Cela ne signifie pas encore que nous soyons capables de réaliser à volonté la photosynthèse "comme dans un bocal," mais nous pouvons de mieux en mieux en étudier le mécanisme, et déjà nous savons les grandes lignes de ce qu'il faut faire pour exalter l'activité photosynthétique des cellules des plantes.

Si le rendement moyen reste encore si bas (de l'ordre de 1 pour 1.000 pour la moyenne d'un an, et sur l'ensemble d'un territoire aussi varié que la France), déjà l'amélioration des procédés culturaux permet d'atteindre des rendements de l'ordre de 1 à 2% pendant la période la plus favorable de culture, et pour les meilleures sortes de plantes cultivées. Mais dans une ambiance plus favorablement élaborée pour se rapprocher de l'optimum du rendement de la photoynthèse, et notamment par un enrichissement de l'atmosphère en gaz carbonique, et par une répartition plus judicieuse de l'intensité lumineuse totale généralement trop grande, il est possible d'atteindre des rendements de l'ordre de 5 à 10% ou même davantage. De tels résultats ne sont actuellement obtenus que dans des conditions de laboratoire, non transposables dans la pratique d'une manière rentable en ce moment. Mais on sait trop combien il est rapidement possible de passer d'une découverte de laboratoire à une utilisation technique, lorque l'enjeu en vaut la peine, pour estimer avec beaucoup de vraisemblance que l'utilisation de l'énergie solaire avec un haut rendement, par la photosynthèse, s'étendra à la pratique agricole ou industrielle dans un délai relativement court de quelques générations, quelques dizaines d'années peut-être.

PERSPECTIVES DE LA CHÉMIURGIE: CULTURES DE MICROORGANISMES; CULTURES D'ALGUES

Nous rejoignons ici des perspectives d'un autre ordre, celles que l'on réunit souvent sous le nom de chémiurgie, c'est-à-dire l'approvisionnement des industries en matières premières plus ou moins élaborées grâce à une culture de plantes appropriées.

On peut citer tous les degrés de réalisation actuelle ou d'anticipation plus ou moins romanesque dans les conceptions de la chémiurgie: par exemple c'est une utilisation actuelle, déjà possible dans la pratique, que celle de la culture du ricin pour fournir la matière première à l'industrie des plastiques et des textiles artificiels. C'est une perspective moins immédiate mais cependant facile à réaliser et qui a été déjà mise en oeuvre dans certains pays, que celle de la culture de micro-organismes, tels que les levures pour transformer rapidement des mixtures à bon marché (formées de sucre et de composés minéraux de l'azote) en matières alimentaires pour l'homme ou les animaux, en protéines d'une haute valeur nutritive. Il est probable que les excédents de betteraves sucrières auraient pu, si l'on avait fait l'étude technologique en temps voulu, être utilisées sous cette forme par une facile reconversion de certaines distilleries, et contribuer ainsi à réduire les besoins en importation de graines fourragères pour l'alimentation du bétail. L'utilisation des eaux résiduaires des papeteries au sulfite pour la préparation de la pénicilline est à signaler de même.

Une autre perspective de la chémiurgie est celle qui rejoint les perspectives de développement des recherches sur la photosynthèse, la culture des algues et, notamment, celles des algues uni-cellulaires, les chlorelles et autres analogues. Ces algues microscopiques sont formées de petites cellules isolées dotées de chlorophylle, et capables de se multiplier rapidement dans des milieux de culture synthétiques (faciles à fabriquer avec quelques sels minéraux dissous dans l'eau). Par insufflation d'air enrichi en gaz carbonique, on élève la teneur du liquide en gaz carbonique dissous, et l'agitation des chlorelles amène chacune d'entre elles à se présenter à la surface du liquide, directement exposée à la lumière du soleil intense, pendant un temps suffisamment court, pour profiter pleinement de cette lumière, puis ensuite à continuer les réactions de la photosynthèse à la demi-obscurité, à l'abri dans les profondeurs. Une telle culture peut être menée d'une manière quasi-industrielle, presque continue; elle a été effectivement réalisée, non seulement aux dimensions du laboratoire, mais à l'echelle de quelques dizaines de m^2 notamment aux Etats-Unis, au Japon, en Allemagne, et récemment en France.

La matière ainsi produite est celle de la substance même des cellules des Chlorelles: elle se compose d'une quantité importante de protéines et de quantités plus petites de sucres et de matières grasses ainsi que de vitamines et autres principes utiles.

La fraction alimentaire est petite; on peut penser que la matière des Chlorelles, convenablement séparée du liquide de culture par centrifugation, puis desséchée et traitée pour perdre ses propriétés hygroscopiques, pourrait constituer une ressource importante pour l'alimentation du bétail; certains mêmes y ont pensé pour l'alimentation humaine.

Grâce aux perfectionnements que la culture des Chlorelles a déjà atteints, le rendement de la photosynthèse y est élevé et des productions de l'ordre de 12 gr. de matière sèche par jour et par m^2 ont déjà été obtenus sur la moyenne d'une année complète. On a même obtenu, pour des durées plus courtes, des productions 4 à 6 fois supérieures. De tels rendements en matière sèche sont 5 à 10 fois plus grands que ceux de la plupart des meilleures cultures agricoles. Dans ces essais en demi-grand, des prix de revient ont déjà pu être calculés: ils varient, selon les estimations, de 55 à 140 fr. le kg. de matière sèche, c'est-à-dire qu'ils ne sont déjà plus très loin d'une possibilité pratique de rentabilité.

Comme de telles cultures n'exigent par rapport à la production finale, qu'une quantité relativement petite d'eau, on voit aussitôt les perspectives que l'on peut imager pour l'utilisation des régions fortement ensoleillées et pauvres en eau, telles que les confins du Sahara.

Mais les algues en culture serviront sans doute à bien d'autres fins que les usages alimentaires: si l'on songe à la diversité des éspèces de ce groupe de plantes, jusqu'ici totalement ignorées de l'agriculture, on peut penser à la diversité des substances qui pourront en être tirées, dont certaines pourront peut-être servir de matières premières pour l'industrie.

* * *

VALEUR DES NOUVELLES TECHNIQUES DE L'AGRONOMIE

Il me reste à porter un jugement de valeur sur les perspectives que nous ouvrent les développements probables des techniques de l'agronomie. Trois points principaux doivent être soulignés:

1) Le progrès technique en Agronomie est en plein essor, et,

par lui, la révolution agricole du monde est à peine commencée;

2) Ses caractéristiques essentielles et originales proviennent de ce qu'il met en jeu l'utilisation de l'immense énergie solaire, et par des moyens biologiques;
3) Il se développe à la fois en vue de pourvoir à la nourriture des hommes en nombre croissant et en vue de satisfaire de plus en plus les besoins industriels, et ces deux buts sont de plus en plus associés. Examinons brièvement ces trois points.

1. Les techniques en agronomie ont devant elles une énorme marge de progrès possibles

Pour être plus lente que la révolution industrielle, la révolution agricole n'est pas moins réelle ni profonde: jusqu'à la Rénaissance inclusivement, l'Agriculture était plus un mode de vie qu'une technique; elle perpétuait par la tradition, un long acquit empirique et suffisait tout juste aux besoins d'un monde en croissance démographique lente. Depuis 150 ans, l'Agriculture se fonde sur des techniques en pleine évolution et sa propre révolution a été la condition primaire du changement rapide qui bouleverse la face de la terre: la population du monde vient de tripler et pourtant, grâce aux progrès des techniques agricoles, les famines aigües de jadis ont pratiquement disparu (sauf en cas de guerre). Il demeure la famine endémique des pays dont l'agriculture est insuffisamment développée.

La capacité d'évolution de l'Agriculture est pourtant loin d'être parvenue à son terme; quand on note que le rendement moyen des plantes, ces "machines végétales," est d'utiliser en moyenne 1% de l'énergie solaire, et que nous savons qu'elles peuvent, au laboratoire, fournir des rendements de 5 a 10% sinon davantage, quand on rapproche cette capacité potentielle de progrès avec la valeur actuelle (au rendement de 1 à 2 pour mille) de la production agricole qui est pourtant de l'ordre du tiers de la production industrielle dans les pays évolués, on éprouve le sentiment profond que la puissance des techniques agronomiques est largement comparable, sinon supérieure, à celles des techniques industrielles. Quand on considère les bases scientifiques des prochaines techniques agronomiques (telles que l'analyse chromatographique et l'emploi des éléments appliqués à la Physiologie végétale, les notions nouvelles d'hormones et de mécanismes régulateurs de la croissance et du développement, la physiochimie des macromolécules appliquée au support des propriétés héréditaires), on peut raisonnablement penser que les découvertes scientifiques changeront aussi profondement l'agriculture du siècle qui vient qu'elles l'ont modifiée déjà durant le siècle qui s'achève.

A court terme, par tranches de quelques mois, ces progrès semblent des utopies et la science ne semble fournir qu'un amas confus de nouveaux détails. Mais l'expérience du passé récent nous apprend qu'à long terme, de nouveaux progrès, toujours plus éclatants, ne cessent de sortir de la multitude des petites decouvertes, de sorte que, au-delá des soucis fastidieux de leur tâche quotidienne, savants et techniciens attachés à l'Agronomie peuvent avoir foi dans l'intérêt et la portée immense de leurs travaux.

2. *L'agronomie tient sa puissance et sa valeur de l'utilisation de l'énergie solaire par des machines vivantes*

L'ampleur des perspectives d'avenir est encore accrue maintenant, lorsque nous considérons mieux la situation de l'agriculture par rapport aux problèmes généraux de la matière et de l'énergie.

En ce moment, le monde, doté de la civilisation technique, vit, d'une part pour l'approvisionnement en vivres, sur les ressources de l'agriculture, renouvelables chaque année, et d'autre part, pour ses besoins en énergie et matières industrielles, sur les ressources des mines de houille, de pétrole et des mines métalliques et autres (inclus les minerais atomiques). Ces ressources minières sont fatalement destinées à l'épuisement. Cet épuisement n'est évidemment pas pour demain: mais dans certains pays comme l'Europe, il surviendra, notamment pour le charbon et le pétrole, dans le délai d'un nombre relativement petit de générations. Seule l'énergie solaire est indéfiniment renouvelable, pour des temps aussi considérables que l'ordre du milliard d'années, et si l'humanité doit subsister assez longtemps, seule l'énergie solaire (qui est d'ailleurs une forme de l'énergie atomique) permettra à l'humanité une survie prolongée.

On conçoit donc l'importance présente et surtout future des études qui s'attachent à la captation et à l'utilisation de l'énergie solaire. Les unes sont fondées sur des procédés physiques tels que la concentration de la chaleur pour le fonctionnement des fours solaires. Les autres concernent l'utilisation notable de l'énergie lumineuse en courant électrique; déjà, de la sorte, des productions de l'ordre de 40 à 100 watts au mètre carré ont été envisagées. On peut donc prévoir pour l'avenir que la production de l'énergie d'origine minière sera relayée, pour une part, par la production d'énergie thermique et électrique à partir des centrales atomiques concentrées en installations puissantes sur de petites surfaces et, d'autre part grâce à la production d'énergie principalement électrique obtenue à partir du rayonnement solaire, par des installations réparties sur de grandes surfaces. Ces dernières installations pourraient même éventuellement remplacer toutes les autres sources d'énergie, si elles venaient à manquer.

Mais la production des matières organiques, soit pour l'alimentation, soit comme matières premières pour l'industrie, telles qu'éléments textiles et matières plastiques, ne pourra être assurée dans l'avenir que par des synthèses tirées de l'énergie solaire par un processus analogue à celui qu'emploient les plantes sinon par les plantes elles-mêmes. C'est là que s'attache l'intérêt fondamental des recherches sur la photo-synthèse et sur la stimulation des végétaux par tous les moyens capables d'utiliser leurs propriétés physiologiques. De plus l'utilisation de l'énergie solaire par voie photo-électrique ou par la photo-synthèse, offre l'avantage de n'accumuler aucun produit toxique de caractère permanent contrairement au risque qui est présente par certaines des utilisations de l'énergie atomique.

La Physique, la Chimie, et l'industrie pure ont donc devant elles une large part des possibilités de capter l'énergie radiante du soleil pour livrer des formes plus utilisables d'énergie, électrique par exemple. Mais la Biologie et l'Agriculture détiennent le quasi-monopole de la production indéfinie de matière à partir de l'énergie solaire. Les machines vivantes qui assument cette transformation se reproduisent d'elles-mêmes par des processus génétiques, avec les propriétés améliorées que nous parvenons à leur conférer. Ce sont là des traits originaux et irremplacables de l'Agronomie. Effacé un moment par le spectacle éblouissant de la révolution industrielle, le prestige de l'Agriculture reparait, avec la disparition maintenant certaine, quoiqu'encore lointaine, des ressources minières de matières premières et avec la prise de conscience des richesses réelles qui sont celles que nous fournit l'énergie solaire.

Dans cette perspective, la face future du monde nous apparaît bientôt comme changée. Si les mines glacées de fer et de pétrole du Canada sont maintenant en vedette, ce sont les déserts ensoleillés comme le Sahara vers lesquels se tournent nos regards pour demain et il nous faut songer sérieusement à une future industrie et une future agriculture des déserts. Ainsi, pour le vieux monde, la notion d'Eurafrique est en train de reprendre un sens puissant; elle constitue, de ce côté de la terre, la grande unité économique d'un futur qui n'est plus très lointain.

3. *Les buts du progrès technique en Agronomie*

Nourrir le monde et fournir les matières premières à l'industrie. L'agriculture étant seule capable de fournir aux hommes la satisfaction de leur besoin primaire, les vivres, il est clair que le but initial et capital de l'Agronomie est d'abord de "nourrir ceux qui ont faim." Sur ce point essentiel, la croissance récente et rapide de la population du monde jette le trouble et provoque de légitimes inquiétudes.

Cependant, ce que nous venons de voir de la puissance et de la capacité du progrès des techniques agronomiques lève le doute, du moins pour le moment: si nous nous efforcions d'accroître la production des vivres sans préoccupation économique, avec la même énergie que celle que l'on déploie pour les productions d'armés en temps de guerre, nous serions capables de procurer à la population du monde entier la quantité de vivres nécessaires pour apaiser sa faim. Il est vraisemblable que s'il en était ainsi, les dangers mêmes que la surpopulation fait encourir au monde s'estomperaient peu à peu, car avec le relèvement des conditions économiques et de la situation sociale, les zones de croissance démographique désordonnée pourraient recevoir l'education et limiteraient d'elles-mêmes leur croissance à un taux raisonnable, comme il est constamment arrivé dans les pays de civilisation technique avancée.

Mais en regard de ces possibilités théoriques, nous pouvons être profondement déçus par la lenteur des progrès actuels de l'agriculture et par le fait que là où les progrès ont pénétré, ils sont aussitôt accompagnés d'un contingentement de la production, comme la leçon de la canne à sucre nous en a donné l'exemple. On pourrait ainsi considérer, au contraire, avec pessimisme les possibilités de progrès techniques que la science offre à l'agriculture. Je crois qu'il ne faut pas en rendre responsable ni les savants, ni les agriculteurs, mais dans une large part le système économique dans lequel nous sommes installés et qui, précisément, ne tient pas compte suffisamment de la puissance des moyens techniques qui sont maintenant à notre disposition.

En effet, à côté du progrès de la science, il faut envisager l'importance des moyens à prendre pour la pénétration du progrès technique dans l'agriculture; il s'agit là d'une autre forme d'investissement, ce que l'on pourrait appeler un investissement dans les cerveaux, qui consiste à fair connaitre les nouveautés déjà techniquement acquises et à promouvoir la volonté de les appliquer sainement.

Sans même envisager les progrès lointains que nous pouvons concevoir par anticipation, il est frappant de remarquer combien est faible la proportion des agriculteurs, pourtant éclairés, qui ont mis en oeuvre les procédés déjà bien au point d'amélioration de la ponte des volailles, de la production du lait, de la haute fertilité des luzernières, des aménagements pastoraux, etc... Cette lenteur dans la pénétration du progrès technique provient d'abord de l'insuffisance en nombre des agents de cette pénétration. Mais fussent-ils plus nombreux, mieux préparés, cela ne suffirait pas encore: chaque fois, en effet, que les agriculteurs des pays évolués appliquent le progrès technique, produisent mieux et plus abondamment, ils risquent aussitôt de fournir des excédents de production qui alourdissent les cours et le résultat final est qu'ils gagnent moins.

Pour parer à cet obstacle, tout le monde est d'accord pour favoriser les exportations. Cette intention est louable, mais les exportations, dans le régime commercial et économique actuel, s'étendent à peu près exclusivement aux pays solvables, c'est-à-dire aux pays déjà riches et techniquement évolués et chez lesquels précisément la surproduction est également menaçante. Par la voie des exportations classiques, la difficulté peut être un peu reculée, elle n'est pas résolue.

Il me semble qu'il faudrait aller plus loin et cela dans deux voies distinctes: la première consisterait à consacrer des efforts beaucoup plus grands à la recherche des débouchés industriels pour les matières d'origine agricole. C'est pourquoi l'exemple du ricin que j'ai cité plus haut me paraît si hautement démonstratif. Toutes les fois où les recherches scientifiques, dans le domaine que l'on appelle un peu pompeusement celui de la "chémiurgie," ajouteront une plante de plus à celles qui produisent des matières premières utilisables pour l'industrie et transformables en biens de consommation autres qu'alimentaires (que l'on appelle souvent des biens secondaires ou tertiaires), la consommation de tels biens peut croître dans d'immenses proportions en même temps que se développe l'expansion économique. On n'est plus limité dans l'écoulement de tels biens par le plafonnement rapide qui résulte de la satiété des vivres. Dans toute la mesure où de tels débouchés s'ajouteront à ceux de l'exportation, l'agriculteur pourra envisager avec plus d'intérêt les progrès techniques qu'on lui propose, car il saura qu'en cas de surproduction, il lui est possible de jouer sur un clavier étendu de réconversions culturales dont les débouchés industriels toujours croissants se trouveront assurés.

Mais sur un autre plan, il faut aussi considérer combien il serait absurde d'avoir à conseiller à l'humanité le malthusianisme des naissances, quand les pays riches pratiquent déjà la restriction de la production agricole, ouvertement par les contingentements et pratiquement par les prix. Or, le fait est là: dans sa majorité, l'humanité a faim, elle grandit et il est utopique de penser qu'elle limitera immédiatement sa croissance démographique. A moins de la décimer volontairement, ce qui est impensable, il faut tout faire pour la nourrir. Il faut qu'elle vive d'abord, pour s'éduquer ensuite, au delà des applications rudimentaires de l'hygiène, pour atteindre le niveau de connaissance où, d'elle-même, elle tempérera sa croissance désordonnée. Si nous ne faisons rien pour nourrir ceux qui ont faim, leur masse ravagera les pays riches et tous périront, nous comme eux.

Pour un problème aussi vaste, la science nous ouvre des techniques nouvelles. Mais elle ne suffit pas seule; car seule elle serait utopique. En même temps que la science, la pénétration du progrès technique doit être développée. En même temps que les vivres, et même pour les produire plus libéralement, l'agriculture devra produire de plus en plus de matières premières pour l'industrie. En même temps que le progrès technique, le système économique doit être amendé: nous ne pourrons pas subsister longtemps si l'abondance continue à tuer le riche sans être d'aucun secours pour le pauvre. Là est la monstruosité dont nous pouvons périr, alors que nous avons techniquement tous les remèdes pour survivre.

CONCLUSION

L'agriculture future continuera à contribuer au développement des vertus fondamentales de la personne humaine

Laissez-moi terminer par une dernière remarque: l'agriculture, transformée par la Recherche scientifique appliquée à ses progrès techniques restera encore l'agriculture, car son trait caractéristique est d'être fondée sur la transformation biologique de l'énergie solaire à bas potentiel, dispersée sur d'immenses surfaces. Dans l'avenir, quelles que soient les transformations, c'est là une donnée permanente de la nature en vertu de laquelle la révolution agricole est plus une évolution continue qu'une explosion brutale. Il s'ensuit que les hommes qui seront appliqués à la marche des machines à énergie solaire, que ce soient des piles photo-électriques ou, mieux, des cultures d'algues, ou des cultures agricoles améliorées, auront sous leur dépendance une assez vaste surface de machines électriques ou de machines vivantes à controler. Ces dernières, surtout, exigent à chaque instant un contrôle intelligent et personnel.

Loin d'être rassemblés comme des automates dans une usine étroite, les agriculteurs de demain, comme et mieux que ceux d'aujourd'hui, auront sans cesse à développer leurs qualités personnelles d'observation, d'indépendance, d'initiative et de responsabilité. La science et la technique appliquées à l'agriculture ne nous conduisent pas à une ère de robots, mais elles contribueront au développement des vertus fondamentales de la personne humaine.

SUMMARY

Probable trends in the development of new techniques in agriculture

Viewing areas of scientific studies which seem to be most fruitful for future agricultural techniques, the author indicates a number of new lines of research which merit attention of studious technicians for adaptation and use in the moment when they can be of practical value.

He cites various ways to achieve a higher drought resistance e.g., by *seed preparation*, *subirrigation* of sand culture of deserts, *desalination* of brackish or *seawater*. (A remark of the Editor cites in this connection for their global significance the successful experiments of *direct application* of highly brackish water and even *seawater* up to oceanic concentration on coastal and inland sands and gravel areas. These experiments, carried out first in Israel, since 1949, proved to be likewise successful in Spain and in Sweden. Thus they already cover a climatic profile from the hot desert climate of Eilat, over the mediterranean coastal plain, in Israel, and the warm temperate climate of Spain, to the cool and humid climate of Eastern Sweden).

Other important results in raising the agricultural potential of our globe can be expected to be achieved by:

- *Leaf-manuring;*
- *Genetical improvement of physiological resistance* to pests;
- Increase of productivity *by heterosis;*
- *Promoted mutations* by radiations of mutagenic substances;
- New systems of *production of virus free crops;*

- *Chemiotherapy against pests;*
- Refined uses of *growth hormones;*
- Many *uses of Phytotrons* for pure and applied knowledge of *growth and development*, and for *shortening of agronomic experiments* on quality and adaptation of new crops;
- Improvement of knowledge of *photosynthetic processes;*
- *Chemiurgy*, the prospects and potential of which are very wide indeed for the production of new plant raw materials for industry. Several examples are given (*Ricinus*, Algae, etc.).

We are reminded that the technical revolution in agriculture, begun and carried out during the last one and a half centuries, is now in full development and still has the potential for much more progress. The importance, and the originality, of agricultural techniques which renew themselves permanently through living biological machines driven by the inexhaustible energy source, the sun, is also indicated. At this time, when the mineral resources of the globe which have brought such prosperity to industry are about to be exhausted (not immediately but in the foreseeable future - only a few generations away), the utilization of solar energy will then take on all its importance and will be able to insure an extended high standard of life in the future.

Agriculture, provided thus with all her potentialities, is technically at least, able to meet for a long time to come the rising needs of men. The difficulties now are psychological and economic rather than technical. It is a slow process to make the millions of growers aware of this technical progress and this is one of our most urgent tasks.

The expansion of the economy of underdeveloped countries is of great urgency, it exceeds, however, the object of this essay. But a trend of world importance would be extending the production of plant-raw-materials for industrial use. This development would free agriculture of the worry of excess production (which throttles the use of technical discoveries), and could thus contribute, indirectly, to a larger and more economic production, also, of food itself.

The meaning of the technical progress of agriculture can, therefore, be expressed roughly as follows:

1) The potential ability to progress in agriculture is enormous in respect to industry.
2) The peculiar characteristics of agriculture are *its use of solar energy by living machines* (plants), exploiting the natural plant physiological process of photosynthesis.
3) The *aim of agriculture* is at first the production of raw material for *food* as well as for *industry*, thus permitting the increase of human population and welfare.

Conditions of the *agricultural way of life* should always be in accordance with the *development of fundamental characteristics of human beings.*

In summing up, the essay reminds us that no matter how revolutionary future agricultural techniques may and can be, they must always conform to the fundamental development of human qualities and oppose man's degradation into a robot. In fact, founded on the use of solar energy, vast but dispersed, and on the play of living machines which demand a permanent control, agriculture of tomorrow, much more than that of today, will be able to contribute to the development of the spirit of man's initiative and freedom.

Science in the Service of Man in Africa South of the Sahara

by

JOHN PHILLIPS

THE CONSEQUENCES OF FAILING TO PLAN ECOLOGICALLY

Even as science may be applied to the service of man, its not being so employed in a sound, integrated and carefully planned manner retards progress and indeed does much harm to the welfare and happiness of all concerned.

The *ecological* approach – that is the seeing of the community of life and its stage, the habitat, in proper relation and perspective – is capable of so much good in the service of the indigenous and other peoples in Africa South of the Sahara, that a failure to think along ecological lines is in the nature of a very serious disservice.

To convey what is likely to happen in the event of man's failure to plan and prosecute the agricultural and related development of Africa South of the Sahara according to certain ecological principles is the object of this essay.

This is no attempt to paint merely a Job's picture of what would happen should development continue to be casual, but rather to convey some impression of what might be averted were the *holistic* approach to be adopted more widely and with wider and deeper knowledge of ecological detail. Some examples illustrating the risks incurred in not thinking ecologically are summarized.

NATURAL VEGETATION

Due to absence of an understanding of the biotic nature, habitat characteristics and ecological development of natural vegetation this is often seriously impoverished by agricultural and related activity.

Failure to relate the *bioclimatic* possibilities to the demand made by nomadic, transitional and settled African pastoralists and by Europeans permanently occupying land ultimately spells the deterioration of natural pasturage and browse, livestock and the soil itself. Open grassland is reduced in the number and volume of the more valuable fodder species at the expense of others less palatable to or rejected by livestock. Again, contiguous with a more xerophytic vegetation such as the Karoo in South Africa, grassland is invaded by useless species from the neighbouring subdesert. Again, subdesert Karoo is converted from palatable browse to a wilderness of relatively useless species in which sheep and goats find little sustenance. Wooded savanna – be this subdesert or arid, subarid or subhumid – through a combination of heavy stocking and withholding of fire, rapidly develops into thickets of woody species, the grass diminishing and often altering in species and pastoral quality.

Today, when water for man and beast can be supplied where this never previously existed, there is even greater danger of the disturbing of the ecological balance, and the consequent accelerated ruination of the vegetation. Examples occur in Southern and East Africa and if the prevalent well intentioned but unplanned provision of water to dry subregions is intensified, there will be ere long examples in arid and subdesert Somalia and in the drier parts of West Africa.

Even mangrove communities are liable to maltreatment, with related alteration in the effects of tidal water on the coastline. Fixed littoral sand dunes steadily are being subjected to excessive pressure from livestock and in places are being deprived of their woody cover for the sake of fuel: the outcome is the advance inland of the sand. Where overgrazed by sheep and goats fixed inland dunes once again become mobile.

Through the influences of uncontrolled shifting cultivation and fire, forest steadily yields to grass and wooded savanna, with accompanying impoverishment in the productive capacity of the soil and, if the area be extensive, of water supplies for the country at lower levels.

It is common practice to use fire in the driving of game, the stimulation of the growth of young grass and browse shrubs, and the conversion of forest, scrub, thicket, woodland and other vegetation to open land for cultivation. Equally general is the tendency of many pastoralists, agriculturists and botanists to decry this practice. Ecologically there is much to commend *discriminative* burning, based on a knowledge of the ecology of the area. Indeed failure to burn grazing and browse at suitable seasons and intervals, in relation to previous or intended utilization of the area by livestock, spells deterioration of the nutritive value and palatability of the vegetation.

Much of the continent already shows the effects of casual or feckless treatment of the natural vegetation – the African and European often being equally destructive.

CROPS AND CULTIVATION

Marginal and thus often subeconomic production of crops is a widespread feature, springing from a lack of realization of the local moisture and temperature conditions. European settlers as well as African tribesmen, for instance, tend to grow maize in areas at the limits of adequate distribution and amount of rain – examples exist from Southern to North-eastern and West Africa in the non-humid regions. Cotton, tobacco, sunflower, groundnuts, sorghum and other crops are often tried beyond their economic range.

In recent years there has been wishful thinking of developing oil palm in parts of West Africa marginal in both the annual total and the monthly distribution of rainfall. Irrigated banana plantations have been established under subarid to arid conditions in Somalia, and run at high cost in proportion to yield and in comparison with rain-fed plantations elsewhere in Africa. Production of sunflower has failed in Tanganyika where attempted under subarid conditions and on a scale rendering satisfactory pollination impossible. Large-scale production of groundnuts in subarid Tanganyika and parts of subhumid Ghana has failed; in the first instance, because of drought and severe soil compaction; and in the second, *inter alia* because of high humidity and a rainfall prolonged into the harvesting period.

Shifting cultivation induces loss of fertility where the return use of a given area is too rapid. Unless applied with understanding and care modern mechanized clearing of vegetation and soil preparation do much damage physically, through loss in fertility and by the disturbance of micro-organisms.

Serious inversion of the soil and subsoil follows the deep ploughing of certain types. In some very heavy clays of montmorillonitic nature a failure to leave the soil rough, that is *not* worked into a fine tilth, before the onset of the rains, creates a veritable quagmire of slushy-like consistency. Conversely, where normal soil conservation contour banks are provided, lighter soils such as sandy loams accumulate water which converts them almost to quick-sand. These soils become useless for crops such as tobacco, maize, cassava, yams and others sensitive to prolonged wetness.

An appropriate cycle supported by improved husbandry, as well as the use of mixed cultures of cereals, gourds, rootcrops and legumes not always rigorously weeded, have been insufficiently appreciated for too long by too many European agricultural officers and farmers. Failure on the part of so many Europeans to understand the ecological common sense of some of the traditional cultivation methods, spells loss of opportunity for raising the productivity of many parts of Africa.

DEVELOPMENT AND CONSERVATION OF WATER

Outside of the humid regions *water* is one of the commodities most prized in Africa. Its development spells so much good to man and beast that it will appear strange not to praise all efforts to provide water more abundantly.

Water poses deeply seated questions in the planning and the management of pastoral areas and the irrigation of certain soils. As noted under natural vegetation, the casual or ill-planned distribution of watering points in country by nature poorly supplied accelerates, in woodland and open woodland, either degradation of the soil or the intensification of thicket. The application of water to soils with alkaline reaction normally induces "brack" or "black alkali" so as to retard plant growth. In siting dams and setting out of irrigation schemes below them error in assessment of the reactions of the soils to irrigation is all too common. A further error is not to take sufficiently into account the heavy losses – up to half their content – from dams of shallower depth by evaporation. Ecological forethought could readily estimate the loss due to this cause and make provision accordingly.

The otherwise excellent practice of establishing soil and water-conserving hydraulic structures on arable land of certain soil types results in excessive accumulation of water, detrimental to most subsistence and cash crops other than rice and other hygrophilous species.

Efforts to utilize drainage lines and flood plains, where vegetation normally conserves groundwater at no great depth, give excellent return, provided flooding is preventable. But experience especially in Southern Africa and elsewhere reveals the devastating losses in soil following this misuse of bottom lands.

If inadequate attention be paid to the ecological phenomena associated with the local geomorphology, the surface wash and erosion, the loss of soil from the uppermost horizon, the change in depth of the water table, the habitat factors both soil and microclimatic, the succession and development of vegetation and the animals associated therewith, the failure of an irrigated project cannot be averted.

As atomic and solar radiation power are developed it is likely that more and more water will be made available from the oceans for irrigation and other purposes.

TSETSE AND TRYPANOSOMIASIS

A wealth of knowledge, scientific and practical, is available for the control of one of the greatest scourges to man and beast in tropical Africa, and one of the most powerful brakes on the planned development of wooded savanna country, from the subhumid to the arid regions, the "fly." No single method is in itself either wholly practicable or all-sufficient, but a combination of techniques properly planned and applied could work wonders over large areas. Up to the present the failure to implement concerted attacks on the "fly", followed by phased settlement and the provision of sufficient suitably distributed watering points, animal health and husbandry services, livestock culling, castration and general control is notorious. Disappointment and frustration hence are inevitable. Ecological awareness is fundamental to the successful combat of the "guardian" of Africa's potential pasturage soils, the "fly".

LIVESTOCK

But slight study has been paid to the interrelations of livestock responses – physiological, ecological and in terms of behaviour. Breed, strain, pigmentation, resistance to drought and heat and to pests and disease, and the capacity of the animals to forage in severe physical and biotic conditions must be examined for the successful selection of cattle for a wide range of bioclimatic conditions. Casual introduction of exotic cattle, sheep and poultry into the humid and the dry tropics is creating many problems in health, efficiency of function, growth and conformation.

Though more successful over a greater amplitude of humidity, sunshine, and radiation than other exotic animals, pigs[1] do present their own special problems. Protection from excessive radiation and, in "fly" areas, from Tsetse, and an assured balanced yet economic diet, are among the conditions all too rare.

Humidity and temperature control is essential to satisfactory incubation of chickens. If livestock is to be farmed successfully in the humid forest region it will prove necessary to select suitable strains of high economic promise in sheep, goats and poultry. Although cattle are more difficult to adjust to climatic and nutritional conditions in the forest, success cannot be expected until there is a well concerted approach.

CONSERVATION AND CONTROL OF GAME

Game – especially antelope, buffalo, elephant, leopard, lion and smaller but abundant carnivores – although much less widespread than a quarter of a century ago, is still abundant to frequent in parts of East Africa and elsewhere.

1. The naturalized "razor-back" pig is probably the offspring of Portuguese "long-snouts" introduced in the 15th century.

In the interest of cultivators and the health of livestock, the control of game is an accepted tenet of policy. How best this can be implemented, so as to prevent the spread of game and therewith associated pests and disease injurious to livestock, is a conundrum for the administrator and the veterinarian. The relationship of game, tsetse and trypanosomiasis in man and beast is among the most significant of the problems confronting vast areas in Africa. Attempts at a solution – not appreciating the ecological network of relations – so far have failed and will continue so to do. Control must be based upon a knowledge of the ecological relations with the vegetation, and their capacity for utilizing the sparse and far scattered water supplies in the dry season.[2]

Conservation of game for aesthetic and scientific purposes is now a practice supported by many governments. Unfortunately in most instances there is still no effort to approach preservation along ecological lines. These would involve selective shooting of some super-abundant species and the encouragement of the rarer kinds. Hence undue proportions of some species – zebra, wildebeest (gnu), impala, and hartebeest (kongoni) being examples – appear comparatively soon. If, because of competition or any other reason there be a scarcity of graze, browse and water in the reserves, the impulse is to move beyond their borders and thus into country cultivated or used for livestock.

LAND USE AND TENURE

The widespread change in economic and social patterns is

2. Representatives of the International Union for the Conservation of Nature (I.U.C.N.), the Food and Agricultural Organisation (F.A.O.) and the Scientific Council for Africa South of the Sahara (C.S.A.) are to meet in 1961 to discuss further the possibilities of *management* of game and other wild animals.

Economic production of game products together with practical control of natural pasturage and browse thus migth be found feasible. To "farm" game migth be a better land use than to "farm" domesticated livestock in areas that are marginal ecologically.

causing much thought to be focussed on the traditional patterns of tenure. A consideration of the inherent issues stresses the necessity for careful investigation before deciding on legal and other changes. Unless granted in some appropriate form and with suitable conditions and controls, individual ownership can cause as many problems in land use, wastage of soil and economic depression as it purports to solve.

Legal, administrative, land use and economic aspects all must be examined in their bearing one on the other. A failure to think and plan *holistically* is liable to perpetuate many of the existing evils in communal ownership and to perpetrate yet others. The more knowledge of local conditions, available from ecological-economic land use survey and from a study of the changing social pattern of the people, is weighed by the jurists and administrators, the less likely are serious errors of judgment. If ever subjects, fundamental to the prevention of soil and vegetation deterioration and to the assurance of human well-being, demand a co-ordinated solution they are the use and tenure of arable land, the responsibility for the usage and maintenance of pastoral areas and the conservation of an adequate proportion of forest, for the production of timber and the regulation of water.

ROADS AND RAILWAYS

Road and railway alignment and the associated drainage, to be efficient, demand an ecological approach. Where road and rail have been established without adequate reference to master climatic factors, topography, soil types and vegetation, there follows, on the land in their proximity, serious sheet and donga erosion. Furthermore, too often are lines of communication established in country ecologically incapable of yielding crops or livestock justifying this expenditure on evacuating comparatively limited production.

Vegetation usually indicates the physical and occasionally –

as in highly arid, calcareous and gypseous country – the chemical characteristics of soils. To fail to draw upon the experience of the ecologists, skilled in the interpretation of aerial photographs for soil and vegetation survey, when planning the course of roads and railways, is to neglect a remarkably effective means of avoiding error.

HUMAN ECOLOGY

Ecologically there is a relation between indigenous human life and the environment in Africa. Were this otherwise the number, the physical and mental capacity and the actual output by Africans would be far less impressive.

There are, however, further adjustments within the grasp of the peoples living intimately with Nature outside of the larger settlements. This is especially true of health, sanitation, housing, nutrition and water supply for primary needs and for livestock and supplementary irrigation in drought periods during the rains. But this also applies to the care of the soil, crop husbandry, and the health and management of livestook through the striking of a balance between the aims of the stockman, the multifarious pests and diseases and the existence of a great game fauna.

The habitat factors and their variation are severe: high humidity to extreme aridity, torrential rain to lengthy drought, monotonous heat to acute cold, intense and prolonged sunshine to many weeks with little or no direct sunlight. Inured as they may be to either monotony or to wide oscillations of climate, Africans leading a simple existence in the wildernesses are, none-the-less, influenced by the interplay of climatic factors. To the more privileged Africans and to members of Overseas races these conditions are even more severe when encountered away from modern conveniences. For Europeans the impress of radiation and humidity, for example, is more serious than for Africans.

Moreover, the presently unexplained, because not yet measurable, tension in the atmosphere toward the end of the dry season and during drought periods in the rains makes the European in the African tropics far less efficient in mental reaction and physical response than in temperate and sub-tropical environments. Whether or not this will be explicable later, on the grounds of specific features of atmospheric ionization, remains to be proved.

Apart from a solution along ecological lines of the problems in health, nutrition and other basic matters already noted, there is also wanted a more realistic approach to clothing, physical excercise and mental stimulus in the several social groupings in their natural milieu.

A failure to plan and labour ecologically for an amelioration of the rigours of the habitat will postpone indefinitely the striking of an equilibrium between man and his environment. Till that day will be withheld a measure of additional happiness for the African people.

It should be remembered that Africans and the people of Overseas origin – especially those of European ancestry – do not easily understand each other. Tradition, moral attitudes and so forth are markedly different – hence it is unwise for either racial groups to be ultra-critical of the other.

An ecological assessment of environment, background, sociology, religion and group ethics would ease the present ready tendency for group criticism. Africans and others have to learn to understand each other far better if they are to live and labour together for the best development of the continent.

SUBSISTENCE AND ECONOMY

Unless the practice of production is based on ecologically sound systems and methods, a struggling existence or permanent poverty is inevitable, instead of a slow but none-the-less real amelioration.

In many parts Africa is very poor; in others she is blessed in mediocre degree only; in yet others she is moderately fertile. She will be poorer throughout unless her people are more successful in relating her natural potentialities to appropriate practices and in realizing the relentless association of cause and effect, no matter how often the forgiveness of Nature tends to hide the mistakes of man. In the educating of his African brother to plan ecologically, the Overseas guide, philosopher and friend is heir to a truly weighty responsibility.

CONCLUSION

Applied to the physical, biotic, racial and economic problems of this ancient continent, the ecological viewpoint and approach could serve as an operative force both realistic and idealistic. It should enable man – black and white – to see life and living *as a whole.* A South African of several generations, who happily endeavoured to serve the Sovereign State Ghana for eight years, pays personal tribute to the holistic creative force of the ecological approach to human understanding.[3]

3. An effort to apply the ecological approach to the sounder development of agriculture in Africa South of the Sahara has been attempted in book form: "Agriculture and Ecology in Africa." (J. F. V. PHILLIPS, 1959, Faber and Faber, London).

La science et l'homme au seuil du désert

par

Théodore Monod

Au sens populaire du mot, le "désert" est un pays inhabité: à ce titre, bien des forêts primaires, bien des montagnes, d'immenses surfaces polaires, comme tous les océans, sont *aussi* des déserts.

Nous n'envisagerons ici le mot qu'en son sens restreint de région où le développement de la biosphère trouve dans la sécheresse un facteur toujours limitant, et, parfois, léthal.

Ces immensités désolées, et assoiffées: un Namib, un Atacama, un Takla-Makan, un Simpson Desert, une Tanezrouft, comme elles sont un lieu propice, et prédestiné, à une méditation sur la Science et l'avenir de l'homme.

Non certes qu'il s'agisse nécessairement de terres "vierges": il n'est sans doute pas dans tout le Sahara un mètre carré qui n'ait été foulé par l'homme – celui du biface, celui de la céramique, celui de la lance ou celui du fusil – et par des animaux: le boeuf, le cheval, la chèvre ou le chameau. Mais ces espaces démesurés – il m'a fallu parcourir au Sahara occidental, entre deux points d'eau et en ligne droite, près de 900 km en 22 jours – appartiennent encore à des aspects singulièrement marginaux de l'oecoumène: l'homme, même nomade, y reste rare, le paysage demeure à peu près intouché, en dehors des îlots, punctiformes, de vie sédentaire et des péjorations du surpâturage, la technique, reine ailleurs, s'arrète encore, hésitante, au seuil du vrai désert, et s'interroge.

La vie traditionelle continue de siècle au siècle, et depuis des millénaires sans doute, le miracle du nomadisme désertique, atteignant avec l'élevage camélin des "grands nomades" un équilibre écologique et une adaptation au milieu qui en fait une réussite humaine à coup sûr aussi remarquable et, on peut le penser, aussi "respectable", que celle des Eskimos les plus septentrionaux.

Que ce style de vie ait à côté de ses lumières ses ombres, qui le nierait? Mais qui, aussi, oserait oublier, s'il était tenté par la vaine stupidité d'un "palmarès", les turpitudes des civilisations orgueilleuses qui se sont arrogé le monopole du C majuscule?

Mais ces dernières, qui ont pour elles la force matérielle, font tache d'huile (ou de pétrole ...): les voici aux portes du désert, prêtes à mener l'assaut de leur machinerie contre le scandale des taches blanches de la carte économique. Les appétits s'éveillent: *auri sacra fames*, comme d'habitude, même s'il s'agit, en fait, de fer, de cuivre ou de "produits noirs" ... mirages de rentabilité et de puissance, espoirs aussi, bien sûr, de substantiels dividendes ... Le désert renferme-t-il quelque richesse désirable? Pourquoi les forts et les habiles hésiteraient-ils à le "sucer", fût-ce au bénéfice de lointains consommateurs, et de quelques non moins lointains actionnaires?

Bientôt la géopolitique et la stratégie s'en mêlent et voici les déserts précipités, de gré ou de force, dans le cercle infernal des querelles des "civilisés". Méritaient-ils semblable promotion? Et que devient, dans ce fièvreux branlebas des mécaniques, l'homme local, l'homme désertique, celui qui est ici chez lui, et le plus souvent depuis fort longtemps? Quel avenir lui réserve-t-on? Quel part recevra-t-il, et sous quelle forme, du bénéfice des investissements industriels? Se pourrait-il qu'on l'oublie? Et que l'on s'apprête à bouleverser sans lui, et comme à son insu, le cadre de sa vie traditionelle?

Contrepartie nécessaire et juste des profits que les puissances matérielles s'apprêtent à prélever sur les déserts, des devoirs, de toute évidence, s'imposent, que certaines entreprises, d'ailleurs, ont la sagesse déjà de reconnaître. Si la technique doit permettre, dans le domaine minière, l'exploitation de richesses souterraines souvent sans intérêt direct pour le nomade, elle ne sera pas moins capable de procurer à ce dernier le seul minéral qui lui soit immédiatement profitable, l'eau. Et, par conséquent, d'améliorer ses conditions d'existence.

En même temps que le recours, désormais possible, à des nappes profondes inaccessibles à la technique traditionnelle, une politique résolue de conservation des ressources naturelles s'efforcerait de rechercher un équilibre raisonné, fondé sur l'observation et l'expérimentation biologiques, entre le pouvoir régénérateur de la plante et les exigences du troupeau.[1]

On sait en effet le rôle de l'homme dans l'entretien et l'aggravation des conditions désertiques par les contraintes qu'il exerce, avec ses animaux, sur la végétation naturelle. Mais il n'est pas douteux que dans certaines régions du Sahara, comme sont en train de le prouver les expériences de mise en défends de parcelles protégées dans l'Adrar mauritanien, le type normal, climatique d'une couverture végétale soustraite aux actions anthropiques, se montrera beaucoup plus dense qu'on eût pu l'imaginer. Il en sera de même, *a fortiori*, des semi-déserts marginaux, à végétation steppique, dans des zones où déjà se posera l'éternel problème de la coexistence nomades/sédentaires, partout complexe et plus encore en Afrique sahélienne où à l'opposition des genres de vie se superpose celle des races et où l'évolution socio-

1. On a parfois qualifié, pour les ridiculiser, ceux qu'inquiètent les menaces que font peser sur les êtres vivants au Sahara: flore, faune, humanités, de "conservateurs du désert": comme si ce dernier n'était pas de taille à se défendre tout seul et comme si nos technocrates étaient déjà capables de modifier les climats ... L'homme moderne peut certes beaucoup, et ses capacités de destruction s'amplifient magnifiquement: il aurait peut-être tort de se considérer prématurément comme omnipotent, car il s'en faut de beaucoup, comme l'océan, les seismes, les volcans, les déserts ou les pôles le lui répètent pourtant assez clairement.

économique et politique actuelle tend à modifier des structures traditionelles de type féodal, avec une aristocratie de pasteurs blancs nomades maintenant en état de servage ou de demi-servage des agriculteurs sédentaires de race noire.

On se gardera donc d'imaginer que le problème de la mise en valeur des déserts ou semi-déserts soit seulement une affaire de technique et qu'il puisse jamais suffire d'ingénieurs ou de machine pour le résoudre. Cela peut être vrai localement, dans des déserts inhabités, s'il en est, mais dans la plupart des cas, il faudra découvrir le moyen d'assurer aux humanités désertiques une part legitime des profits des exploitations industrielles et, dans certains semi-déserts, agricoles, envisagées.

Non certes qu'il s'agisse de contraindre le berger touareg ou bédouin à se transformer obligatoirement en salarié ou en client, et à aventurer sa liberté aux périls de la cité ou de l'usine. Mais si la science accepte de prendre au sérieux, par delà les calculs du profit ou de la puissance, son pouvoir de libération et le soulagement qu'elle peut apporter à la séculaire peine des hommes, elle trouvera au désert ample occasion d'exercer cette haute mission.

Mettre généreusement au service de l'homme, fût-il le plus humble, le plus "attardé," le plus attaché au style de vie le plus différent de notre comportement occidental, les ressources de la technique moderne, voilà le devoir d'une science digne de ce nom, capable de se faire enfin l'efficace auxiliaire du labeur des êtres, de régir les *choses* pour affranchir des *personnes*, et, en soulageant travaux et soucis de l'*homo oeconomicus*, de favoriser le développement d'un *homo cogitans*, d'un *homo aestheticus*, d'un *homo orans*.

Au seuil du désert, la science s'interroge. Elle s'apprête à livrer bataille et à vaincre une nature hostile. Mais quel sera l'enjeu de la lutte? Le profit, la puissance, le prestige, l'orgueil, une économie destructrice, la *Raubwirtschaft*, comme d'habitude, ou, désormais, le fraternel service des hommes, dans le respect de ces différences qui constituent, dans la symphonie planétaire, leur irremplaçable richesse?

LA SCIENCE ET L'HOMME AU SEUIL DU DÉSERT

SUMMARY

Science and the Man in the Heart of the Desert

The author stresses the responsibility of science and of technical power in the deserts. These come increasingly in the foreground for various reasons (mining or oil interests, geopolitics, a.s.o.): but what of the inhabitants? What benefit – if any – will they derive from the industrial exploitation of their country? If man, with his tremendous material abilities is really what he claims, a sapiens Primate, what will be his aim: profit, power, prestige, pride or, henceforth, the brotherly service of men, respectful of those differences which constitute in fact, in the planetary symphony, irreplaceable riches?

Human Needs and the Need for Ultimate Orientation

by

H. F. Infield

What we witness today is a change in orientation from one looking towards origins to one turning towards aim and purpose. This is probably the most significant characteristic of the "crisis of our times." This is the great change, of which every thinking person today is aware, and to which the different leaders of thought give different names. There is no reason to assume, as many of these leaders do, that this change is necessarily for the worse or that there are simply no ways and means of controlling and steering it in a desirable direction. It is true that, impressed with the advance of our technology, we may be inclined to overrate our control over our natural environment and to believe that there is nothing which, given the necessary means and time, we cannot accomplish. It is also true that it needs only a substantial earthquake, a hurricane, a flood or a dust storm, to make us aware again of our essential helplessness in the face of natural powers. But the change of which we are speaking is not a geological or atmospheric but a social one; and in this respect our position and possibilities are quite different.

Interestingly enough, it is only now that we become aware of our capacity to shape our social environment. It is a curious feature of mankind's development that it took it all this time to realize this fact. The explanation, probably, is that being fully involved in the process that we call society, we find it extremely difficult to attain the necessary attitude of detachment and objectivity. Possibly also, because of the genetic orientation, the tribe, the state was viewed as part of a plan preordained by the Creator. Now, however, with our predominant attitude becoming more and more ontological and operational, we begin to realize that as much as our natural environment is given, just as much our social environment is man-made. We can at best modify nature, and only to a relatively very limited degree at that; but the social environment, if we really want to, we actually can shape wholly to our own devices.

This opens possibilities – wholesome as well as noxious – of which we only now become aware. Social engineering is a growing discipline – but it can be beneficial only if it remains conscious of its limitations. In this sense, it can play a useful rôle only when and so long it is guided by and remains oriented towards the needs – and all the needs – of man.

In a paper on "Recent Developments in Personality Studies" (American Sociological Review, October 1948) already a number of years ago H. GOLDHAMMER observed that the "re-emergence of a strong emphasis on what are variously called drives, impulses or needs," is largely responsible for the fact that "intentionality or purposiveness has won back its place in the analysis of human conduct," that behaviour is again viewed as "goal-directed" (p. 555). Concern with these factors, however, is not new. Thus, for instance, the rediscovery of universal drives – or "invariants" – as ANATAL RAPPAPORT puts it in his *Operational Philosophy* (N.Y. 1954, Harpers) – such as the need for survival, for belonging or for "self-extension," for order, and for security (p. 94ff), can be shown to be actually only a newer version of the old four "fundamental wishes" – the desire for new experience, for security, response and recognition – (of THOMAS and ZNANIECKIS *The Polish Peasant*), which had dominated the discussion for so long. The shortcoming of all such classifications is that they reify what is only a *modus agendi*. This procedure goes back to the old philosophical distinction between *noumena* and *phenomena*. It is present in KANT's distinction between pure and practical reason, between the Ding-an-sich and experience. It has reappeared, in more recent times, in the so-called "instinct theory" of McDOUGALL, where "instinct" is the a priori substratum of behaviour. This question of needs is important because any genuinely "goal-directed" chartering of the next step in human development depends on it. We shall try, therefore, to sum up here in some detail our own thinking on the subject.

A FUNCTIONAL THEORY OF NEEDS

To approach the matter in the light of modern scientific method, it seems that needs cannot be viewed as "substances" but rather – to use REICHENBACH's term – as *illata* or "inferred things" such as "internal states" that can be inferred from certain "reactions of the body." [1] These reactions themselves can be understood fully only in the context of certain functional relations. In connection with an attempt to arrive at a sociological definition of culture this context was described as follows: "Culture is an acquired aggregate of meanings attached to and implemented in material and non-material objects which decisively influence the manner in which human beings tend to interact in order to satisfy their needs." [2] And it was added that "like any true functional interrelation, the one presented in our definition can be analysed by starting from any one of its terms." If we start with meanings (the old material and non-material "values" of the anthropologist) we can show how they, by way of the mode of social interaction which they determine, affect the nature of the needs. Similarly, if we start with the mode of social interaction, we can show how it serves, so to speak, as a

1. HANS REICHENBACH: "The Rise of Scientific Philosophy." Univ. of California Press. 1951. p. 263 f.
2. See this writer's: "The Concept of Jewish Culture and the State of Israel," in Amer. Sociol. Rev., August 1951.

relay system between meanings and needs, and vice versa, which are both affected by it. And taking the needs first we can show how they actuate the mode of social interaction which in turn affects the "selection, acceptance and cultivation of specific meanings attached to material and non material objects." As in any truly functional relation, primacy can be assigned to any given term only by arbitrary postulation. When man's mind reaches that state of lucidity which enables him to conceive of these terms and to reflect on them, they are already "in function." As is the case with regard to dialectics – which offer only a limited and simplified application of the functional view – it does not make sense to argue in this context who was first, the egg or the chicken; both are given when we begin to reflect on the fact that they exist. The difficulty consists rather in being able to keep in mind simultaneously the different terms of a multiple functional relation, or, in other words, the difficulty is one of being able to think functionally. Any particular term may become of special interest, given a specific issue. If what happens to interest us is the meaning of meaning – the "decision-criteria" of modern communication and organization theory – we would concentrate on the implications of this term; and so with the mode of social interaction, or with needs. Different disciplines, philosophy, sociology, and social psychology, specialize in such considerations. But they all fall short of offering real understanding of any of these terms because, or at least in so far as, they fail to view each of the terms in its functional context, which is its relation to the other terms. Thus it might be said that philosophy falls short because and in so far as it neglects the sociological and socio-psychological aspects of meaning, while sociology and socio-psychology do so because and in so far as they lack philosophical orientation.

In starting with the needs we do so not because we assign to them any primacy, but because of all three terms this is the one that is of special interest to the issues of our present discussion. In dealing with them, we should keep in mind that we do so in the light of the functional view. For it is this view, we believe, that can help us to find a viable solution to one of the most vexing issues of the theory of needs, which is classification. Attempts at the classification of needs, in the modern sense, can be traced back as far as the end of the eighteenth century; they continue to be made to this very day. A useful survey of the more noteworthy of such "systems of basic motives," made by BERNARD NOTCUTT, covers a period from 1788 to 1947 and reproduces lists constructed by authors such as THOMAS REID, the first who, using the term "active power," treated motivation in a way "similar to that used by modern authors"; of WILLIAM JAMES and W. McDOUGALL; of F. H. ALLPORT, H. A. MURRAY, and A. H. MASLOW, to name only the better-known ones. There is neither the place nor the need to go here into a detailed discussion of these lists. As of special interest to us we may mention perhaps the list of MASLOW who, finding it "impossible as well as useless to make a list of fundamental physiological needs," insists that no need exists independent of other needs and that the relation between them is a hierarchical one. This in the sense that certain needs have to be satisfied first before others can assert themselves. In his view this hierarchy shows the following order: "1) physiological needs 2) safety needs; 3) love needs (for affection and belongingness) 4) esteem needs; 5) need for self-actualization."

Examining the different lists, NOTCUTT concludes that there is "a large measure of agreement" between several of them, "and only minor points of disagreement." However, what he finds missing is a "clear-cut criterion," on the strength of which it would be possible to decide which of the lists is the correct one. All that can be said, he suggests, is that they all can be more or less convenient, depending on the use to which they are put.[3]

3. All the above quotations are from: BERNARD NOTCUTT, The Psychology of Personality. Philos. Library, New York, 1953. ch. VI. pp. 88–115.

In our own view, a survey of this kind raises several interesting points. Firstly, it appears that all the lists presented, although they may prove to be convenient in one respect or the other, lack an adequate principle of division. A mere inventory of needs, however, can never be exhaustive, simply because the nature of needs is essentially dynamic and their range infinite. The issue resembles that of the closed systems in philosophy. Any attempt at finality is doomed to failure in the face of the continuous – spontaneous or, as in our society, deliberately induced – emergence of new needs.

Another point worth stressing is the fact that none of the lists contains any reference to the spiritual or religious need. The justification for this omission, it would seem, can be traced to McDougall who, like E. L. Thorndike – to quote another writer on the subject – "rejected the religious instinct" because, he argued, "religious emotion is no single and specific expression of one instinct. It is too complex and diversified to be the product of a single motive but develops in various ways from multiple causes."[4] We may suspect, however, that the real reason was not so much fear of oversimplification as the materialistic bias of the times which kept shy of anything that smacked of idealism and transcendence. "Need" still for many means chiefly or even exclusively material needs.

Finally, a word or two might be said about Maslow's hierarchical order. His basic principle – which, and because it accords with the dynamic nature of needs – undoubtedly is sound. Needs, it is true, vary in their strength, but not in a way that would justify their ordering into higher and lower. Such ordering would presuppose that the strength of each need is constant, which contradicts the basic dynamic principle. The nature of needs being dynamic, implies rather that the strength of each need varies in itself, and will be

4. See: Paul E. Johnson: Psychology of Religion, N.Y.-Nashville. 1959. Abingdon Press. p. 59.

greater or smaller, depending on circumstances. In this sense, a need ranked as higher by Maslow may become potent before any of the lower needs have been satisfied. As we shall see later on, there exists a functional interrelation between needs, obstacles, and the "aggregate of meanings" called culture. Where a specific need meets with an obstruction that proves to be insuperable, it will be either abandoned, or the energy that activated it will be deflected into another field or context.

It might be convenient to distinguish between the different "fields" or contexts of human needs in the traditional terms of material, emotional, intellectual, social and spiritual. This distinction, however, by no means intends to represent a classification of needs. When subsequently we use expressions like "material" or "intellectual needs", it should be remembered, therefore, that we do so in this conventional sense which refers rather to the different fields or contexts as here indicated.

An actual classification of needs, in order to be consistent, will have to be based on criteria that are in accord with their nature. Since we found that this nature is dynamic, the criteria of classification themselves will have to be dynamic. A criterion of this kind, we believe, can be found in what sociology would call the mode of social interaction. Two such basic modes can be distinguished: one that implies doing things chiefly by and for oneself; and the other that implies doing things with and for others, and sharing the results equitably. To avoid those somewhat loose and unprecise terms, competition and cooperation, we may call the first the "disjunctive," and the second the "conjunctive" mode of social interaction. It is this distinction which offers us the necessary principle of division. It enables us to divide all the needs, the manifest and the potential, into two mutually exclusive classes. All needs, we can say, are either disjunctive or conjunctive, dependent on what kind of social interaction they require for the sake of their satisfaction.

As can be seen, this classification is dynamic and "open". Although it helps to order needs systematically, it does so in a way that takes into account their potentially infinite range. Its effectiveness asserted itself in the construction of a Test of Needs, or the "Cooperative Potential Test", as it came to be known.[5] This self-rating test was designed so as to yield a quantitative estimate of the relative potency of the two kind of needs, the conjunctive and the disjunctive, felt by a given individual. There was actually only one, but two-pronged, question asked by the test: to what degree are your needs of the one or the other kind. However, in order to counter any attempt at "beating" the test, the needs to be rated by the individual were divided into the five conventional contexts mentioned above, and arranged according to an underlying key, by means of which the answers could be ranked from extremely and fairly conjunctive to fairly and extremely disjunctive. In this manner the test asked five times the same question, concealed by the arrangement of the needs, and produced a five-fold self-rating with respect to the cooperative potential.

THE DYNAMICS OF NEEDS

The classification of needs just described is based, we said, on their dynamic nature. It might be well, therefore, to consider this nature somewhat more closely. We may begin with the observation that there are certain dynamic aspects of needs which are inherent partly in their own nature and partly in the nature of the factors inhibiting their satisfaction.

As inherent in the nature of needs can be considered chiefly what we might call their conspicuity or manifestness, and their valence or intensity.

The manifestness of needs can be graphically represented

5. Cf. this author's The Sociological Study of Cooperation. An Outline. Loughborough, 1956. p. 39 f., and p. 67 f.

as a continuum ranging from below zero to infinity. Below zero we can place "unfelt" needs, or needs that are only potential in the sense that one is not aware of them at a given time. They can be activated by a change of circumstances, or by deliberate manipulation, as through advertising campaigns. The range of such activation appears to be a continuum to which no limit can be set. This refers particularly to material needs. Many of those we consider as acute today were "unfelt" not so long ago and are still so in most of the "undeveloped" areas of the world. The other needs in principle are probably no less malleable and can be just as infinitely activated given the right approach. It is the extreme malleability and fecundity of probably all needs that militates against any attempt at their conclusive inventorization.

Valence, or intensity, is an aspect that has sensible reference only to "felt" needs. It is an index, or a rate, of the reciprocal relation between such needs and the factors inhibiting their satisfaction, or obstacles. This relation is not uniform. Strong needs that meet with strong obstacles may be either intensified or frustrated, dependent on the relative, objective, or subjectively experienced insuperability of the given obstacle. The manner of coping with such obstacles will depend largely on the individual temperament. It may lead either to a stimulation of inventiveness, or resignation. Paradise is a nostalgic conception of a human condition in which there are no obstacles to the satisfaction of all needs. There is reason to assume that, contrary to common belief, such a truly utopian condition would produce not bliss but rather apathy and stultification.

The malleability of needs, finally, may be seen as related to the persistence of achieved satisfactions. These can be more or less lasting or more or less temporary or passing. More or less lasting satisfactions prevail only where the total human condition is subject to small and hardly perceivable changes, as in relatively stationary societies. Where technological and social conditions change as rapidly as in modern society, new needs, especially of the material kind, constantly arise and have to be activated, chiefly because of the commanding requirements of an "expanding economy." As a consequence, all satisfactions become transitory. They serve as mere stepping stones to new needs. This, in spite of an unprecedented abundance of achieved satisfactions, cannot but result in a pervading sense of frustration or dissatisfaction.

The intensity and malleability of needs as just described makes it possible to formulate a general rule of human behaviour based on the dynamic aspect of what we called "factors inhibiting their satisfaction." We may say that between all needs and their satisfaction human beings will find interposed some obstacles. The resulting effect will vary depending on three factors: the relative intensity of the given need; the size of the obstacle; and the means available for overcoming it.

The important fact to keep in mind is the functional interconnection between these three factors. They are correlated in the sense that the manifestness and range of each factor is determined by, and in turn determines, the manifestness and range of the other two factors. Thus the nature and intensity of a given need cannot be viewed correctly without taking into consideration the nature and intensity of the obstacle which it will have to overcome on its way to satisfaction. In addition, there will also be the question of the ways and means available and needed in order to overcome it. In the simplest case, a material need will be up against obstacles that are material and will aim at material satisfaction. If the obstacle is too great, the result may be either resignation and frustration, or deflection. Resignation and frustration means abandoning the need, temporarily or permanently, and thus admitting defeat. Deflection may lead to stimulation of other types of needs. For instance, deflection from a material need may lead to activation of intellectual needs. This may express itself in inventiveness that may be applied to the overcoming of the material obstacle; or to substitution of intellectual satisfactions for the material ones. Intellectual frustration may activate material, emotional or spiritual needs, etc. The question is whether and to what degree such deflection is possible between the five types of needs. The stronger a need, the larger the obstacle with which it can cope. The more desirable a satisfaction, the more intensive will be the need, and so on. But even the most intensive need may be stymied if the obstacle to its satisfaction proves insurmountable with the available means.

As observed before, frustration in one context can prompt a shift to another context. Perhaps a theory could be formed based on the assumption that each person is endowed with a certain vital energy which enables him to secure the satisfactions he considers as desirable. Such desirability will be largely determined by two factors: the meanings dominant in a given culture, and what for want of a better term we may call temperament.

As to the meanings, they will influence, and will be influenced by, the development of means to their realization and thus tend to put at the disposal of the individual certain techniques effective in achieving the satisfaction. Where, as in our culture, material satisfactions are deemed to be the most desirable, the technology developed makes their achievement appear so easy as to virtually obliterate awareness of the existence of any obstacles. Still there are even in our society people whose temperament makes them pursue other than material satisfactions. This, for instance, is, at least temporarily, the case in adolescence, when emotional needs become dominant; or in people who devote themselves to intellectual pursuits (scientists) or to the search of spiritual values. The prevalence of such needs will tend to reduce the intensity of the other needs. People in pursuit of emotional needs, e.g. love, may lose desire for food; and people who experience conversion may lose interest in all other human needs but the spiritual ones. In our culture such needs are taken to be marginal; in other cultures they may, at least theoretically, be dominant. Even physical survival may then – as in the case of cultures in which religious or for that matter political values predominate – be subordinated to the satisfaction of such needs. There is, though, this difference. Spiritual or emotional needs in extreme cases may make saints or martyrs, heroes or victims; material needs only profiteers or paupers.

Though no priority can be assigned to any need in its functional relation with obstacles and satisfactions, a ranking appears to be possible among the different kinds of needs. Such ranking, as mentioned before, will be determined by the "aggregate of acquired meanings," or by a given culture. Thus, in our predominantly materialistic culture, we are inclined to accept as pertinent the consideration that though man does not live by bread alone, he certainly cannot live without it. This implies a primacy of the material needs. Without their satisfaction no other satisfactions appear possible. This, however, is by no means as self-evident as it appears to be. Thus, for instance, even on the level of plant existence, satisfaction of the bare physical needs seems to be not always sufficient. Some people find that "loving care" makes plants grow that would otherwise wither. This would seem to imply that even plants have emotional needs, the satisfaction of which may make the difference between death and survival. This may be the reason for the effectiveness of the Chinese intensive agriculture – in which wheat is planted instead of sown – each seed, so to speak, being given individual attention. We know of the stories of dogs who starve to death on the graves of their masters. They cannot survive the deprivation of the specific emotional satisfaction derived from their master's affection. Man, too, could not survive if he were incapable of pursuing any but purely material needs. Their very pursuit would be impossible without attention to his intellectual, emotional, spiritual and above all social needs. In this sense, the priority assigned to any need will not depend upon its intrinsic potency, but rather on the scale of values implicitly or explicitly accepted by a given culture in general, and by any given sub-culture – be it that of business, science or art – in particular.

THE EXTENSION AND REFINEMENT OF NEEDS AND THEIR SATISFACTION

This brief outline of the dynamic nature of needs is still evidently only an outline and in obvious need of further refinement, if it is to serve as the basis for our program of action.

Since the kind of action we have in mind is one that proceeds from and remains oriented toward man's needs, their fullest possible understanding is indispensable for such an undertaking. There are quite a few aspects that a complete theory of needs would yet have to elucidate. One is the problem of their relation to what we call "instincts" and the other, to what we call "interests." Both seem to share a certain paradoxical tendency for being elusive. The bane of all high minded leaders and teachers of mankind is its capacity for disregarding its own real needs and best interests and of pursuing, instead, those that cause all the trouble of which human history offers such a disastrous record. This tendency appears to be so pronounced as to make it possible to speak, as FREUD does, of an instinct for self-destruction, or Todeswunsch.

This would bring up the problem of whether it may not be just as important to know what needs not to pursue. The decalogue seems to be conceived in this spirit. Of the ten commandments only two, the third and fourth, refer to what man ought to do, the rest are rather interdictions. Is this an ingenious indication of a pessimistic, or shall we say realistic, view of human nature?

A related problem would be what we call inhibitions. Some

of these are "internalized "taboos of our culture; but there are also those that are self-created. These are the ones that arise from shyness, "inferiority complex," a sense of inferiority that has no objective justification, and all the other "complexes" with which man in our civilization tends to torture himself and to block his chance for the satisfaction especially of some of his basic emotional needs but, as a consequence, also of his material and social needs.

An interesting undertaking would be to try also to visualize the refinement of means available for overcoming obstacles to the satisfaction especially of the emotional, intellectual and spiritual needs. The greater urgency of the material and, to a much lesser degree, of the social needs, has forced mankind to concentrate all its energies on the conquest of the natural obstacles to their satisfaction. This has spurred an advance in technology, which, since the design and refinement of the experimental method, has led, at least in one country, the U.S.A., to a state where the "venom of want," which still poisons the lives of most of the human race, has become virtually obsolete and has been replaced by the "perils of plenty." It is possible that a similar advance in the techniques that serve to cope with the obstacles that inhibit the satisfaction of social needs will follow the application of the experimental method to social innovation, such as suggested by the experimental cooperative communities.[6]

As to the other needs, however, we seem to be satisfied to abide by the standards accepted by our ancestors at the very onset of human civilization. This lag becomes startling when compared with the diversity and complexity of our material satisfactions. Love, friendship, enjoyment of beauty in art and nature, and our other emotional satisfactions are all essentially not different in kind from those known in Antiquity. Virtually no progress has since been made in Western Civilization, and in the Orient the stagnation is of much

6. See this writer's: A Prototype of Sociological Experiment-The Modern Cooperative Community. In: Int. Arch. of Sociology of Cooperation, Vol. I, No. 1. 1957.

longer duration. The same can be said about spiritual satisfactions. Essentially they are the same as established by the founders and first followers of the Great Religions, of which the most recent one, Islam, dates back to the 7th Century. It is true, that certain variations have been introduced, for example in Protestantism, in respect to some of dogmas of the Catholic Church.

But the basic form of faith in JESUS, as the Son of God and Saviour of humanity still is essentially the same. The situation is very similar, if not identical, in all other Great Religions, the only difference being the loss of adherents, as in Parsism, or their growth in numbers, as in the Christian faith.

In contrast, it would seem as if we had made considerable progress in our intellectual proficiency. The estimate here will depend on the standards by which we judge intellectual progress. There can be no doubt that what we know today, and the way we know it, is a far cry from what was known, for example, to the ancient Greeks. This knowledge, however, refers chiefly to knowledge derived from the observation of a very limited area of our universe, the physical environment. There seems to be only very little advance in our thinking about all the other contexts of human existence, the social, emotional, spiritual, and yes, the intellectual itself. Despite all the efforts of the giants of philosophy in the last two thousand years, our epistemology and logic have made hardly any progress. We know of course, or we think we do, more about psychology; and symbolic logic constitutes an interesting attempt to break with Aristotelian logic; which, however, still provides the rules that dominate most of our present-day thinking.

We seem to be ready today to question this state of affairs. We begin to feel, prompted probably by the unprecedented extension and refinement of our material satisfactions, that the satisfactions of our other needs are similarly extendable and refinable. One interesting symptom of this feeling is the popularity of the so-called science fiction. I have in mind not so much the attempts to imagine and depict mechanical inventions of the future, but the attempts to anticipate probable future ways of thinking, of feeling, of living together, and in general to conceive new cosmogenies. In a less fictitious vein, signs of such exploration of new and more subtle ways of satisfying our emotional, intellectual and spiritual needs, and of opening the way to their refinement, can be found at the margin of the disciplines that deal with the context of these needs. The distrust of the, essentially conservative, majority of people for such attempts expresses itself in a generally derogatory attitude. The poets who experiment with new and more subtle possibilities of the aesthetic, as the Neo-Romanticists at the end of the last century, will be called "decadent"; any spiritistic medium who is caught cheating, will gloatingly be taken as proof that the whole business of extrasensory perception is a hoax; any scheme, literary or activistic, to explore the feasibility of a better society, will be dismissed as futile or "utopian"; "mystic" becomes an invective levelled against even the most serious search for more rarefied spiritual satisfaction.

Viewed more dispassionately, such reaching out on the part of a relatively few into areas of human experience as yet beyond the reach of the many, is probably nothing else than a sign that those few are already sensitive to needs as yet unfelt by the others. Once these needs become accepted as legitimate, and once the techniques for their satisfaction approximate the effectiveness of those available today for the satisfaction of material needs, man may well become transformed into a kind of human being as far ahead of man as we know him today as he himself is of the cave dweller.

These considerations should not be taken as flights of fancy, as vain daydreams of glory. Rather, they follow naturally from a theory of needs that is functional and not genetic, that instead of concerning itself with the origins of the drives responsible for human development, about which we can only guess, tries to comprehend them in a way that can be confirmed by direct observation and that at the same time helps us to trace their extension into the immediate future. It is on the basis of a theory of this kind that the operations can be suggested which, when carried out, will produce certain effects that, if nothing else, will help man in what probably is his most ambitious task as man, the realization of all his potentialities. The formulation of the ways and means leading to such realization may well be the fulfillment of what WELLS had in mind when he spoke of the Bible of Civilization and what might well come to be called the Bible of the Future.

MAN'S POTENTIALITIES, AND WAYS AND MEANS TO THEIR REALIZATION

It may sound presumptuous, if not preposterous, to contemplate such an undertaking; but the task is actually less awesome than appears to be. The new "dispensation" can be new only if it differs in kind from the old ones. It will be new in the sense that it does not claim to have its source in divine revelation, but in the social experimentation prompted by the search for the satisfaction of certain human needs. The commandments of the new "Bible" can derive their strength not from an alleged and inscrutable divine authority, but from a validation in terms of human performance. In other words, the commandments of the new Bible have to be operational. It is not enough – and it has never been enough – to decree "thou shalt not steal" or "thou shalt not kill" and to expect people to obey because God is supposed to have said so. In order to enforce such obedience, we seem to depend today rather on two means: police and prisons. Both, as our increasing rate of crime and delinquency shows, prove to be quite ineffective. The commandment of the future will not be a decree, but a design of ways and means that will create conditions in which unwanted behaviour will have only an irreducible minimum chance of occurring.

That such conditions are practicable is shown by the experience of cooperative communities, those of the past, such as the Hutterites, as well as those of the present, such as the Kibbutzim. In those groups stealing, for example, hardly ever occurs. And this not because of an abundance of material goods. Frugal as are the conditions under which these groups exist, the fact that they hold "all things in common" deprives of any sense the very idea of stealing. Since every one *de jure* and *de facto* owns and is entitled to use according to his needs everything that belongs to the group, theft would mean stealing from oneself. Such infractions as may happen can be due only to momentary attacks of greed or to psychopathological impulse.

In a similar way, the question is one of designing ways and means for the fullest realization of man's potentialities. Since we start from the present state of affairs, seen from the vantage point of a country with the most advanced material standards man has ever known, we may disconsider the issue of material needs. The American economy of today proves that we already possess the know-how necessary not merely for their satisfaction but even over-saturation. As to emotional and intellectual needs, our awareness of their possible range is so spotty that even the most complete inventory of available knowledge on the subject could at best be more suggestive than enlightening. It should be attempted, by all means, even though it may yield not much more than first leads. A real advance, however, will depend on opportunities to explore actively the unfathomed ranges of our emotionality and thought, and to exercise, systematically and intensively, any uncovered faculties. Research and training of this novel kind obviously will require an institution for "advanced studies." These studies will be "advanced" in more than one sense. They will aim at advancing the range of our emotional and intellectual needs and satisfactions; and they will be oriented by the, for the time being, tentative assumption of an unlimited perfectibility of man's faculties.

An experiment of this kind cannot fail to be useful either way: in positively enhancing man's development to the very limits of his possibilities; and negatively, by determining in an objective, verifiable manner the real limits beyond which man cannot go, at least for the time being. It should throw light also on the interesting problem of the actual relation between man's potentialities and their realization. In this respect man, generally speaking, may act in four different ways. He may:

1) Want to do what he can do;
2) Not want to do what he cannot do;
3) Not want to do what he can do;
4) Want to do what he cannot do.

The first and the second case offer no problem; the behaviour they imply is simply reasonable. More of a problem is the third case. The reason for such behaviour may be lack of awareness, emotional inhibition, simple laziness, etc. In the relation to an "ever-expanding" economy, these mental blocks are of crucial importance and are intensively explored by so-called "motivational research." Some of the findings indicate that more generally oriented research in this area would produce valuable insight into factors determining choice and decision making. Most intriguing is our fourth and last case. It would be simple, if we knew with any degree of finality, what we can or cannot do. In one field, that of technological development, the experience of our lifetime tends to make us perhaps over-sanguine in this respect. The things we knew in childhood as fairy tale stuff have become today articles of daily use: the horseless carriage, the magic glass mirroring events taking place in the far distance, the flying carpet, and so on. There is much in the mental climate of today that makes us inclined to believe that if only we can imagine a thing we can also make it. The only things it would seem, we cannot do are those that we just did not yet happen to think of. This is what SANTAYANA calls, "The indomitable freedom of life to be more, to be new, to be what it has not entered into the heart of man as yet to conceive ..."[7]

However, this virtually unlimited optimism with regard to the possibilities of material development – somewhat dampened just now by the adverse aspects of the release of atomic energy – turns to diffidence when it comes to man's other faculties. Our folk- as well as religious-lore is replete with the dire forebodings about the pitfalls sown in the path of any uncommon intellect. From the stories of Adam and Eve, who lost Paradise for us all because they would not keep away from the Tree of Knowledge, and the men of Babel, who were smitten with confusion when they raised their sights too high, to the wet nurse apprehension about the child who cannot be "long of this world" because it is too bright, the American glorification of the low brow and the equation of "controversial" with "subversive," there is one persistent long line of anti-intellectual bias. No wonder that the results are what they must be: intellectual timidity, if not outright stultification. Thus timid thought and timid emotions create a mental climate in which the real faculties of man remain unexplored and, because not exercised, shrink far below their actual and potential range.

On the other hand, it might be said, in view of the damage done to mankind by "supermen" such as Alexander "the Great," Nero, Napoleon and their more recent emulators, the Hitlers, Mussolinis and Stalins, apprehension about all God-like ambition of man might not be quite unjustified. All that these monstrous criminals – who escaped the law only because, and so long as they made it – in fact did accomplish was disaster for themselves and for all those whom, willingly or unwillingly, they were able to drag down along with themselves. Intellect, it seems if carried away by the obsession with power, is capable of destruction of truly

7. GEORGE SANTAYANA: Three Philosophical Poets. Anchor Books, New York 1953. (First published 1910) p. 181 ff.

megatonic proportions. It looks even on the cobalt bomb as just another handy tool of its ambitions.

The issue seems to boil down to a basic dilemma: if man accepts the so-called dictates of God and is meek and humble before him, he forsakes his chance of a full realization of his potentialities; if, on the other hand, he disregards the dictates of God and overreaches himself, he invites disaster for himself and others with him. However, like all such "either or" dichotomies this, too, is misleading. For the question is not necessarily one of either obeying or disobeying the dictates of God, nor is it one of being either meek and retarded or ambitious and malignant. Presupposing, as most of us do, that we need some vision, some signification of a supreme idea, of an ultimate meaning, of a Value of Values, in order to derive from life its fullest and noblest satisfactions, the question is one rather of whether the commandment to realize our potentialities to the utmost is not the truest expression of such vision.[8]

Put in this way, the question we will want to answer will call for two things; an open-minded, matter-of-fact, precise determination of the actual range of our potentialities and faculties, and an imaginary point of spiritual reference set high enough to serve as the apex of all our aspirations or, in other words, a concept of God that would satisfy our own present-day need for such a spiritual perspective.

The first will require a prolonged and painstaking experimental investigation concerning the nature, the range and the limitations of our intellectual and emotional capacities as well as the testing of techniques conducive to their fullest exercise.

This kind of research requires a setting in which exploration can be closely combined with implementation. It requires a group of people highly intelligent, highly sensitive, highly inquisitive and highly articulate, who are capable of

8. This, of course, presupposes that our potentialities are healthy. But if not, whose responsibility is it?

initiating the necessary experimentation and who, at the same time, are willing to serve as its substance. What is needed in short, is an experimental group akin to the cooperative community but distinct in its concentration on emotional, intellectual and spiritual rather than material and social needs.

THE NEED FOR ULTIMATE ORIENTATION

What interests us here is the fact that fruitful, and indispensable, as we believe that such experimentation might be, there is no overlooking the fact that it is beset with grave dangers. To push to the very limits of possible experience is a natural tendency in a man of free spirit. He will yield to this tendency even if in the process he has to brave customs and mores, which frown upon such daring, and orthodox religion, which condemns it as sin. To us, such daring appears as the very essence of material progress. That beyond a certain point it may turn into a serious threat to such progress is the lesson forced upon us by the advance of atomic physics. Succeeding in smashing the atom which, not so long ago, was looked upon as the last indivisible particle of matter, the physicist was stunned by the catastrophic consequences of his success. The bottled-up energy, which had seemed to be only begging for release, once freed, not unlike one of the evil jinn, has turned into a monster that stuns its "liberator" with the threat of total annihilation. In their first shock the atomic scientists, or at least the more sensitive among them, would have been glad to put nuclear energy back where it came from. Since this proved to be impossible, they formed the well known Emergency Committee of Atomic Scientists. Grown out of concern over the results of their doing, it set itself the task of mitigating its consequences. Among the palliatives proposed, most consummate probably is that recommended by ALBERT EINSTEIN himself. What we need, he feels, is nothing less than a complete overhauling not only of our ways of thinking but of our ways of living together. "The Atomic Bomb," he observes, "has altered profoundly the nature of the world as we know it, and the human race consequently finds itself in a new habitat to which it must adapt its thinking." [9] And as to the corresponding form of the social existence he remarks, more laconically: "Today we must abandon competition and secure cooperation." All this, if we are not mistaken, is indicative of the unfortunately belated realization that experimentation if not guided by some ethical principle may overreach itself and thus defeat its own purpose. Instead of extending man's mastery over his environment it may create, as this experience shows, a real threat to his very survival.

Thus, if we do not want to end up with an emergency similar to that in which the atomic scientists find themselves today, we would do well, it would seem, to equip ourselves with some guiding and controlling principle before we embark on the project of exploring to the limit our potentialities. The most effective of orientations that saves man from overreaching himself – which is the "original sin" – is what KIERKEGAARD calls "the absolute relation to the absolute," with all that it implies in terms of "good faith" and commitment to a Summum Bonum.

This concept immediately brings us face to face with a dilemma, which the issue of religion presents to the sensitive person of today. Realizing the urgency of the need for an "absolute" commitment to some form of the "absolute," he finds all the traditional forms of such commitment unacceptable to his present day experience and sensitivity. The taste for myths has changed today and, as SANTAYANA says, "those of us who still dream do so today in a different key." The religions as we know them have, for us, become myths

9. ALBERT EINSTEIN: Only Then Shall We Find Courage. E.C.A.S. pamphlet, undated.

that are obsolete. Does this mean that we have to abandon the idea of religion? For those who see the question as dichotomic, or two-valued, as a question either of religion as we know it or no religion at all, the answer will be simple. They will call, as so many whose thinking on this subject is obsolete or reactionary, for return to "old-time" religion. Others, sensing the sham of such return, will resign themselves to agnosticism. Those, however, who feel the need for and the indispensability of a transcendent, even if imaginary, point of ultimate reference, will see this dichotomy as a false one. For them, who feel just as strongly about the spiritual as about all other needs, the question will not be one of either "old-time" religion or none at all, but rather one of whether it is possible today to conceive of a religion, which would satisfy their spiritual needs; and if so, what should be the nature of such a religion. This way of putting the question seems to be the way of all those who, like SANTAYANA, recognize the need for a "new religion." Such recognition, however, is too general and abstract to represent more than a necessary first step. It leaves open all possibilities, even the possibility that this "new religion," for all we know, may be of a kind so different as to require a different name. This is suggested by the manner in which SANTAYANA, perhaps the most discerning contemporary thinker on this subject, formulates the issue. What we need, he says, is "to establish a new religion and a *new art*, based on moral liberty and on moral courage." [10] The passage that follows in the text from which this quotation was taken shows that the kind of religion SANTAYANA anticipates is not so much a new religion as a new art. It is the poet rather than the prophet to whom he looks for that "double insight" into art and religion which, he feels, is needed in order to "reconstitute the shattered picture of the world." And he hails him "from afar" as the "ultissimo poeta," "the highest possible poet."

The "supreme poet" who "is in limbo still" may or may

10. SANTAYANA, op.cit.

not put in his appearance one of these days. Instead of passively waiting for this to happen, it might be more appropriate for an experimental group of the kind envisaged above to attack the task independently.

SANTAYANA describes the qualifications of the "genius" capable of performing it as follows: "he should live in the continual presence of all experience, and respect it; he should at the same time understand nature, the ground of that experience; and he should also have a delicate sense for the ideal echoes of his own passions, and for all the colours of his possible happiness." [11] These, no doubt, are qualities that are exceptional in an individual; and even if potentially present, only a very rare combination of personal development and external circumstance can bring them to fruition. In order to cultivate them purposely and consistently it needs, it would seem, not one individual alone, but a group of individuals united by the interest in such cultivation. As the history of the Kvutza shows, such a group, though its minds may be hardly above average, can, by putting them together, develop powers of divination equal to, if not surpassing, those of a creative genius.

In approaching the task of determining the actual scope of man's spiritual potentialities, and taking themselves as the substance of such experimentation, a set of interconnected assumptions will suggest itself to the participants of the group. The primary of these has already been mentioned. It is the assumption that the satisfaction of spiritual needs is just as vital to man as is that of the other needs, and that this claim in certain respects, especially in respect to personal integrity, antecedes, and lends meaning to, that of all other needs. In this sense, dissatisfaction with traditional religion would signify that it is religion as we know it that is obsolete and not the need for it. If this is so, the exploration of spiritual potentialities becomes oriented to a proximate aim, which is the search for a more satisfactory religion. The acceptance of

11. SANTAYANA, op.cit.

these assumptions will naturally lead to the consideration that there can be no true and universally valid religion, but that each reflects certain ways and means of coping with the exigencies of living, characteristic of given periods of mankind's existence. Each culture and each epoch, we might say, produces and accepts its specific concept of religion and of God. The question, then, that our exploration will want to answer is: what concept of religion and what image of God corresponds to our own epoch and to our own culture?

There is reason to believe that such an exploration of the nature and scope of our intellectual, emotional and spiritual potentialities can produce invaluable insights and open new and unsuspected vistas of human possibilities. In order to do so, it will have to be open-minded, relatively free of bias and preconceived notions, and as uncontaminated as possible by wishful anticipation of the results. It will have to be objective and rigorous, not in the sense of the tautological truth-value of a science so pure that it becomes irrelevant to human actuality, but in the sense of critical control, validation and interpretation of every step in the conduct of the experiment. That, and in what way such criteria are applicable to experiments of this kind, in which the people concerned serve at the same time as their initiators and their substance, has been demonstrated by the experimental groups known as modern cooperative communities. These communities are part of the Cooperative Movement, of which they form the most advanced stage, characterized by a practice of cooperation that is comprehensive or communitarian. Like the Movement itself, these groups owe their origin to spirited people who refused to resign themselves to frustration which competitive economy imposed on them. When other action failed, they resorted to cooperation. In the process they discovered ways and means of securing material satisfactions otherwise unattainable to them. Being comprehensive in scope, these groups seek to apply the cooperative principles to other than purely material aspects of social existence. In doing so, their cooperative ingenuity is mapping out a pattern of social innovation comparable to the method of physical science experiment, but modified so as to accord with the nature of social phenomena. This ingenious application of the experimental method to other than purely physical matters is a momentous pioneering feat. It constitutes not only the most significant contribution made by the modern cooperative communities to the advance of social science, but it sets a precedent and a model for the exploration of all the other human potentialities referred to above.

Practical Notes on Politics and Poesy

by

Lyle K. Bush

"Have you ever seen an inchworm crawl úp a leaf, cling to the very end, revolve in the air ... reaching for something?"

The immediate response to this chance retinal presentment is merely visual; but the cognitive mind goes to work on it. First, it becomes a *dissatisfied* worm, wriggling for a fresh satisfaction. The spectacle then becomes slightly amusing, ludicrous, evocative of whimsicality; initiates botanical or zoological conjecture, enlists momentarily the gambler's fascination with fortune. Will he get it? Launched from an ocular pad, this larva of a geometrid moth has become a projectile of the mind, passing through a sequence of firings, each of them releasing a *meaning* until the final stage resolves into the release of a spirit of reckless imaginative daring. This new condition of orbitual suspension achieved, the measuring worm commands an amazingly expanded view. What has happened to the *inch* of the inchworm?

The thought makes no pretense of originality. In the worm as a constant and in the mind's expanding view as a variable, it is hoped that one will catch the echo of Whitehead's "Exactness is not enough," and Oppenheimer's world of "changing views". Scientist, poet, philosopher, and artist have revealed their awareness of the inchworm analogy, but many others have not, and like the fleet companions of the desert wind have hidden their heads in the Saharan sands. What is the germinal source of the malady which has rendered mankind myopic to the wealth before him? What accounts for the distortion in his view?

It was the painter-poet ALBERT PINKHAM RYDER who thrust the inchworm into our vision as a homely symbol of the wriggling and the reach of a creature that is, and always has been, and ever will be ourselves. He can be discerned in the dull-witted troglodyte directing his gutteral murmurs from squatted position at the mouth of a bone-strewn cavern toward the magnificent but discomfiting mystery of a borealic splendor. And one of his more cogitative descendants must have become even more baffled by the mystery of Time's disintegrative influence on human handiwork as he sat atop one pyramid and viewed the crumbling masonry about him. A more sensitized but still perceptibly vermian Crusader must certainly have sipped a fresh elixir of mystery in a land where milady was veiled so tantalizingly in the traditional obscurity of the East. And generation after generation of inchworms have revolved at the ends of generations of leaves and reached ... why? There are inchworms and inchworms. Life is acquisition, but of what? The ill-nurtured RYDER ignored uncashed checks because of a great hunger ... a hunger of the active imagination. His was the reach of wonder, as MALRAUX was to describe it: "The sacrifice to a cause beyond comprension that restores richness to man."

And as the prodigal inchworm of today has devoured sufficiently of his resources to begin wriggling at the tip of his leaf ... reaching ... there occurs a freshly mystifying anomaly. The fruits of a magnificent automation are about to pull the stars together and to reveal secrets of the universe, but the precious store of invigorating wonder that characterized our ancestors has diminished perceptibly as automation has brought dreamless sedation to our bed, packaged nutrition to our board, and has piped pleasurable indulgence to every centre of our recreative desire. A diversion of the benefits of this automation toward indulgence in a gluttonous consumption seems to have left us in a sun-soaked apathy, stranded on the shoals of meaningless boredom by the receding tide of time. A few create the die, a few others pour the mould, and the rest of us consume the product without necessity for curiosity or reach of imagination. There is much pith and little wood in NIETZSCHE's words that "He who knows a Why of living surmounts almost every How."

Traditionally, the humanist has accepted responsibility for viewing the ebb and flow of major currents in the broader areas of human activity. The instability of his position in the cloud echelons has raised the question of his competence. The physical scientist has adjusted his microscope to each topographic detail in its turn, until the revelation of universe within universe appears to have resolved what was once a divorcement between schismatic spheres of enlightenment into fleeting glimpses of a truth whose validity can be attested only through envisionment of the specific, and the general embraced by a reality of constantly changing views ... a world that is existential in terms of change. Such a world was suggested by WILLIAM JAMES, "unfolded by thought ... always more than any of its unfoldings." It was a prophetic awareness of its unfolding that prompted EINSTEIN's plea for "a new kind of thinking in order that we may survive." And it is the unfolding itself that is the world of OPPENHEIMER with its "open mind" and "changing views."

The role of the inchworm in its reach for fresh securities within changed realities was played quaintly by ALBERT PINKHAM RYDER, the painter, in a curiosity-driven quest for the unfolding world of JAMES, the wishful survival of EINSTEIN, and the changed views of OPPENHEIMER. The artist's reach was an intuitive one, but RYDER had this explanation for it: "I went into the fields determined to serve nature as faithfully as I had served. In my desire to be accurate, I became lost in a mass of detail ... The scene presented itself one day ... framed in an opening between two trees ... As I worked, I saw that it was good and clear and strong. I saw nature spring to life on my dead canvas." RYDER began with an exactness which WHITEHEAD has suggested is not enough. The painter attained a view that his friend MARSDEN HARTLEY has described as a "music of some faraway world which was his laughter." Like BEAUDELAIRE, he presumed to have attained a view which enabled him to "see only the Infinite through every window."

Brief for this intuitively generalized and transitory reality has been held rarely with firm conviction in the occidental world, but the oriental ancients have clung to it tenaciously for nearly thirty centuries, not without observable material losses but with discernible spiritual gains. The Indian Vedas initiate the concept of "being" and of "not being." The world of *drista*, the seen, and of *adrista*, the unseen, are united by a mystically golden shaft, *Vishvakarma*, the Creative Principle. RABINDRANATH TAGORE attunes the concept with the nineteenth-century kinetics, with the convertibility of mass into energy, and with the resolution of a previously conceived static existence into one of dynamic metamorphosis. Indian ontology has always subscribed to a Universal Consciousness as the essence ... the stuff ... which precedes, modifies, and qualifies the impression of environment on the ego, even as PLATO may have received nurture from it. TAGORE poetizes the conception in the *Gitanjali* with "The same stream of consciousness that runs through my veins night and day runs through the world and dances in rhythmic measures."

And now we have drifted precariously across the no-man's-land that lies between the objectively existent fact and the subjective response to it. Yet when THUCIDIDES cited man as the "measure of all things," the Greek acknowledged human attitude as a qualitative, as well as a quantitative factor in the measurement of fact. This would explain, and we hope would justify an apparently presumptuous exploration of matters that are more psychological than they are philosophical or scientific. It is quite admittedly a resort to OPPENHEIMER's view from high, and dubiously secure altitudes in order to discern the directions and their possible effects upon all people.

In the delicate exploratory surgeries of the mind in the quest of "wills-to-" something, the most highly revered and widely known is that of SIGMUND FREUD. His discoveries have been reminiscently Cyrenaic, but are doubtless far more intricate than most of his interpreters have viewed them. And the will-to-pleasure is mirrored unmistakably in each facet of a darkly mutable splendor. Recent historical events and ADLER have supplemented it with a will-to-power. But ADLER's will-to-power can acquire an approximate coincidence with FREUD's will-to-pleasure. As one man's pleasure can be another's pain, and as another's power can become pleasure or pain to himself or to others, we must retreat mildly discomfitted into CONFUCIUS's semantic complaint known as "The Rectification of the Names." We can accept two wills to somewhat indeterminate ends. Power and pleasure are certainly major desirables. They can be worth all the strategic planning and tactical maneuvery necessary to obtaining fulfillment and they should be preserved as jewels of the Crown, but as the terminology is employed within the profession, they are subject to a conditioning that can greatly enhance or completely nullify the embodied values.

The work of Dr. VICTOR E. FRANKL of the Medical Faculty at the University of Vienna is most pertinent to pleasure and power as integrative variables. Dr. FRANKL describes in his recent work, *The Psychology of Meaning*, his opportunity to observe the phenomena of *Weltschmerz* at work during four years of imprisonment at Auschwitz. He noticed that the typical question voiced by his unfortunate associates was, "Will we survive? If not, life has no meaning." He gave the question much thought and became convinced of its inconsistency. He rephrased the question until it expressed to him not a life of meaning dependent upon survival, but a survival warranted only by meaningful living. "Has life meaning? If not, *why survive*?"

The utterly disarming logic of this different approach as the result of a changing view is first grasped with a chuckle. It is then followed by the cleanly cutting edge that severs civilized man from the beast in the field. Pleasure and power, as values to humanity, are conditioned by *meaning*. One reflects anew on the since-fatuous, but really surcharged and now psychologically practical Goethean view that "The highest happiness of man as a thinking being is to have probed what is knowable and to revere what is unknowable." The thing, for instance, called "love" is that thing on the terms and in the existence of, and in the perpetually refreshing change of its "view." It probes what is knowable and reaches reverently into the unknowable. Love without curiosity is monotony; love in the spirit of inquiry is revelation. Love is a habit and a nothing, or it is a state of wonder. There is a will-to-understanding which sublimates our exercise of power and which renders our pleasure transcendent.

ARCHIBALD MACLEISH has expressed the view that a distinguishable time in history is created not by the event ... the battle ... but by the response to the event ... the heroic or craven reaction to it of the generation which experiences the event. When this thought is lifted from the context of his Commencement address at Smith College in June of 1956, it appears at first to suspend the world of the actual in a most precariously pendulous fashion. Facts are dethroned by human attitudes. Philosophies of history become involved, and series of consecutive, interdependent events become warped in the weft of revisions of attitudes in distances of time. Battles are fought under the motivations of wills-to-power. The meaning of that power is the by-product of changes in view. Had the meaning of an Anschluss been clear to all who were involved in 1938, understanding would have changed the course of history. And a comparable will-to-meaning today could be expected to dispel some of the prevailing delusion that the United States, to use MAC-

LEISH's phrasing, "can deal with the enormous forces now at play in the world merely by resisting one of their more disturbed manifestations."

With this and each passing hour there must be acknowledged the existence of an impending *impasse* from the lack of a will-to-meaningful understanding that can, as the poet SEAN O'CASEY suggests, "frighten hope from the human heart," or on the other hand it can inspire the conviction that the world really "has grandeur and life has hope," and that it is man's heroic spirit that will save him. For O'CASEY the poet, "The Harp of the Air Still Sings." This soaring minstrelsy carries the indomitable faith of the distinguished physicist PERCY BRIDGMAN in the "feeling in our bones that we know what we are doing," and that we can be expected to carry it through. "It is the nature of knowledge," declares Dr. BRIDGMAN reassuringly, "to be subject to uncertainty."

Of this uncertainty, one can be certain. But of the knowledge with which to meet the uncertainties to which a lack of knowledge can render us subject, one is still uncertain. Bard and scientist have both composed passages of melodic sweetness, but the composition is subject to the interpretation of the performer. The performing artist of the moment is the statesman in the government of peoples. His performance may be accompanied by tenor saxophone, slide-trombone, or drum. And what of the statesman ... the politician ... the purity of his tone, the adequacy of his techniques, the accuracy of his tempo, the meaningfulness of his artistry? An extended but searching view of our political world, of "politics," suggests the strong possibility that within this bland culture of ours, the poet, the composer, the artist, and yes, the scientist have lived too long and are still living, alone.

One should pause sufficiently at this point to note that SEAN O'CASEY as poet, and PERCY BRIDGMAN as scientist would seem to have been cited rather arbitrarily as presenting a strongly optimistic view. A pessimistic one would of course involve the negation of hope, and would serve no purpose whatever. Such a view would be a denial of FRANKL's will-to-meaning as a preface to survival. But when an optimism is the result of critical discrimination, it becomes an active, and therefore a meaningful idealism. The optimism of the poet has been, traditionally at least, contingent upon the intuitive response of the internal life to an external environment. We accept this optimism as an active idealism in terms of its subjective validity. The optimism of the scientists has been, again traditionally at least, contingent upon the facts which are rendered, as effectively as possible, independent of internal life and viewed in the light of externally apparent validities. We accept this optimism in the terms of its objective validity.

The search for a comparable political optimist *and* idealist with whom to complete a triumvirate in estimates with that of scientist and poet is not to be made without considerable effort today. We are confident, however, that there are those who are searching for an optimism out of which there can emerge an actively workable idealism. There is courageous statement, and wishful thinking as well in the conclusion of Mr. ADLAI STEVENSON, speaking in the February 7, 1959 issue of the *Saturday Review of Literature.* To quote Mr. STEVENSON: "All politics is made up of many things – economic pressures, personal ambitions, the desire to exercise power, the overriding issues of national need and aspiration. But if it is nothing more, it is without roots. It is built on shifting sands of emotion and interest. When challenged, it can give no account of itself. When threatened, it is in danger of collapse."

A courageously stated truth can be a hard but a heartening thing, and we would expect it to come from Mr. STEVENSON. But his conclusion is followed in the February 21, 1959 issue of the same publication by an equally disillusioning one. In this instance, Dr. ROBERT M. HUTCHINS speaks of a political configuration which has been established on principles including the rights to life, liberty, and the pursuit of happiness through the instrumentation of government of, by, and for the people, but which has lent itself to restatement in later decades and has resulted in a "pressure group state, which cares for the welfare of those who are well enough organized to put on the pressure."

Dr. HUTCHINS is one whose activities we have associated primarily with the academic world, but whose view lends further support to an indictment of matters political from the externality of his position if not from detachment. Mr. STEVENSON cites a phrase of the late A. POWELL DAVIES as of critical pertinence to a situation that could be expected to inspire heroism only at the cost of disheartening disillusionment. "The world," once declared Mr. DAVIES, "is now too dangerous for anything but the truth, too small for anything but brotherhood."

If this were to become recognized as a "truth of truth," it would become far easier to realize the value of a discovery that humanity is humanly and naturally addicted to wills to pleasure and to power to the point of an unimaginative resort to immediate expediences and that panaceas are not to be found by fixing upon them as constants and by approving them in many of our institutions of higher learning. If there is a discipline involved, it is not to be applied so much in terms of curbs or pressures or legislative mandates; it is a "discipline" more suitably administered through exercise of the mind in the attainment of levels in resourcefulness and imagination which can lead to basic and toward "ultimate" meanings in the sense of the Aristotelian concept that the major importances to mankind are to be discovered in the discriminations between what is enduringly good or bad for man. It is prefaced with new promise in FRANKL's *will-to-meaning*. Like OPPENHEIMER's changing view, it is to become a search *toward* apparent constants that are among, and subject to the ultimate influence of variables.

To face the "variable-constant" whether or not it may be

fraught with danger is to become permeated with imaginatively creative fire. Not to face it imaginatively is to deteriorate inevitably from flaccidity into morbidity. When confronted with a choice of alternatives between destruction without comprehension and preservation through imaginative insight, one choice involves a denial of meaningful creativity, but the other is to direct the imagination toward, for instance, an almost untouched Gargantuan wealth of natural resources hidden beneath the oceans. It may well be that such a diversion of human interest and resourcefulness as a tremendous under-sea release of natural resources would involve is the *only* remaining alternative to the slash of major areas of population, with but faint hope for a maimed residuum. Such a diversion of human energy into creative productivity could be expected to initiate an era of invigorative purposefulness such as history has not previously shown. And in the rush of wonder that would attend it, differences of race, color, party, ideology, or ethos could also be expected to wane. Cocks know not why they fight, but it is hoped that man has attained and can maintain a condition of reaching toward the envisionment of human perfectibility that nurtures his existence with the *meaning* of each changing view.

The rhythmic flight of the imagination is not the landed estate of a poetic gentry. Nor is poetic exercise, strangely believed by many, merely a fanciful form of catharsis. The approach and the attitude of poetry, one can humorously, seriously, but always genially insist, is valuable in all human activity. Suppose one were to select Mr. STEVENSON's courageous allusion to a political operation so appallingly impoverished of meaning as to invite challenge to render account of itself. This is, both in whimsical and serious substance, a plea for the stuff of poesy in the sphere of politics. The rhythms and the imageries of poetry, without the necessity for formal versification, comprise the stuff of which great men are made. The poetic consciousness traffics in imagery in order to see facts and ideas clearly in terms of their meanings. The poet's incomparable gift of character portrayal dispels the umbrage of causal human understanding. To poetize is to intensify and to sensitize human emotion. It is an antidote to boredom. A high majority of the sins of the world are committed in boredom. Poetry often vies with the sciences in the prophecy of truths that would otherwise escape us ... Its procedure is rhythmic, like the flow of rivers and the laving of waves upon the shore and the gently measured metamorphosis of ideas in the minds of people. Above all, it is imbued with effortless emotive power. It is sublimely nuclear, cordially intercontinental, and suspends itself in caressive orbitry through infinitudes of space and eons of time. And it has a way of becoming so incisively and disarmingly truthful that scientists can live it throughout their daily lives in the crystalline world of galaxy, snowflake, and atom. Scientist and poet respond to and attune themselves with these universal laws of form. Man, in the honesty of his innateness, wants to. We should become entranced, along with the rest of the world, to see a member of the Congress imbued with an unmistakable will-to-the-discovery-of-the-meaning-within-a-sense-of-wonder. In the face of this highly unusual thing, the ideologies of the peoples of the earth might take at least one step toward a global ethos.

It is in the spirit of an enforcedly restrained desperation that one reflects upon five milleniums of richly cumulative devotion to the arts and sciences, and still admits that one must carry DIOGENES' flashlight to discover the night-chilled spirits of those who retain the key to an ever-enlightening human happiness. Quite clearly today that key is not in the hands of those politicians who now can and do openly paternalize helpless populations of spoiled boredom. And clearly the key must be transferred to the hands of those who have reached into wonder, have created for all because they cared for all and were able to do so because they first cared enough to wonder. These creative ones now stand benumbed at the spectacle of growing panic that stampedes countless unmeaningful selves toward the brink of an already dangerously comforting emptiness.

There was once a tired Swiss painter named KLEE. In the China that once was, he would have been called both painter and poet for they were considered the same, even as there was a *scientia* in the West. He explored wills to pleasure, ignored wills to power, and in the disillusionment that can occur in an apparently rotting world, he ascertained his will-to-meaning: "What artist would not like to dwell where the central organism of all temporal and spacial change – call it what you will, the brain and heart of creation – is ordering all the functions?"

In spirit, PAUL KLEE was artist, philosopher, and scientist. His was the spirit of AQUINAS' *Theologia*: "Delicate and not exclusive, he will yet be of our day; his heart, for all its contemplation, will yet know the works of men." And it was the spirit of LEONARDO: "The love of anything is the fruit of our knowledge of it, and grows as our knowledge becomes more certain." This LEONARDO DA VINCI was GEORGE SARTON's hero, and in defining LEONARDO's indomitable will-to-meaning, SARTON imparted a spirit in his phrase that was also SARTON's own: "His outstanding merit is to have shown by his own example that the pursuit of beauty and the pursuit of truth are not incompatible. He is the patron of those men, few in number, who love art and science with equal fervor. One might add that without love there can be no real knowledge." And finally, KLEE's question conveys between its lines the infinitely ponderable conclusion of the one man who could phrase it more simply and more satisfyingly than has any other. This was ALBERT EINSTEIN, who dissolved the question and answer into one with a startlingly anachronous humility: "The greatest thing in the world is a sense of wonder."

CHESTERTON's fastidiously disdainful witticism that "The

world will never starve for want of wonders, but only for want of wonder," leaves the scientist and poet unscathed. But with deadly aim it finds and pierces the targets of prevailing ennui on the part of peoples and the political activities that this ennui condones. It is an ennui for want of will-to-meaning ... the thing that prompts a sense of wonder.

Somewhere along the way humanity appears to have lost what inspired the Greek *euphoria*; or the "stream of consciousness" of TAGORE "that runs through the world and dances in rhythmic measures;" or the "Why" of NIETZSCHE. We try without that *why* to find the practically expedient *how*. We proceed to manipulate without identifying with the Platonic Good.

The meaningful life is but a search, of course; a directive, with symbolic markers along the way. Our quandary is not new, but simply more cosmic to us in its malignity. WALT WHITMAN met this quandary in his *New Themes Entered Upon*. "After you have exhausted what there is in business, politics, conviviality ... Nature remains."

There was a poet-Emperor of China who crept to the end of his leaf of bamboo and reached with a sense of wonder as he composed the lines,

"*The whispering pines are living harps,*
And fairy hands were there ..."

This was CH'IEN LUNG's meaningful if not entirely conclusive answer to the question that HAEKEL addressed to his universe: "Are you friendly?" And this reach for meaningful attunement with his world may have helped him appreciably in ruling his body politic with statesmanlike distinction. His was the spirit of the scientist and the poet. But of course there were then still in a reverent state of conservation the natural resources that are necessary even for the antics of an inchworm.

The Goal

Science and Engineering - and the Future of Man

by

W. Taylor Thom, Jr.

INTRODUCTION

Through the Ages past Man has toiled upward from savagery and barbarism along an ascending road, until he now stands poised at the summit of The Great Divide – where he can either turn toward the Right, and enter a World of Justice and of Peace – or he can continue straight ahead, and downward, along the old way of Imperialism, of Injustice and of War – a course which leads inescapably to the destruction of civilization and probably to the destruction of all Humanity as well. Man *is* free to make his own clear choice – whether he *will* consciously, and intelligently, seek the road to peaceful progress, or whether he will stupidly continue on into World War III.

In this situation the scientist and the engineer bear particular responsibilities for giving such aid as they can toward the definition, and solution, of the world's current problems. For Science is concerned with the discovery of "that Truth which sets Men free" and Engineering is concerned with discovering how to make proper and effective use of Natural Law; of natural forces; and of the world's material and tangible resources – in order that "the World which is" may be transformed into "the World which should be."

Science and Engineering tell us that the Creator who

established the ordered and changing Universe also gave Man the opportunity, the ability, *and the responsibility*, for choosing his own destiny and for building his own future. To this end the Creator not only established Natural Law, for the guidance and control of the processes of the Universe, but also established Moral Law, for the guidance of human choice; of human action, and of human participation in the work of Creation, in so far as this involves the development of Life upon the Planet Earth. "Justice", "Opportunity", "Responsibility", and "human choice" are the key words which relate to the Future of Man. For Man is capable of choosing whether he will be active, or inactive; whether he will be progressive, or retrogressive; whether he will seek Good, or Evil; whether he will seek to exploit and oppress his weaker fellows, or whether he will strive to work with them in building a peaceful world – and in creating a genuine world-wide "Brotherhood of Man."

History has given convincing scientific proof that human progress has depended upon the acceptance of proper spiritual motivations; upon a wise choice of human objectives; and upon well-planned and effective practical action. It has been obviously true that no individual has been *forced* to be diligent, rather than slothful; that no individual has been *forced* to be wise, rather than foolish; and that no individual has been *forced* to heed the guidance of the Spirit within, rather than worldly wisdom, and the counsel of selfishness. Every human being has been free to choose whether to do that which is right and sensible, or to do that which is wrong and foolish. Moreover, experience has shown that Man is not justified in expecting that "God" will do for him those things which he could, and should, have done for himself. These things are axiomatic. That is to say that they are self-evident truths – to those who are willing to accept the Truth.

The sum total of History has demonstrated three things: *First*, that every human individual is *potentially* capable of making unique and important contributions to the progress of Mankind. (This despite the fact that many persons fail to realize their potentialities);

Second, that the basic needs of men can be best served by the cooperative effort of all;

Third, that in the building of an orderly and peaceful world "Force is objectionable" for "it destroys that which it seeks to preserve."

In developing his story of "Science and Engineering – And the Future of Man" the writer will take up, successively, the following seven topics:

1) The role which has been played by basic human aspirations and motivations in the production of many, successive, civilizations – within a frame-of-reference which has been established by Cosmic Trend coupled with the Limiting Dimensions of Space and Time.
2) The controlling influences that natural-resource conditions and geographic factors have exerted upon particular civilizations – with a discussion of the ways in which environmental conditions have determined the forms, durability and energylevels of particular civilizations.
3) The prime causes responsible for the psychological and political crises now afflicting our modern civilization.
4) A diagnosis of the nature of this current world-malady.
5) The kinds of action that must be had – if the prescriptions called for under (4) are to be effectively implemented and successfully applied.
6) Summary.
7) Conclusion.

HUMAN MOTIVATIONS AND THE ORIGIN OF "CIVILIZATION"

Certain basic emotional and mental motivations and spiritual aspirations have given rise to civilizations, at many times and in many parts of the world. Human affection, within the family, and group-loyalty, within the general community, have provided the invisible but real foundations upon which all civilizations have been built. Also mental curiosity, and reason, have again and again provided imaginative and intelligent leadership, capable of evoking enthusiastic and coordinated action on the part of major population groups. Likewise natural (and largely sub-conscious) spiritual aspirations have been of ultimate importance in determining the choice of the group-policies which have resulted in the building of civilizations. For Man does aspire to be a worthy and a self-respecting individual. He does aspire to be a worthy, and respected, member of his community and nation. And he does aspire to be a worthy servant of that Creator who has established Life-on-Earth, within an orderly and infinite Universe. Civilizations have, then, arisen as natural, practical, expressions of particular impulses which continuously arise within the hearts and minds and souls of human individuals and of human groups. Consequently, in order to understand why and how "The Future of Man" should be developed, in proper and satisfying fashion, we need to consider carefully Man's nature, and his basic aspirations.

The Nature - and Aspirations of Man

Man's true nature manifests itself only within the Silence – for in Silence the souls of all men become as one in the presence of the Creator. For whether savage or saint; whether humble shepherd or Imperial Ruler, it has been Man's nature – since the Beginning – to gaze with reverence and awe upon the wonders of Creation.

Mountain solitudes; the vast expanse of the ocean; the overwhelming fury of the storm; the beauty of spring flowers – in desert, in meadow, and in grove; and the silence and majesty of starlit nights in the desert – all have spoken to his soul of the Power and Glory of God the Creator.

Man has also instinctively sought to know, and to conform to, the will and purpose of the Creator. Priests, Prophets, Wise Men and Saints have prayed to receive revelations direct from God. Philosophers have sought understanding and wisdom, through orderly and logical consideration of all information relating to Natural and Moral Law. And scientists have sought to learn, indirectly, about the nature and purposes of the Creator through their discovery (and verification) of the Natural Laws which have been established by the Creator, for the guidance and control of all parts of the Moving Universe - whether these parts be animate or inanimate, whether material or mental or spiritual.

The Shaping of History by Cosmic Trend, and by the Dimensions of Cosmic Space and Time. It is a basic Natural Law that all things and all situations change and progress, and that this change, and this progress, go forward systematically by means of cyclic and rhythmic or recurrent movements, according to the Creator's established Cosmic Trend (or the Direction of Movement of the Universe). Day follows night. The lunar phases and the seasons follow each other in due course. Living Creation grows and reproduces and passes on - to make room for on-coming generations. Scientists thus have learned much about *how* the progressions of Life, and of the Universe, go forward - but as to *why*, they can only echo the answer given by the Prophets "It is the Will and Plan of God, the Creator."

The existence of this Cosmic Trend or of the "Causative Directional Dimension", both in Earth History and in Human History, becomes clearly apparent if one considers the sequence of events on Earth, as these have taken place in Space and Time.

The Cosmic and Human Significance of Space and Time. Space and Time are matters which are of little interest and concern to

Stone Age savages but are ones which have become more and more important to human beings as their ability to observe, and to reason, has increased. Consequently Man has, from time to time, developed better and better hypotheses as to how Cosmic processes are related to human history, although all who have developed and set forth such hypotheses have been handicapped in two ways. First, because finite human minds are not able to grasp the fullness of Infinite Truth, and second, because of the inability of one person to communicate to others, exactly and accurately, his thoughts and the Revelations he has received – because the same words have different meanings for different people. Hence, as all scientists know, the results of a developing inquiry can advantageously be recompiled and reanalyzed from time to time, but always with the corollary proviso that preliminary understandings are not to be accepted as proven and final until they have been adequately checked, tested and confirmed.

Unfortunately all past seekers after Truth have not appreciated that preliminary findings should be regarded as tentative only, until they have been fully corroborated – with the result that many theologians have not even yet comprehended two facts: 1) That the Dimensions of Cosmic Trend and Space and Time have always applied, and still apply, both in the Realm of the Spirit, and in the material world. And 2) that the Story of Creation, as set forth in the First Chapter of Genesis, was qualitatively correct, but was quantitatively inaccurate with respect to its statements regarding the Space and Time Dimensions involved. In consequence, because of these dimensional inaccuracies, various theological confusions and erroneous interpretations and doctrines have arisen, and have continued to beset and be-devil multitudes of people, for many centuries. Regarding this matter it has been said: "Men concerned with Religion, Philosophy and Science long ago developed the Story of Creation, as it is recorded in the First Chapter of Genesis – a story which, considering the remoteness of its period, was amazingly accurate qualitatively, but one which was distorted – because the Space and Time dimensions included in the story were not correctly comprehended – as has since been demonstrated."

The Space-Dimension in the Story of Creation. The Space-Dimension is highly important in the Story of Creation. But at the time when Genesis was being recorded the Planet Earth was believed to be the central feature of all Creation and it – and Man – were regarded as objects of the Creator's principal interest and solicitude. Whereas we now know that the Earth is only one small planet within one solar system, that our Sun is a relatively small star among *many* millions of stars and that some of the galaxies and nebulae, visible through modern telescopes, are many billions of billions of miles distant. Therefore, whereas it still remains true that Man had, and has, a special significance in the realm of Creation – it is nevertheless also true that Man, and our planet, obviously do not occupy nearly such prominent places in the Creator's Universal Plan and scheme of things as was postulated by the authors of Genesis.

The Time-Dimension of the Story of Creation. Because the authors of Genesis had no effective means for measuring the length of past spans of time they spoke, in their statement, of the "Six Days" of Creation, if the translations are correct. Or they may actually have used a more general expression which was equivalent to "six periods of time" – these being later translated, freely, as "six days." However that may have been, modern scientific studies have transformed the terms of the Time-dimension in the Story of Creation just as drastically as they have the Space-dimension. For now, with modern studies of intra-atomic structure, and of the rates at which radio-active decay proceeds in minerals, it is possible to determine with approximate accuracy the time which has elapsed since the world was formed; since Life appeared on

Earth; and since the different plants and animals began to develop. Such studies now indicate that the Earth is about 4,000,000,000 years old and that the first recognizable traces of Life-on-Earth date from about 2 billion years ago, whereas Primitive Man appeared on Earth only about 1 million years ago. Nor is this the only important modification of the Time-element in the Biblical story which needs to be made, in the light of wellverified scientific information now in hand. For the Process of Creation did *not* cease to operate at some given time in the past, just after Man was created. Instead, change and progressive Creation have not only gone on throughout the 4 billion years of Earth History, as is proven by the geologic record, but they are still in operation and reasonably will continue on until such time as the Creator's purpose has been finally and completely fulfilled, and "Perfection" has been finally attained. As to the continuing operation of the Creative process we can assure ourselves, by our own observations, since new episodes of Creation take place in Nature during every Spring season, while each new-born infant is likewise a miracle of new Creation. For within each tiny body there resides a new Soul and a new Life, created and placed there by God Himself.

The combined influence of the Space, Time and Universal-Trend dimensions upon the course of events in Geologic and Human History can be most easily comprehended if we construct for ourselves a Pictorial History which shows in proper Space – and – Time perspective the times of arrival upon the Earth of the different forms of Life – Plants, fishes, "creeping things," "beasts of the field," and "fowls of the air" and, lastly Man. For such a pictorial History, when viewed from a distance, would confirm the belief that the general *sequence* of Creative events was reported with substantial accuracy in the First Chapter of Genesis. But when examined more closely this Pictorial History would also show a cyclic or rhythmic recurrence of events within the broader terms of the total story. For as each new Life-group appeared its members, in turn, went through an essentially similar developmental process. For at the outset the members of each such group progressed in numbers; in physical size; and in the complexity of their bodily structures, until they reached a stage where one of three things happened: Some members of the group might cease to progress further – whereupon they would begin to lapse into greater and greater obscurity and unimportance; Or some members of the group might become dominant in worldly affairs – by developing monstrous size and terrifying appearances – after which they would, almost immediately, become extinct; Or some members of the group would progress onward and upward, quietly step by step, until they had passed around one loop of the Spiral Path of Life, and had given rise to a *new* Life-form, which occupied a next-higher position upon God's scale of living creatures. That Living Creation *has* moved forward and upward along a spiral path is obvious if both the distant and the close-range views of the Pictorial History are considered. For the several new Life-forms created – fishes, reptiles, mammals and Man – have appeared at successively higher and higher positions upon this spiral Path-of-Life.

This pattern of creative progress, so clearly illustrated by the histories of the lower forms of Life, is perhaps even more evident in the total History of Man. For as the Earth-record shows the first primitive Man-brute, though he possessed a "sense of right and wrong" (that is to say a sub-conscious awareness of the direction in which the Universal Trend of events is *supposed* to flow) – he was nevertheless still chiefly a brute withal. Then *families* of Stone Age savages appeared. Then came *clans* and *tribes* of New Stone Age cannibals. Then rudely-organized *primitive Communities* of Bronze-Age barbarians came into being. Then pastoral and agricultural civilizations developed and with them came the Great Prophets – and civilizations concerned with Beauty, with Truth and with Natural and Moral Law – civilizations which were

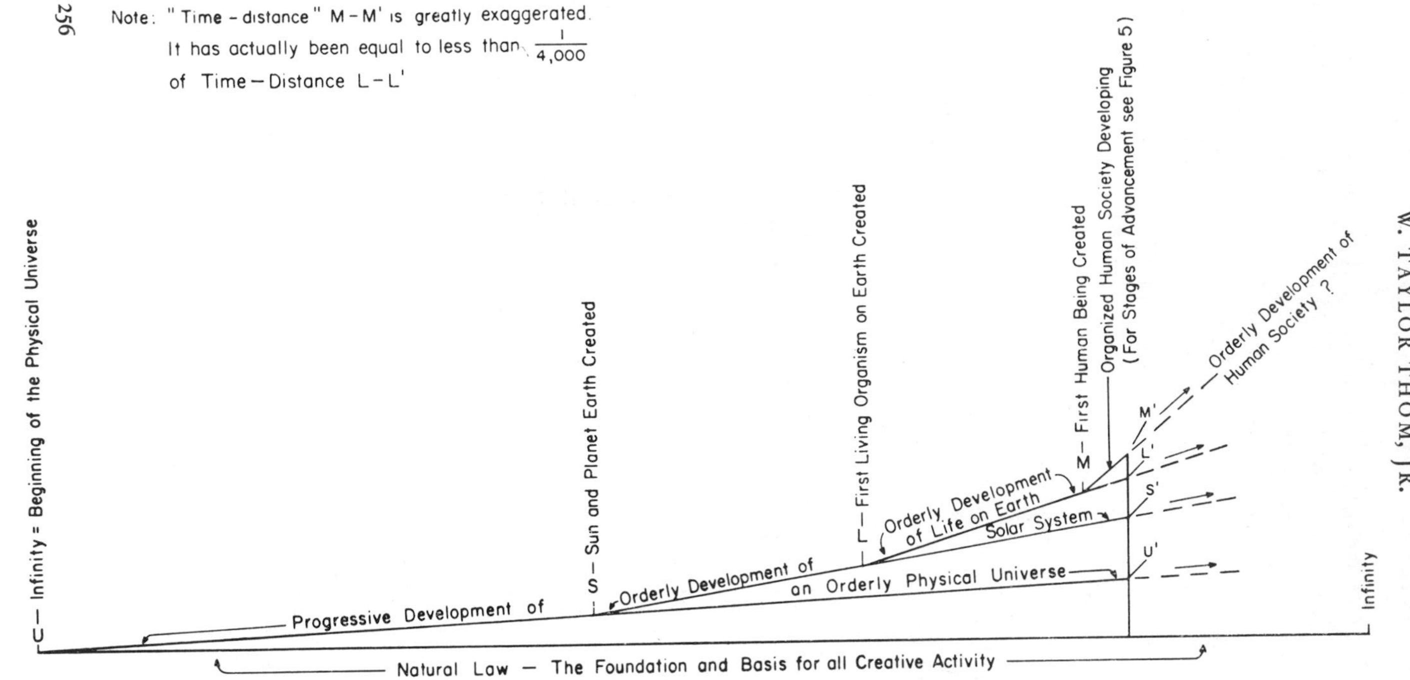

Figure 1 Diagram showing time-Dimension in the Progressive Creation which has led up to man's present situation

advised by one more of those Messengers of the Creator – the Prophets – as to Man's responsibilities with respect both to God and to all of his fellow human-beings. (The admonitions which have been thus received are, as of this moment, more than ever important, because it is only by a conformance with the instructions thus provided that we can be able to create – and enter – that World of Tomorrow which we so desire).

In order to convey somewhat more specifically how the Universal Trend-direction (or direction in which the whole Universe is moving) and Space and Time relate to the development of Life and of Man upon the Planet Earth, the writer has constructed a diagram (Figure 1) which seeks to give a graphic description of these relationships – a description which is subject to at least one drastic criticism, in that the duration of the human portion of the story has been exaggerated by about 4,000 times – in order that it could be easily observable.

THE CONTROLS WHICH HAVE BEEN EXERTED BY ENVIRONMENTAL INFLUENCES UPON THE FORMS, HISTORIES AND ENERGY LEVELS OF OLDER CIVILIZATIONS

Natural-Resource and Geographic Dimensions have exerted, and will continue to exert, decisive influences upon the forms, life-histories and energy-levels of particular civilizations. It is therefore important for us to consider how and why these "dimensions" have thus been determinants of the size, growth-characteristics, energy-levels and life-histories of four types of civilization, these including, respectively, ones which have developed in the Pastoral Lands of the Near and Middle East; in the well-watered lowlands of the Near, Middle and Far East; in Ancient Greece and in the Occident.

Environmental and "physical-state" characteristics of the Ancient Pastoral Civilizations. The civilizations which arose long ago in the Pastoral Lands of the Near and Middle East were ones which developed within an environment that had only two obvious dimensions – those of Earth and Sky – and only one mental and spiritual dimension – that of Religion. It was therefore natural that a Psalmist, living in such a region, should have written that

> "The Heavens declare the Glory of God
> And the Firmament showeth His handiwork.
> Day unto day uttereth speech
> And night unto night showeth knowledge.
> There is no place nor language
> Where their voice is not heard."

Water, and grass were, to be sure, vital matters. And the grazing lands were dotted with oases and were bordered by well-watered lowlands. But the Pastoral Peoples were never, in any sense, hemmed in. For they could move across the desert, or along its semi-arid borders, at will, as a thinly-spread, highly-fluid, and highly-energetic patriarchal civilization, which continually lived and moved in The Presence of a Creator who had made not only Heaven and Earth, but also Life, and Man.

It was to these peoples that Great Prophets came – those Messengers of the Creator who brought the revealed Will of God, as expressed in words which indicated Man's duty both to his Creator and to his fellow human beings. Likewise these Pastoral Peoples worshipped the Creator directly, without the intervention of priests or the employment of symbolic rituals – other than such as were provided in and by Nature. The whole of their lives was spent in The Presence, and it was therefore their firm belief that if they lived according to the Creator's (Natural) Law then, indeed would "all things needful" be added unto them.

Forms and Energy-Levels Characteristics of the "Lands of the Fixed Horizon."

The civilizations which arose on the fertile alluvial plains of Ancient Egypt, Mesopotamia, India and China differed amazingly from those which originated within the Pastoral Lands. For the Pastoral regions were essentially limitless in their extent and their peoples were therefore almost as free as the winds of Heaven, whereas the dwellers on the arable lowlands occupied by the ancient agricultural civilizations were surrounded by all-but-impassable mountain barriers and deserts. Consequently the agricultural peoples, as their numbers increased, became ever-more-tightly compressed within their fixed and immovable limiting barrier-boundaries. And hence these "fixed-horizon" civilizations became essentially crystalline in their formal structures, attitudes of mind, political and social systems, and mass energy-levels – since by assuming frozen, crystalline, structures and forms the impacts and frictions between the crowded component human individuals would be held to a minimum, and the orderly life and economic stability induced would make it possible for a maximum number of people to subsist in orderly and peaceful fashion within fixed limits and bounding horizons which had been established by Nature.

Thus the ancient Agricultural Civilizations rested upon broad bases, composed of unfree agricultural workers and slaves, augmented, when necessary, by forced-labor levies. And from these "mud-sills of Society" the pyramid or tiered temple or pagoda rose in orderly and symbolic fashion toward the "fortunate few" near the top of the social structure, and to the "God-Emperor" who sat at the summit – his position assured not only by the convergent self-interests of those below him, but also by the cementing influence of that "Power Behind the Throne" – the ecclesiastical hierarchy. For this hierarchy not only provided the scholars and civil servants who could write out (and preserve) the needed legal documents and property records – and diplomatic and business messages – but it was also the duty of this hierarchical group to advise the people comprising the lower courses of the pyramid that it was *their* duty to support the God-Emperor at the top without question and without complaint. And it was even more particularly the responsibility of the members of this priestly system to advise those in bondage, at the base of the social order, that *their* hopes for freedom and happiness were ones which could be realized in the *Next* World – a world which they would be allowed to enter *only* if they were sufficiently meek and uncomplaining in this one.

Social and political order were thus maintainable (despite birth-rates which were limited only by natural biological potential) because there was a constant "draining-off" of those born in excess of the natural carrying-power of the land – this surplus population being recurrently eliminated by flood or famine; by disease or war; or by over-work, coupled with a gradual downward movement among the poorer people near the bottom of the social structure – where unfortunate persons passed successively from poverty to destitution; from destitution to beggary; and from beggary to oblivion.

Thus did environmental limitations, imposed by Geographic and Natural-Resource Dimensions lead to the typical development and flowering of civilizations which were at once, massive, orderly, static (and therefore "peaceful") and relatively devoid of those energies which are prerequisite both for aggressive expansion and for effective self-defense – when conquering hordes pour in.

These ancient and long-enduring civilizations also produced great Prophets and rare and beautiful flowerings of the mind and spirit – flowerings which were brought to pass by fortunate individuals living near the summit of the cultural pyramid – who were therefore in position to enjoy that quietness which is indispensably necessary for thought, for meditation and for creative effort. But these great civilizations were essentially tree-like in their slow and continuing growth, and in their demonstrated lack of interest in the sufferings, frustrations and deprivations of the vast unfree masses of people at the base of the total, crystalline social structures. Hence such civilizations have been almost powerless either to improve the living-standards of their peoples, or to resist attacks from abroad, when attacks have come.

The Mineral-Resource Dimension - and the Rise, and Collapse, of Athenian Culture. The decisive influence which may be exerted by mineral natural resources upon the growth and decline of human cultures has been made evident in most spectacular fashion by the rise, and collapse, of the Athenian (and Grecian) culture of the so-called "Golden Age." For the enormously large and rich silver mines at Laurium, near Athens, provided directly the material foundations upon which Athenian culture was based, besides being, indirectly, a principal source of support for cultural developments throughout all of ancient Greece.

The wonderful capacities of the Greek mind and temperament; the favorable climate of Greece; and the inspiring Grecian landscape - blending and contrasting mountain and plain; and shore and sea - all contributed to Grecian greatness. However the ancient Athenian culture was, in essence, like the mythical giant Antaeus. For Antaeus was reputedly able to maintain and increase his strength only as long as he was in effective contact with the life-giving qualities of his parent, Mother Earth. And so it was with Athenian culture.

For centuries the huge Athenian mines poured out silver in millions and millions - with the result that Athens was a tax-free city - where labor was done by slaves purchased with silver from the mines at Laurium; where the safety of the state depended upon mercenaries hired with silver from the mines - or upon the subsidized armies of the other Grecian states making up the Pan-Hellenic League. Athens was, therefore, a city where men of ability and genius could spend their time in scientific investigation; in logical, mathematical and philosophical study and discussion; in creative art; and in athletic sports, including "Olympic Games." It was, indeed, an ideal and idyllic state of affairs – until the silver mines became exhausted. Economic and political collapse, of course, then ensued, practically at once – as it has, on a lesser scale, at so many times and in so many mining regions. And the defenseless remnants of the ancient Grecian culture were largely carried abroad by Greek scholars, artists, scientists and engineers who had been taken captive by the Romans. Sic transit gloria mundi!

Perhaps it should be reported at this point that a mining engineer – who had been in contact with the situation at Laurium after the old lead-silver mines had been redeveloped for zinc – has stated that in the course of these modern redevelopments more than 2,000 ancient mine-shafts were found and more than 100 linear miles of underground workings. More recently another eminent geologist has estimated that the silver which had been taken from Laurium, over the centuries, had had a purchasing power equivalent to that which would have been provided by 36 billions of (1946) U.S. dollars. No wonder that the Athenians could afford magnificent public buildings and works of art. And, having heard that Xerxes, the Persian had become interested in securing the Laurium mines, it is no wonder that the Athenians felt that they needed to build that fleet with which they defeated the Persians at Salamis.

Environmental influences in the Occidental "Lands of the Expanding Horizon."

The cultural developments, social attitudes, patterns of thought and "energy-levels" which are characteristic of the Occident are almost exactly antithetical to those which persisted for so long within the "Fixed- Horizon" civilizations of the Orient. For the peoples who moved westward and northwestward into Europe – as the glacial ice-cap melted back – knew *no limiting horizon* – geographic, intellectual or spiritual. They were fierce, strong and adventurous peoples who aspired to personal freedom in all phases of human life – mental, economic, political and spiritual. It was their attitude from the beginning, that adventure and discovery were the breath of life; that men discovered what they could – and held by force, if they could, that which they had discovered. Consequently the human tides advancing toward the northwest did not pause long at the North Sea's rim, but pressed on, – spreading laterally along the Atlantic Coasts, and westward to Iceland; to Greenland; to the East Coast of the Americas; and ultimately on to the Pacific. Nor was this westward progression all.

For the westward, and ultimately global, explorations of the Occidental peoples were paralelled by similar extensions and expansions of their interests within intellectual, scientific and technological fields of endeavor. Scientific and mechanical principles which had long been known among the Oriental and Mediterranean peoples were either learned about or were re-discovered, and extended – particularly after the onset of "The Industrial Revolution" – which was actually expressive of the World's Third Technologic Revolution – the two earlier ones having been related, respectively, to the discovery and use of the wheel; and to the discovery of methods for smelting ores and for making alloys and forged tools and weapons.

The First Industrial Revolution

The so-called "Industrial Revolution" was born of gunpowder and of the invention of the steam engine. For when gunpowder – long known, but not highly regarded in the Orient – became known in Europe, its military-and-political importance was soon recognized, and guns and cannon thereupon became important. Consequently more iron ore had to be dug and more iron and steel had to be forged. Charcoal fuel ceased to be readily available for smelting and forging - so coal began to be of prime importance, both for metallurgical work and for corollary purposes. And as mines ware dug deeper it became imperative to invent some mechanical contrivance which could pump water from coal mines and ore pits. And so the steam-powered pumping engine was invented and with gunpowder and iron (and steel) available, and with the supra-human energies and power of the steam-engine at command - the (First) Industrial Revolution moved on toward its maturity, with two profoundly important consequences. First, because it became unprofitable to use slave labor to do work which could be done more cheaply, or better, by steam-powered machines, and secondly (in the political realm), because a few little Western European nations, despite their small size and minor human populations, were able to establish world-empires, through their ability to apply irresistible naval and military pressures to vastly larger populations, which had long been so organized as to be incapable of resisting concentrated military – and – political force.

However, the general history, and manifold consequences of this (First) Industrial Revolution are so widely known that they require no further exposition here. That this "Revolution" provided the power-basis upon which the early-modern worldempires were built, is obvious. That it was also a necessary pre-requisite to the abolition of slavery and serfdom, and to the establishment of high standards of living, is less frequently remembered, and seldom mentioned. Nor does it seem to be generally realized that the economic-and-political needs of the growing populations of North-western Europe, and of America, continued to foster and accelerate scientific exploration and discovery, coupled with the development of inventions and procedures which made possible the effective technological-and-engineering application and employment of known scientific facts and principles. In this manner were the seeds of new technological revolutions planted, in the Occident, long before the national leaders concerned realized that new conditions were developing which would, again and again, tend to transform the world's social, economic and political situations or that repeated crises would result if these impending transformations were not foreseen, and were not prepared for - in time.

The Coming of the Fourth, Fifth and Sixth Technological Revolutions. Three more Technologic Revolutions have been going on more or less simultaneously during the past 80 years - ones which have been based, respectively, upon developments in the Chemical and Chemical Engineering, Electrical and Electronic, and Automotive fields.

The one related to Chemistry and Chemical Engineering may be regarded as dating from the end of the Franco-Prussian war, when the union of Ruhr coal and of Lorraine iron ore, plus the development of the byproduct coke oven, began to make it possible to transform and transmute a few basic natural-resource raw materials into all manner of new products and new ersatz or synthetic materials, thus building up that industrial - and - military power which was displayed with such telling effect during World War I.

The Electrical Transmission and Telecommunications Revolution resulted in the invention of the telegraph, telephone, electric light, radio, radar and television (and related appliances, techniques and arts) and has, of course, made world-wide communication essentially instantaneous, besides making long-distance transmission of electric power a standard modern practice.

The Sixth or Transportation Revolution has resulted from the development of the internal-combustion motor, whereby the energies of petroleum have been made effective through the use of automobiles, airplanes and trucks; also of Diesel-powered tractors, earth-movers, locomotives, farm machinery and ships.

The Onset of the Seventh Technologic Revolution. The Beginning of the "Limitless Age." The discovery of processes for bringing about controllable atomic fission, and the prospective harnessing of the limitless energies that can be had from thermo-nuclear fusion have confronted Man with the necessity for deciding whether these discoveries are to cause an early annihilation of the whole human race – or whether they are, indeed, to become the heralds of a "Limitless Age." For we, the peoples of the whole world do now either face, together, a future world of Hope, and Justice and Peace and Freedom-from-war, or we face no "Future" at all, beyond a few months or perhaps a year or so.

Atomic fission, thermo-nuclear fusion and recent developments in rocketry and in the region of interplanetary space have, indeed, brought us to the threshold of a "limitless" future, depending upon the outcome of the currently-developing Sociological World Revolution – a revolution that has been sired by the belief that "All men have been *created* free and equal," and that was quickened when it became possible to substitute machine-power for the labor of serfs and slaves.

The Beginnings of the Sociological World-Revolution. The Sociological World-Revolution is being born amid economic, political, social and spiritual crises of the most profound importance. And if Man is to survive he can do so only if this new World-Revolution leads to suitable action within the United Nations Organization, and under the guidance of three vitally important concepts:

First, that in the Realm of the Spirit "all men *have* been created free and equal," since they are all children of the same Creator.

Second, that *Equal Justice for all persons* must be the Rock upon which a World of Peace and Progress can be founded. And

Third, that "Government of the People, for the People and by the People" must provide the method by which equal justice is to be assured, if, indeed, it is to be had. Under this kind of government real justice can be established – for society and government are thereby joined in seeking to provide a real equality of opportunity for every adult person and, particularly, for every child.

Also, since all persons will not accept their responsibilities fully, and in equal measure, real Justice will also require that rewards be made proportionate to performances, and that *earnings* be received in proportion to the value and quantity of useful work done (due provision also being made for persons suffering from illness or disability).

That the guiding principles just set out *can* be applied successfully has already been indicated, by the experience of some peoples, and also of some corporations, which have been wise enough to comprehend that Fair Competition, properly enforced, is a key to Justice, to Progress and to Peace. Whereas monopoly, whether economic or industrial or political, is retrogressive, is evil and has always given rise to Revolution, to Cold War and to Red War.

THE NATURE AND PRIME CAUSES OF THE CURRENT WORLD-MALADY

The world is afflicted by a malady having characteristic symptoms and particular causes. The nature of this complex disease is such that it goes through prolonged Cold War incubation periods characterized by mounting economic – and – political tensions, which, in due course, give rise to outbreaks of (military) World War. (Relative to which it may be commented that those who actually trigger the next

World War outbreak will also be destroyed by it – as will all other persons.)

Therefore, for the sake of all concerned, let us now consider how a knowledge of scientific principles and conditions; an understanding of Technology; and an acquaintance with Engineering Science and Art may provide us with both such diagnoses, and with such corollary prescriptions, as can guide us to the cure of that world-malady which currently threatens the Future of Man.

Causes of the Present World-Crisis

The existing world-crisis has been brought on by acute maladjustments in all three of the fields which have basic human importance: the material, the intellectual and the spiritual.

Maladjustments in the material world. Basic maladjustments exist in the material world, as is made evident, graphically, by Figure 2, shown below – since this Figure compares and contrasts the standards of living which now prevail in different world-regions. The mere existence of such inequalities, within a world closely linked by radio, by television and by air-post, has naturally excited great dissatisfactions and certainly calls for strenuous efforts, in all quarters, to find a remedy.

Maladjustments in the mental realm. It is Man's nature to wish to make proper, full and effective use of his mind and of his creative capacities – and with respect to such aspirations many peoples are as yet desperately frustrated, for they have been prevented from developing and operating their own governments; have been, by contrast, prisoners of foreign political powers and economic imperialisms, and have been manipulated, for profit, by industrial monopolies and cartels,

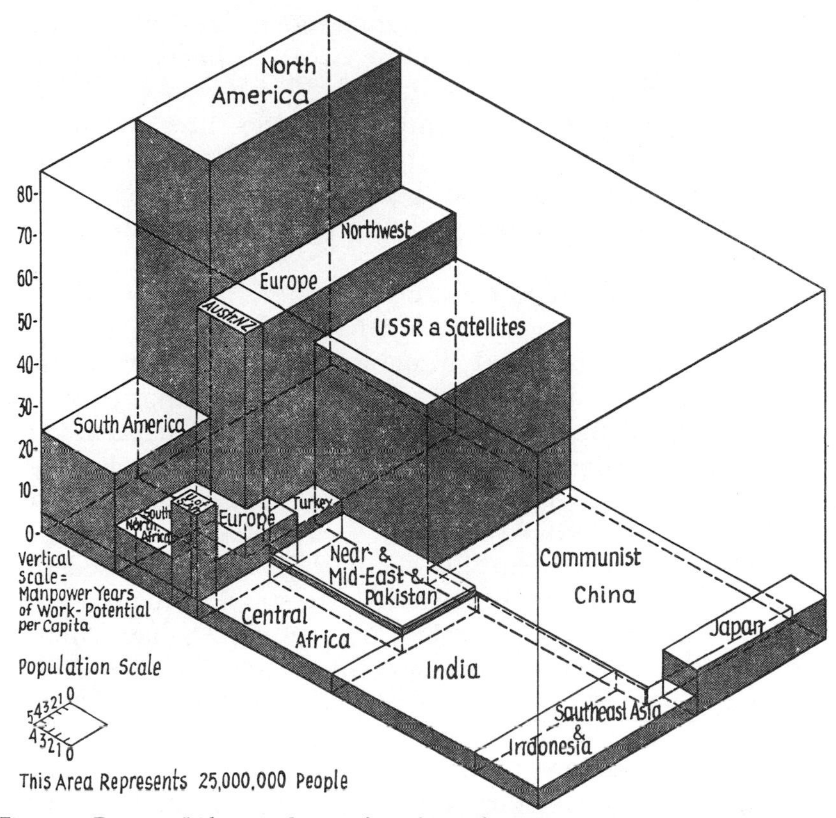

Figure 2 Diagram Indicating Potentials and Populations of Various National and Regional Areas

some privately-owned and some owned by totalitarian and despotic governments. Such conditions have become increasingly intolerable, so the important question is "How can the needed national and international transformations be accomplished, with justice and fair compensation to all concerned, and without bloodshed?"

Maladjustments in the spiritual realm. The writer believes that the members of different civilizations have operated according to one or the other of three differing religious points of view, expressive of contrasting interpretations of how Divine Revelations, reported to us by the Great Prophets, relate to the practical affairs of everyday life. (With respect to this matter is to be noted that no one of the three, religious points of view, as thus far interpreted, has as yet provided a generally-satisfactory and workable correlation between revealed Creative Purpose and the practical direction of daily human activities.)

For some of the Great Religions have been primarily quietist and contemplative and many of the peoples who have held those faiths are in danger of perishing, as of the present, because under this type of spiritual approach to Earthly problems the peoples concerned have been left inadequately supplied with even the absolute minima of food and other material necessities needed to support existing populations – whereas the populations are still growing – and the "surplus" people have now refused to continue to solve their problem by merely dying quietly.

The adherents of another Great Religion have lived constantly in the Presence – and the members of this Faith were not only at one time a Great Political Power but were also, educationally speaking "The Light of the World" – at least in so far as the Occident was concerned. But then they lost the spark of scientific inquiry; their educational systems became formal and static; and "education," apparently became regarded as a process of learning by rote Truths which had been inherited from centuries past – without effective appreciation of the fact that change goes on constantly, and that education should prepare the oncoming generations to use *their* minds, and *their* imaginations, to meet new conditions and solve new problems – but without forgetting that it is Man's duty to serve God.

Crisis likewise prevails among the allegedly "Christian" Occidental peoples, because they have, in the main, not regarded Christianity as a *Religion* – to practice at all times and live by, but rather as a salve for troubled consciences and as a means for escaping punishments (in a Next World) which have been more than earned by improper and inhuman conduct in this one.

Past Occidental economic and political actions have seldom been guided by ethical or religious considerations – up to about 30 years ago – and normally have been guided by secular attitudes and by exclusively worldly and "practical" considerations. Consequently, under these conditions conflicts of selfish interest have been frequent and acute in the international area and a complex of world-crises has been built up, by long-continued Occidental provocations. (For it is only recently and, as yet a limited degree, that conscience and religious motivation have – belatedly – begun to have significant impact upon Occidental affairs, and have begun to create a genuine, though as yet embryonic "soul" within the gigantic mass of secular western materialism.)

If the foregoing opinions are wellfounded, and the writer is convinced that they are, then how can the World proceed to aid The United Nations Organization to establish such a "Unity of Difference" that the collective efforts of the World can accomplish three things – *without War*:

1) Enable the needy to *earn* a decent living?
2) Make freedom obtainable by those who now are either economically, industrially or politically unfree?
3) Enable the adherents of the World's various Religions to *prove* the special merits of *their* particular Faiths – by proper demonstrations of their desire – and ability – to be of aid and comfort to their less-fortunate fellow beings? For truly it is by their *fruits* that they shall be judged.

Anatomical Relationships and Physiological Functions of Civilizations – and Derangements Which Have Been Induced by Foregoing Causes and Maladjustments

The existing world-crisis has given rise to clearly-evident

symptoms of disease, symptoms which have arisen as natural consequences of the several causes of illness just enumerated. Our effort should be to relate, and analyze, these causes and symptoms in such a way that we may be led to appropriate prescriptions and to proper curative measures. But before we can write suitable prescriptions and devise proper treatments

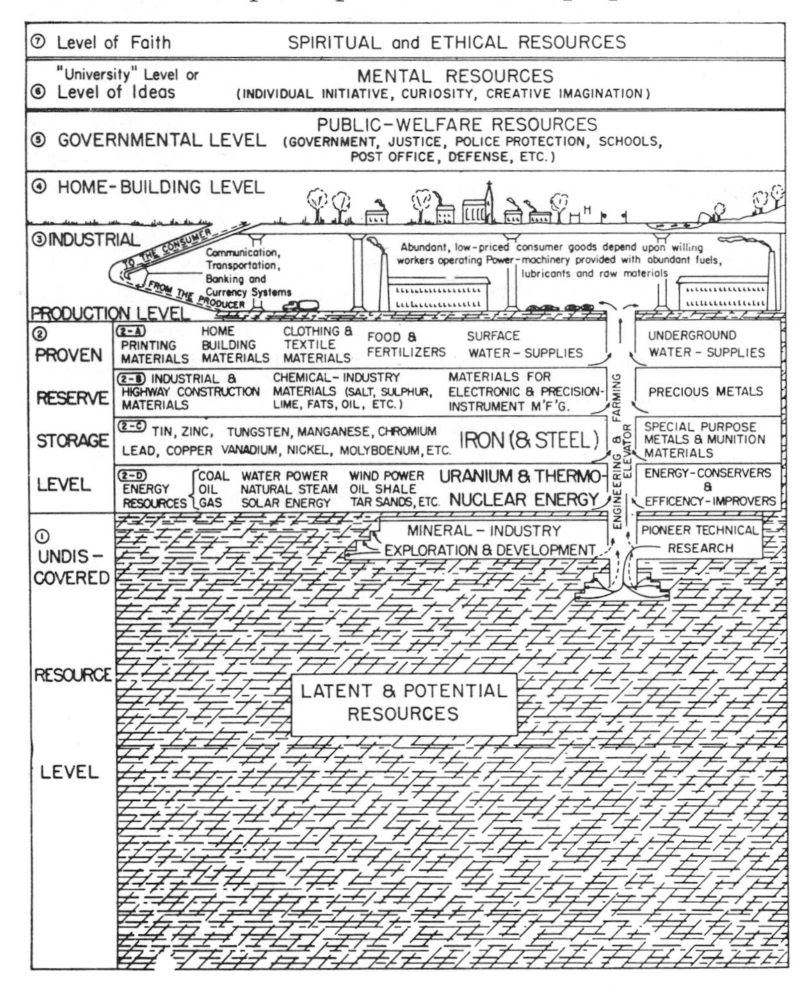

Fig. 3 World Natural-Resources

we need to have clearly in mind the nature of the anatomical structures and the nature of the physiological processes with which we are called upon to deal. For beyond all reasonable doubt various types of civilization do have characteristically differing anatomical and physiological features and processes.

Two figures of speech are believed to be descriptive, respectively, of the older Oriental and Occidental types of civilization. Thus the ancient agricultural civilizations of the East have been essentially tree-like in their morphology and mode of growth. (See Figure 3). Whereas Western civilization has been characterized by a mobility, a physiological circulatory system, and a stage-by-stage pattern of growth of the sort which is made visibly evident by the life-processes of the creature which we know as the Chambered Nautilus. (See Figures 4 and 5).

Anatomically-speaking the material phases of the life of a modern civilization proceed at Levels 1 to 5 of Figure 3 – the activities taking place at these five levels corresponding to those which occur in Nature in the root-zone, trunk, bark and vascular system, reproductive system and bough-and-leaf zone of a tree. Moreover, just as the life of a tree depends not only upon the soil, but also upon the atmosphere within which it grows and upon the life-giving light of the Sun, so also the life of a civilization is similarly dependent upon activities in the realm of the mind (Level 6 of Figure 3) and in the realm of (Spiritual) Enlightenment and Faith at Level 7 of Figure 3 – thus relating us to Cosmic Purpose and Trend. So let us consider briefly the essential matters pertaining to the anatomy and physiology of a simple civilization – as these are diagrammed in Figure 3.

In detail the story to be gotten from Figure 3 is one of fairly simple and fairly obvious interrelationships – for the safety of a civilization depends upon wise and sound operation at the "governmental level" (Level 5). But such operation at Level 5 depends upon the existence of an intelligent and reasonably prosperous voting population living on the "Homebuilding

Level" (Level 4). And in order that there may be satisfactory standards of living on Level 4 the operations on the "Industrial Production Level" (Level 3) must go forward, with general satisfaction to all so involved. Also, if farms and factories are to operate satisfactorily at Level 3, it is necessary that there be available, at reasonable prices, adequate supplies of all of the essential fuels and fertilizers and ores and minerals, obtainable from the "Proven-Reserve Storage Level" (Level 2). And to keep the reservoirs of proven-resource reserves on Level 2 from running dry (which would induce a collapse of civilization) it is imperative that adequate exploratory and research-and-development work be arranged for and be carried on at the "Potential and Undiscovered Resource Level" (Level 1). Which interestingly enough, brings us back again to Level 5 – because adequate discoveries of new essential-resource supplies will continue if, and as long as, the operations of industry, on a basis of fair competition, is guaranteed by impartial enforcement of Justice under Law – a condition which prevails where a "Government of the People, by the People and for the People" makes the laws, and provides for law enforcement. For under popular self-government the citizens try to pass just laws – such as assure each individual and each *group* of citizen-workers (or "company") of a fair opportunity to use individual imagination, individual skill and individual energies on a basis of fair competition, – so that the greatest rewards will go to those who have *earned* and *deserved* most – by rendering greatest service to society.

In countries where "Fair Competition" is thus encouraged (and enforced) new and better ways of doing things are continually being invented within the Realm of Mind, which is situated at Level 6 of the foregoing diagram. Such invention can take place because it *is* true that "to the Free Mind all things are possible" – and it *is* true that "Pioneer Research is the key which can unlock those greatest energy-resources of all the God-given powers of the human individual;

and the assembled and integrated powers and capacities of an ideal modern civilization, a civilization which operates under spiritual guidance (from Level 7) and therefore organizes and directs its activities according to what is right and reasonable – and according to "Justice under Law."

Changing our figure of speech now let us consider, first, how the internal circulation proceeds, at any one time, within the body of a Nautilus-like Western industrial (i.e., non-agricultural) type of civilization (see Fig. 5-A), and

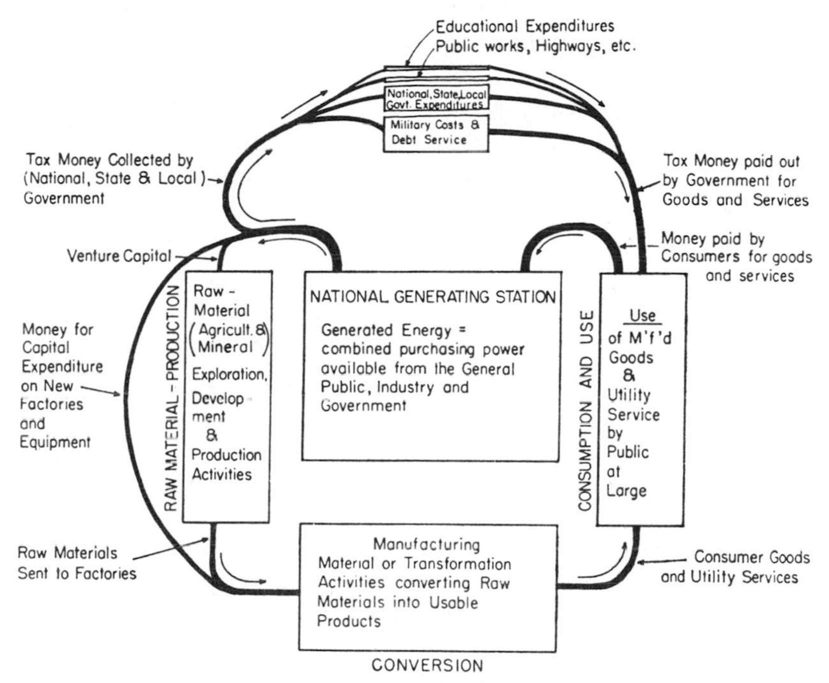

Figure 4 Functional Relationships and Flows of Goods and Capital Characteristic of an Autarchic or Wholly - Independent (National or Regional) Economy

second, how the continuing growth of the creature recurrently forces an almost complete reconstruction of its bodily mass within a new and larger living-chamber, coupled with an almost complete re-development of the creature's circulatory system – these changes being forced partly by the mere increase of bodily mass, and even more particularly because changes in the animal's metabolism call for (steadily increasing) supplies of a constant growing variety of vital nutrient substances (see Level 2 of Figure 3) – and this in a world in which vital natural-resources are of very unequal and irregular geographic occurrence.

Within a wholly self-contained, and therefore independent or "autarchic" political-and-economic circulatory system, such as is shown in Figure 4, human need or "consumer demand" can generate an adequate equivalent supply, providing:

1) That the economy can operate under conditions which assure the creature's capacity for self-defense;
2) That the animal's new living-space is of large enough geographic size to include adequate sources of all essential nutrients – both old and new – which are currently indispensable to the creature's continued growth. And also providing that this living space is large enough to include all necessary capacities for the manufacturing, distribution and marketing of consumer goods, and for the generation of adequate "venture" and constructional capital and of adequate tax revenues. And
3) That the animal can develop under conditions such that its bodily growth (i.e., population increase) will proceed in reasonable balance with the rates of increase of available supplies of energy; and of raw materials; of manufacturing capacity, and of available scientific, technologic and engineering capacities.

However, because healthy life does induce healthy growth, an industrialized civilization, like a Nautilus, does gradually outgrow its former living-chamber, and so, in time it must again re-develop itself within new and yet larger living-spaces. To meet this kind of need – for a recurrent re-development of its body and of an (*unimpeded*) circulatory system – the Nautilus continuously builds its (political) shell

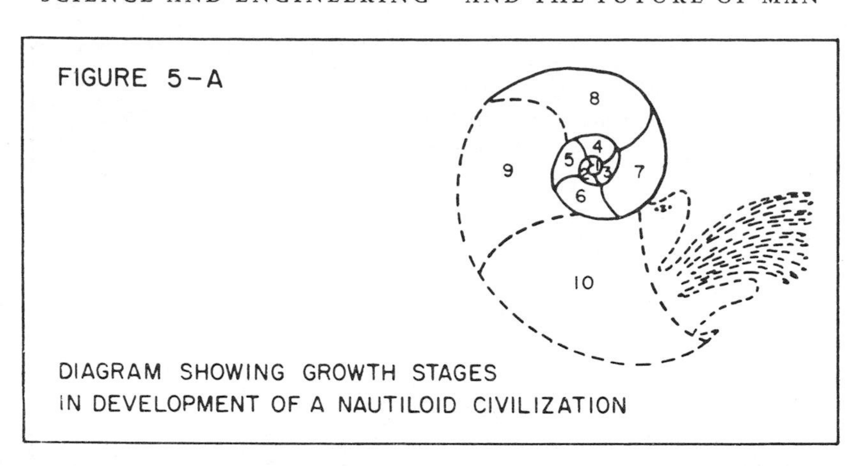

DIAGRAM SHOWING GROWTH STAGES IN DEVELOPMENT OF A NAUTILOID CIVILIZATION

forward – in order to be prepared to house its growing bulk (See Figure 5-A). Then, in order to maintain the structural strength of its shell, it inserts new cross-septa from time to time, whereupon it must, each time, move almost the whole of its body out of its former living chamber and into the new and larger one just created. Human cultures and social organizations have grown in like manner and have undergone recurrent political re-developments and integrations, as per the Stages shown in the Table opposite Figure 5-B. In terms of the Stages listed in this Table Western industrial civilization has outgrown both Stage 7, the "sovereign-state" Stage and also the (composite) "national" Stage (Stage 8) and should, ere this, have proceeded to the ninth Stage – that of Regional Economic Union – moving all the while toward the Tenth, and ultimate Stage, wherein the present United Nations Organization can (and will) become an effective World-Economic Union, created through a voluntary (Constitutional) union of Regional Constitutional Federations.

Man's cultural and social development has followed a forward-and-upward trend, as is shown by both Figures 1 and 5-B. Growth taking place (according to this trend) has naturally called for a corresponding and continuous en-

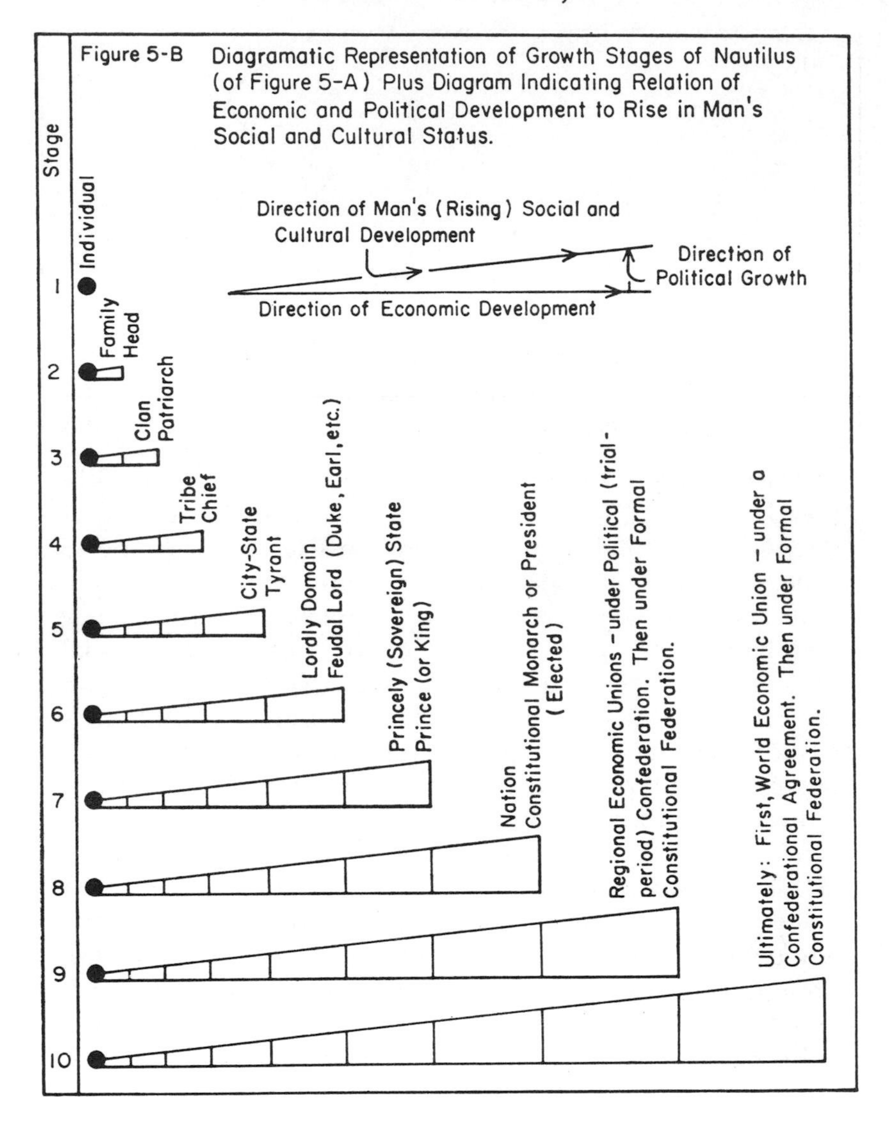

Figure 5-B Diagramatic Representation of Growth Stages of Nautilus (of Figure 5-A) Plus Diagram Indicating Relation of Economic and Political Development to Rise in Man's Social and Cultural Status.

Stage	Characteristic (Most Advanced) Organizational Form of Human Society	Characteristic Type of Culture	Type of Political Structure	Type (or Title) of Leader	Characteristic Pattern of Economic Activity
1	Human individual	Brute	None	None	None
2	Human Family	Semi-Brute	Embryonic	Head-of-Family	Hunting and Scavenging
3	Clan	Old Stone Age	Patriarchal	Patriarchal	Hunting, Herding, Handicraft Work & Barter
4	Tribe	New Stone Age	Tribal	Chief	Hunting, Herding, Handicraft Work & Barter
5	City-State	Barbarism	Local Despotism	Tyrant	Farming, Mining, Primitive Handicraft Mfg. Ship and Caravan Trade
6	Lordly Domain (County)	Embryonic Civilization	Feudal	Lord, Earl, Duke etc.	Agriculture, Mining Guild Mfg. Organized Trade
7	Princely (Sovereign) State	Local Civilization	Absolute Monarchy	Prince	Agriculture, Specialized Mfg. Organized Hemispheric Trade
8	Nation	Regional ,,	Constitutional Monarchy, or Union { of Province / of Soviets / of States } Outdated	President, Prime Minister, Premier, etc. Outdated	Power Mfg., + (Imperial) Colonial Exploitation and impoverishment of Raw Materials and Market Areas
9	Regional-Grouping of Peoples	World-Civilization	Constitutional Regional Federation of Self-Governing Nations	President (Elected)	Rise of Constructive and Creative (= Welfare) Capitalism, Strong Unions, Machine-Power Mass-Production, and High Standard of Living
10	World-Grouping of Peoples		Constitutional Federation of Self-Governing Regional Federations	President (Elected)	World-wide use of methods of Creative (= Welfare) Capitalism. Aboliton of National or Regional *Military* establishments. Use of revenues for the raising and equalizing of living standards.

largement of the supporting economic or material base, upon which the growing civilization rests (Figure 5-B). And this growth, as in the case of the Nautilus, recurrently makes it necessary for the developing creature to move forward into a new living-chamber – with the major difference that the new living-space for the civilization is not produced by a simple extension and enlargement of the old one, but is produced by a fusion and welding together of the living-chambers of a number of formerly separate and independent creatures. (Such a fusion may take place temporarily and abortively because of imperialistic pressures or may take place properly and naturally through voluntary, constitutional, economic and political federation.

Once the development of a genuine community of legitimate self-interests has induced such an Economic Union as that of the Benelux countries, then a new, unified bodily circulation can develop as a replacement for the several, previously-existing circulatory systems – this unification being accomplished by a unification of currencies; by an abolition of intra-union tariffs (with proper indemnification to those injured by such abolition); by free intra-union movement of persons; and by the creation of an adequate and uniform intra-union system for proper legal contract-enforcement.

Once we understand why such economic-and-political integrations and transformations become necessary, recurrently, as a civilization develops, then one main reason for the existence of current world-tension becomes obvious. For modern industrial civilizations simply *cannot* function, successfully and prosperously, within the "sovereign-state" or national boundaries of even the most extensive countries (such as the Soviet Union, China, Brazil and the United States) for the simple reason that *no single nation national area* can now, alone, provide *all* of the essential natural resource materials upon which modern life directly depends. Either (voluntary) union or (involuntary) imperial combination has been made inevitable by modern scientific, technologic and engineering developments – and that the imperial method is both wrong and self-defeating should, by now, have become axiomatic. Pending the improvement and equalization of regional living-standards, voluntary economic and political federations can be developed successfully on a *regional* basis only – though as soon as "population pressures" on the opposite sides of regional governmental boundaries (see Figure 2) have been equalized, then these boundaries can be, in effect, wiped out, and an Economic World-Union (and economic circulation) will become possible, as well as necessary.

A DIAGNOSIS OF THE CURRENT WORLD-MALADY

To diagnose the existing world-malady one must really make three sets of diagnoses, relating, respectively, to the material, mental and spiritual phases of the total problem. These may be stated, in turn, as follows:

Diagnoses relating to material and natural-resource problems: Three principal causes of social illness exist in this "area:"

1) Human populations continue to outgrow their material means of support, partly because unbalanced applications of Biological and Medical Science have provided means for reducing human death-rates without having discovered and made available proper and equally effective methods for keeping birthrates at a materially-supportable level.
2) The standards-of-living in the various world-regions are very unequal and are, in general, very unsatisfactory – due partly to the too rapid increase of populations.
3) The scientific, technologic and engineering exploratory capacities, now available as factors capable of offsetting

mineral-resource depletion, are almost unknown in many parts of the world and have nowhere been adequately developed and employed.

Diagnoses relating to the world's mental and intellectual-resource problems.

4) Human economies have long since outgrown national boundaries, despite which the needed, corrollary, political growths (by voluntary unions and integration) have not taken place, except within the Benelux and, in a preliminary way, in India. Elsewhere either disintegration rather than integration has taken place – or efforts have been made to solve the problem by a re-employment of the old Imperial Great Power-plus-(colony or)-satellite pattern.
5) There has not yet been a proper development of Regional Constitution Federations at Stage 9 of Figure 5-B such as are permissible under The United Nations Charter. Consequently it has not yet been possible to compell a substitution of Fair Competition Capitalism for old-style, exploitationist Monopoly Capitalism (either privately-owned or State-owned).
6) As the World is now set up economically and politically, Science and Engineering and Fair-Competition Industry are not now able, and will not be able, to conduct the mineral-resource explorations and developments which must be carried out, if world standards of living are to be either maintained or improved.

Diagnoses relating to the World's spiritual problems:

7) A disunited World has refused to admit the validity of the old proverb that "as ye sow so shall ye reap." But a continuation of this attitude, within a world which has been made one by technologic invention, can only mean that a further employment of violent methods will lead to renewed World War and to oblivion.
8) It is all too little realized that proper loyalty is indispens-

able to continued human survival. But unless there be proper loyalty within the family; within the nation; and within the Brotherhood of Man, then we shall have proved our *disloyalty* to the Revelations of the Divine Will, and we shall be like "the flower of the field" - "for the wind shall pass over it, and the place thereof shall know it no more."

9) The world, as yet, despite the existence of the United Nations, has developed no sure means for controlling Injustice and Tyranny. People still profess to believe that Peace can be "won" by war. People still try to settle both spiritual and political problems by force - despite the validity of BURKE's dictum "Force is objectionable. It destroys that which it seeks to preserve." People still refuse to admit to themselves that they who practice injustice will surely reap injustice. People still seem to believe that Freedom - both spiritual and political - can be gained by a voluntary acceptance of spiritual slavery - and of political and economic subjugation instead of being earned by effort and suffering. For they have not, in general, as yet accepted in practice that "Truth which sets Man free."

SPECIFIC ACTIONS NEEDED FOR THE CURING OF THE WORLD-MALADY

Certain specific actions are needed if the diagnoses of the world-ills, just made, are to form the basis for proper prescription and for proper treatment. The paragraphs to follow will therefore suggest how these several diagnoses can (it is hoped) lead to effective cure, through particular action.

Problem (1). The problem of population increase: The world's populations, for the most part, have been reproducing practically up to the limits of their biological potentials.

Besides which the praiseworthy efforts of Biological and Medical Science to save human lives have contributed notably to the production of a situation in which human numbers are increasing more rapidly than are the available material resources upon which the support of human life depends. It therefore seems to be the clear responsibility of Biological and Medical research workers to learn more about the natural laws which relate particularly to the biological factors involved in the process of human reproduction – for there seems to be no reason to doubt that answers can be had to the "population problem" – which are not only right and proper but also effective. For proper answers *must* either be thus provided – or improper ones will be had, through the further use of mass-genocide.

Problem (2). The problem of unequal regional standards of living. The problem of unequal regional standards of living can be solved – if the problem of *over*-rapid growth of population can be properly solved. And to show how and why this can be true let us again consider Figure 2.

As Figure 2 shows, almost half of the world's people now live at barest subsistence levels – a condition which grows ever more critical as populations continue to increase faster than do supporting material resources. But if one considers the relationships shown by Figure 2 – in the light of scientific understanding and engineering experience – then a solution of the problem presents itself. So in order that the nature of this solution may become clear let us consider Figure 2 again in the light of four postulates, which run as follows:

1) That the all-inclusive, rectangular outline of Figure 2 corresponds to the outline of a box-like Ark, and that all of the World's people are aboard this Ark.
2) That the members of particular nations or groups of nations have all gathered together in particular parts of the Ark's hold – with each person being allocated an

equal amount of floor-space (with the result that such "national areas" are proportional to the size of national populations).

3) That the national floor areas, so occupied, have been walled about by vertical bulkheads, such as subdivide the hold of an ocean-going ship, and that these bulkheads have been fitted with watertight doors, such as can be closed tightly, or can be left partly or wholly open, at option. And

4) That the populations within the several compartments, thus established, are, figuratively, living upon the surfaces of rafts which are floating at different levels, as shown in Figure 2 – according to the relative per capita productive capacities (or standards of living) prevailing within the several compartments.

With reference to the disparities between national living standards, indicated by Figure 2, various well-intentioned persons have proposed that the world's ills be cured by generous action on the part of the more prosperous nations – so that the needy peoples can be cared for out of the abundance of the less needy. This should of course be done, in so far as it is practicable, but a single glance at Figure 2 shows how completely inadequate, volumetrically speaking, such proposals are. For if all of the bulkhead doors were opened wide, simultaneously, a consequent sudden readjustment and equalization of levels would occur – with catastrophic declines of standards of living taking place in all high-standard countries, but without more than minor and ephemeral improvements of living conditions in the other, larger, areas occupied by the more impoverished populations. And the word "ephemeral" has been used advisedly, for under present mores and patterns of thinking such temporary ameliorations of living conditions as would occur within the low-standard countries would be almost immediately cancelled by an almost explosive growth of populations within those countries. So that within a short time the same tragic poverties would again be prevalent – only they would be suffered by many, many more people. One basic problem of Man is, then, to devise a way by which living standards can be raised, differentially, until all have become substantially equal, whereupon all bulkhead doors *can* be opened wide without causing any serious disturbance of equilibrium in any quarter. From what has just been said, it is obvious that the problems flowing from present unequalities in standards of living cannot be solved or resolved by mere charity, or by the use of mere arithmetical subtraction and addition. But they can be solved by an intelligent and constructive use of the "technologic processes of multiplication." And this is where Science and Engineering *and* Technology *can* provide the answers needed.

For the rafts supporting the populations within the several compartments are not held up by water but are supported by a mobile material of a very different nature – a material which is essentially like bread-dough. Furthermore, if we review, mentally, how the bread-making process proceeds, we shall see the answer to our problem. For we will recall that flour and salt are mixed with a liquid (with nothing more than a mere *addition* of volumes) and then yeast is added and is given time to leaven the lump of dough – with the result that the volume of the dough increases and increases until the bread is ready to be baked (and eaten). And so it is in the international process. In order to keep the raft-borne populations supported, new supplies of "dough" must be continuously developed beneath the rafts, as the finished product is drawn off and used. And in the international dough-making process the "flour" is composed of a suitable blend of all the many essential-resource materials which have been listed at Level 2 of Figure 3. Whereas the liquid to be added consists of "liquid capital" or, in other words, of the machines, the manufacturing plants and the agricultural, mining, constructional and transportational equipment required for modern industrial production. And the 'yeast" is made up of scientific knowledge, of technologic methods and appliances, and of engineering planning, administration and "knowhow." Moreover this yeast of civilization, like the yeast familiar to breadmakers, can, if wisely handled, be shared practically without limit – without causing decrease in the supplies which remain available to the donor. So the three practical problems remaining to be solved, if world standards of living are to be improved and equalized, relate to the reduction of human birthrates; to the availability of adequate supplies of suitable natural-resource "flour"; and to the availability of adequate volumes of productive liquid capital. Solution of the first of these three problems must rest with the workers in Biological and Medical Science. The second problem can be solved through cooperative action within regional groupings of nations which, among them, possess adequate sources from which to draw a full suite of essential-resource materials. And the third can be cared for either by a direct barter of surplus natural-resource raw material for needed capital-equipment, or by means of loans obtained from or through the World Bank – with the assistance of one or the other of the agencies of the United Nations Organization.

Problem (3). The problem of the exhaustibility of essential natural resources. Human thought, and public policy, relative to the development of essential natural resources, have been, and are being, continually de-railed by the general incompleteness of human understandings of the world's natural-resource problem. For non-scientists and non-engineers have definitely failed to appreciate that we are here dealing with Time, Space and Energy problems to which "relativity-theory" definitely applies. Or, stated in another way, they have failed to appreciate the validity of a thought expressed by an eminent scientist (who is also a great industrial executive) who wrote, substantially, as follows: "Creative imagination, controlled and applied is the wand which can reveal the

GEOLOGICAL ENGINEERING
AND
OTHER ENGINEERING

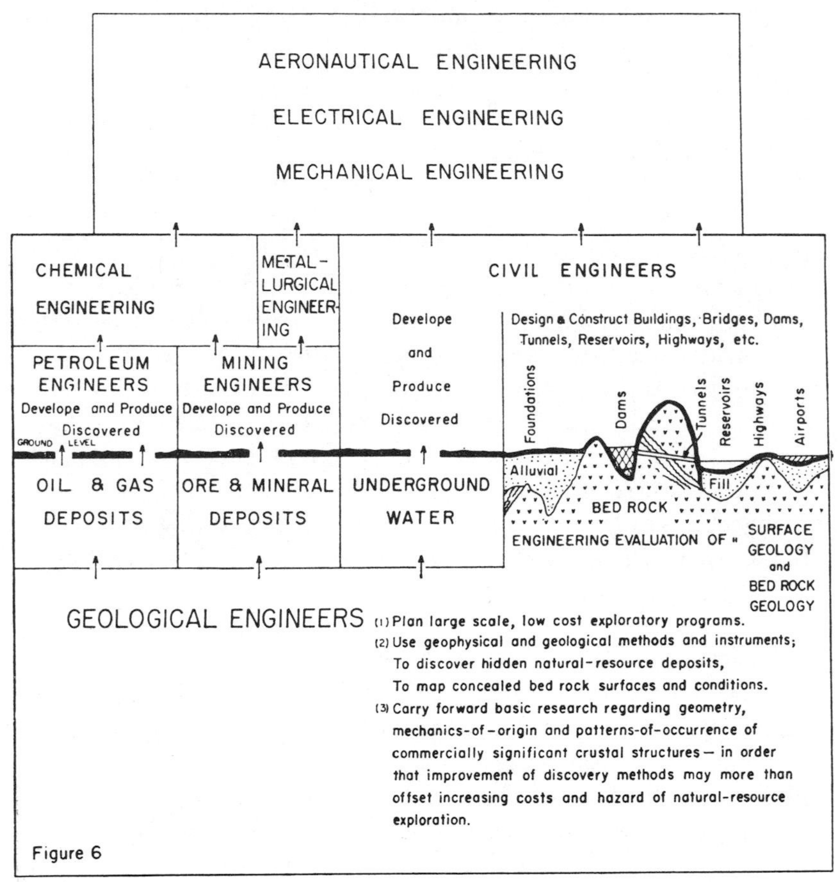

Figure 6

invisible; transform the useless into the useful; waste into raw material of great value; exhaustible resources into inexhaustible resources." For if the capacities of Exploratory Engineers (see Figure 6) to discover new deposits (of many degrees of richness) continue to be increased progressively, by new advances in geo-exploratory science and technology, then other engineers, employing newer and better methods and equipment, can produce and transform mineral raw materials more and more cheaply; thus converting larger and larger lower-grade deposits from submarginal to commercially-valuable resources. Wherefore, even though each *single deposit* will be exhaustible – ultimately – yet the *totals* of the deposits presently available will continue to increase, as more and cheaper energy becomes available (from intra-atomic and thermo-nuclear sources) as Technology advances.

If one assumes, as the writer does, that the unlimited energies of thermo-nuclear fusion can soon be made controllable and usable for constructive purposes, then Man should never lack for the material necessities of Life, provided that his planning for the Future is done cooperatively; on an engineering (and "engineered") basis; and according to what is kind, what is proper and what is reasonable. For providing that a suitable growth-rate can, indeed, be maintained by Exploratory Engineering (Figure 6) within the "root-zone" of civilization (Level 1 of Figure 3) then the activities postulated for Levels 2, 3, 4 and 5 of Figure 3 can proceed in a satisfactory manner. And proper developments *can* be assured at Level 1 of Figure 3 if suitable intellectual and spiritual guidance can be had from Levels 6 and 7 of Figure 3. So now let us turn to:

Problems 4, 5 and 6: the problems of proper and effective international integration in the economic and political realms. The essence of these problems can be summed up in one single question "How can human knowledge, intelligence and experience be so employed as to provide Man with the practical means for "Life, Liberty and the Pursuit of Happiness?" And the answer is believed to be "through that guidance of constructive engineering activities which can be provided by the combined advice of the several scholarly and professional groupings which, added together, constitute "a university" in the full sense of the term. (See Diagram 1).

As Diagram 1 indicates, Religion, History and the other Humanistic subjects can provide understandings regarding those basic human aspirations and motivations which have led to the growth of human cultures and to the rise of many civilizations. Likewise the Social Sciences can demonstrate, and are demonstrating, the nature of the economic and political procedures which have been found to be successfully applicable to the short-term hour-by-hour and day-by-day direction and management of business and government. So, also the Natural Sciences, in general, can give advance warnings, when newly-made (or impending) scientific discoveries are about to alter the whole course of history (as

DIAGRAM 1

A University includes

<table>
<tr><td>Religion
History
Philosophy
Other Humanities</td><td>Which provide</td><td>Insights into Man's spiritual nature and moral and social responsibilities
and
Into basic human motivations – and normal responses thereto.</td><td rowspan="3">Engineering
Which employs that combination of Art, Technology and Science, under guidance contributed by all other University scholarly and professional groupings, whereby creative imagination, natural resources, human capacities, and intellectual and spiritual wisdom can be so integrated and supported as to serve constructively, the needs and worthy purposes of Mankind.</td></tr>
<tr><td>Psychology
Social Sciences and Law
Geography</td><td>Which provide</td><td>Insights into the objectives, methods and patterns of short-term, constructive, social and political action.</td></tr>
<tr><td>Biological and Medical Science
Earth Sciences
Natural Science and Mathematics</td><td>Which provide</td><td>Insights into the basic principles of Natural Law; Into the world-geography of essential natural-resource occurrence; Into the prospective and long-term human significance of recent scientific discoveries; and into the probability of yet further revolutionary scientific discovery and invention.</td></tr>
</table>

is happening today, through the discovery of the feasibility of obtaining prodigious energies from atomic fission and thermo-nuclear fusion). In other words the Natural Sciences can, in relation to the long-term problems of civilization, function as do the headlights of an automobile, being driven at high speed, along an unfamiliar road, and after nightfall. For they can tell us, well in advance, that drastic changes in policy-direction *must* be planned (and prepared) for, if a fatal crash is to be avoided. And, lastly, the Earth Sciences can contribute, in a similarly constructive fashion, to the advance shaping of national and international policy – for they can tell us how the irregularity in world-occurrence of essential mineral-resource deposits (see Figure 1, Level 2) will, perforce, limit and control the inter-relations between nations and national groupings, when economic survival and military security are at stake. For it is only on the basis of such adequate advice (from a whole "university") – as to objectives, methods and limiting circumstances that Engineering can so build – effectively and expeditiously – that human beings may be able to earn their right to survive. And that Civilization may be able to continue to advance – in all three of the realms in which Humanity lives – these three being, respectively, material, intellectual and spiritual.

What, then, does "university-type" knowledge and experience tell us about the steps which should, and should not be, taken – if we are to be able to relieve worldtensions, and are to give rise to an orderly, just, peaceful and satisfactory world? The answers needed can, it is believed, be gotten from Figure 7.

Figure 7 tells us, among other things, that the use of monopoly and of (imperialist) exploitation – at any level and under any circumstances – is self-defeating – though it is, temporarily, advantageous to the strong. Whereas the hopes of all Humanity can be realized, *in the ultimate*, only by the conversion of the United Nations Organization into a World Economic Union and then into a (voluntarily-formed)

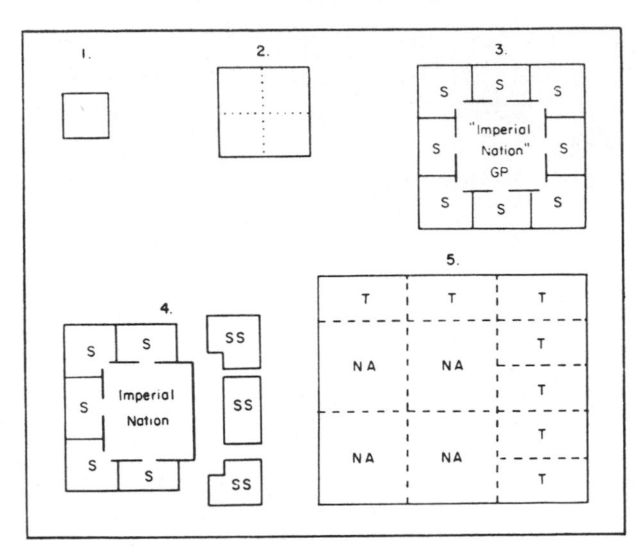

Fig. 7.

1. A Princely State, or Local Kingdom, or "Sovereign State."
2. A Nation, or United Kingdom, or Union of "Sovereign States" formed for mutual Economic and Security Advantage.
3. Developed Empires, consisting of a Great Power Nation (= GP), surrounded by forcibly-held "Satellites" or "Colonial Areas" (= S).
4. A partly disintegrated Empire, plus (economically non-viable and theoretically) "Independent Nations" or "Sovereign States."
5. (Now Needed) Regional Economic Unions, including both "National Areas" (= NA), already Selfgoverning, and also "Territorial Areas" (= T), which are being assisted to improve their living-standards, while they are preparing themselves for local self-government, within the framework of the larger "Economic Union."

Constitutional Federation of Self-governing Peoples – a Federation which will be capable of assuring and enforcing Peace, and also "Justice-under-Law" – on a world-wide basis.

In reaching this ultimate situation certain preliminary steps must be taken by the "colonial" peoples, and by the citizens of "princely" or "sovereign" states. For if the legitimate desires of such peoples (for national self-government) are to be realized then they must be realized in a fair and reasonable manner, and in a fashion which not only provides for *their* automomy (or "independence") in the management of their internal (national) affairs – but also solves the problems arising from wider vital natural-resource *inter*dependences – through voluntary (regional) Economic Union with other, similar, governments – all powers being reserved to the national governments which have not been specifically granted to the Region Grouping concerned by the terms of its Constitution, or Charter, as ratified. That such double objectives *can* be satisfactorily and effectively realized has been recently demonstrated by the peoples of Belgium, The Netherlands and Luxembourg, who have retained their national governments but have done so under a now supra-national Economic Union, whereby the three economic circulations involved (see Figure 4) have been fused into a *single* economic circulation, with the result that their combined domestic trade has been trebled in ten years, and their foreign trade has been doubled. Because of the success of the Benelux experiment a larger Economic (and political) Union is now in the making, including West Germany, France and Italy, in addition to the Benelux countries.

This process of federation (for mutual benefit) has, of course, been used in India and is now in progress in Africa and in the Near and Middle East and elsewhere, and should proceed until the vital natural-resource requirements of *all* nations have been safely provided for, through the establishment of about five or six (voluntary) Regional Unions or Groupings – as is permissible under The United Nations Charter. Within such *regional* unions the several national currencies concerned would be replaced by a single currency; the same system of law and justice would apply throughout the region; and all intra-regional tariffs would be abolished (with fair indemnification to those injured by such abrogation).

That seeming economic miracles can be brought about by such unions has already been proven by the Benelux Economic Union experiment. For under such a union, properly developed:

1) Tax-*rates* can be greatly reduced, even while annual taxyields are being simultaneously increased;

Fig. 8. Map showing nuclei of Prospective Regional "Economic Union" Governments. As defined by geologic (and geographic) occurrence of essential natural-resource materials.

2) Because, under such unions *Annual* incomes from goods and services rapidly become doubled and trebled;
3) Raw material production, manufacturing and marketing can be carried forward with confidence; with increasing employment; and with increased earnings in all quarters – due to the absense of currency, tariff and legal uncertainties and obstacles. And
4) Adequate volumes of both venture and developmental capital can be generated – both for internal purposes and needs and for sound foreign loans – these latter to be made, presumably, through United Nation agencies.

With suitable and natural integrations of inter-regional activities (to be accomplished through the UNO), the enormous sums now being tragically diverted to only

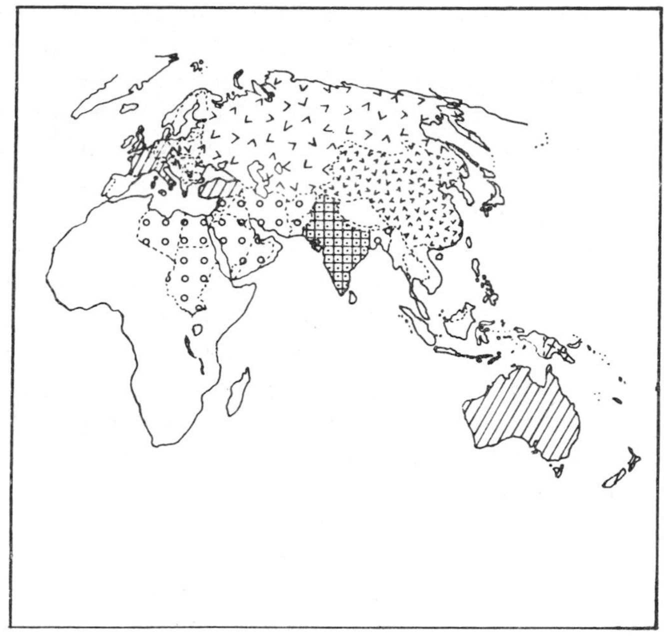

partly-productive (military) purposes could be used for the improvement of world living-conditions. They could also be used for education; for the construction of urgently-needed highway systems; for the enlargement of water-supply and irrigation systems; and for a variety of other public-works and community purposes.

One more matter, fraught with utmost immediate importance, needs to be considered now – a matter which has to do with devising of proper arrangements for ending the Cold War – before it has plunged us into World War III. In this connection we need to realize that existing (vital) natural-resource inter-dependencies will continue to make necessary a regional economic-and-governmental grouping of the Central European and Soviet peoples, even if the Soviets grant these peoples full selfgovernment subject to the condition that they do continue on as member-nations within a Regional Economic Union, patterned on the Benelux Union

Let us also realize that the Soviet leaders are almost certainly unaware of the fact that the recent enormous industrial progress of the United States has been the result of a progressive development (within the United States) of "Fair-Competition Industry" and of "Welfare Capitalism," which are exact opposites of the kind of monopoly, or cartel or imperialist-exploitationist capitalism which was known to KARL MARX and which has been so familiar to so many European peoples – to their sorrow. Furthermore let us realize that it will certainly be impossible for the Soviet leaders to believe in the sincerity, honesty and peaceful intent of the United States, so long as "foreign aid," granted by the United States for the promotion of common safety, is continuously, flagrantly, dishonestly and cynically employed by some beneficiaries, who seek to continue to impose upon *their* colonial peoples a denial of rights to autonomy in local governmental affairs which we, the people of the United States, also fought to gain – in the course of *our own* Revolution.

Perhaps the several misunderstandings and uncertainties involved could be most easily removed if responsible Soviet leaders could come to America as guests of American Labor – in order that they might both satisfy themselves as to our peaceful intentions and might also come to see that the legitimate self-interests of the Soviet peoples, and of all peoples, could be better solved by a peaceful "competitive cooperation" or "cooperative competition," rather than by mutual extermination, through a new World War.

The people of Japan, of China, of "Southeast Asia," of India, of the Muslim world, of Germany, of the USSR, of Britain, of Brazil, of North America, and of many lands, – all are capable of making uniquely-important contributions to the progress and welfare of the world. So let us at least tentatively give the Soviet leaders credit for being sincerely interested in the promotion of the welfare of the Common Man – and in bringing local self-government, coupled with

Region Union, to the world's colonial peoples. And let us hope, too, that we can convince the Soviet peoples that we are similarly interested. For the only hope of human survival lies in that direction.

In saying this the writer is not proposing that broad assertions or unsupported assumptions be taken at face value by *anyone*. For if we pause to think we shall realize that the world's peoples are *not* stupid, and that if professions of peaceful intention are but transparent cloaks for new or old imperialisms, then the whole world will soon recognize that fact and will unite solidly against such imperialism (or imperialisms). What we need now is a focussing of attention upon the constructive steps which need to be taken for the benefit of all peoples. The actions about to be taken in the UN Assembly will plainly show which governments really are in favor of Peace and human progress, and which, if any, are old-fashioned "wolves in sheep's clothing."

SUMMARY

Dedicated scientific search for Truth has led Man from knowledge to understanding and may, by now, even be leading him from understanding to wisdom. For thanks to scientific search and discovery four things have become clear.

First. Astronomy has shown that the Heavenly bodies have been moving forward through infinite Space in orderly fashion during eons and eons of Time.

Second. Nuclear physics, and the study of decay-rates of radio-active minerals, have now also shown that the Time-Dimension in the History of the Earth is measurable in billions of years.

Third. Geological and geophysical studies (of Earth Processes and of Earth History) now give us quantitatively-correct perspectives upon the history of development of Life, and of Man, upon the Earth – thereby transforming conventional "History' 'from a factual and descriptive narrative into a study which has profound human significance and scientific importance.

Fourth. Scientific studies, in total, show that the whole of the Universe has, since the Beginning, moved forward in orderly fashion toward the ultimate fulfillment of the Creator's underlying Plan and Purpose. And therefore Man, being spiritually perceptive of this fact, has possessed (and does possess) an innate ability to distinguish between that which is properly progressive and accordant with the Trend of Universal Motion, and that which is retrogressive and directed counter to the Creator's Cosmic Intention. Or, as the matter has usually been stated, "Man possesses an innate ability to discriminate between that which is (properly Progressive or) "Good" and that which is (retrogressive or) "Evil."

Adding these conclusions together it can be stated that Science has now provided essentially correct "Space" and "Time" perspectives upon World-History. And geographic and geologic studies now can tell us about the environmental conditions (and environmental changes) which have led to the rise, and to the decline, of past civilizations – thereby making it possible for us to gain understandings regarding the anatomical structure and physiological processes which have been characteristic of those invisible organisms which we term "civilizations." Moreover it is now similarly possible for us to distinguish between three types of civilizations. Some have been rooted and tree-like in their form and manner of growth. Others have been mobile and animal-like in their nature and have lived according to the "Law of the Jungle" – with the physically stronger dominating and preying upon the weaker. And a third type of civilization (still embryonic, rather than fully formed) is one which is essentially "human" in its attributes, possessing not only intelligence but a sense of social responsibility and a "sense of Right and Wrong." This latter type of civilization, in its developing form, resembles a great river, wherein waters from many sources will gather, successively, to form rills, and streams and larger tributaries – until they all ultimately join and mingle, as they move harmoniously toward that Infinite Ocean in which the Creator has set Man's Destiny.

CONCLUSION

The World of Man, as it has existed, up until the present, is dying. Moreover its death may come suddenly, as the result of human savagery, selfishness and willfulness – since atomic and thermo-nuclear weapons now make it possible for a modern Samson to destroy himself and all people, by starting a Third World War. Several dictators have stated repeatedly that according to their gospel a Third World War is necessary and inevitable. And that such a war *will*, consequently, happen soon, is probable rather than being merely possible.

But however that may be, a new kind of civilization is struggling to be born – a civilization which, *if* born, will be vastly different from all of those which have gone before it. For if and when it *has* been safely born we shall have entered a world which is animated by a Psychology of Cooperation and of Peace – differing thereby exactly from the older civilizations which have been ruled by a Psychology of Monopolistic Imperialism, Violence and Oppression, and War. Man's fate will, of necessity, soon be sealed by his own conscious choice and by his own decisive action – a choice arrived at within and proclaimed through, the Assembly of the United Nations Organization. For this Assembly represents the collective will and conscience of all Humanity.

If, in making their fateful decisions, the delegates to the United Nations are merely guided by "the backward look" – and by the many bitter hatreds which have been bred by past oppressions and injustices – then, indeed, the World of Man will perish amid flames, as did Sodom and Gomorrah and the "Cities of the Plain." But if, on the other hand, these delegates feel that they are trustees responsible for the safety, and heritage, of *all* of the World's children – the children of Today and of Tomorrow – then they can, through wise, proper and generous decision, make it possible for Science and Engineering to transform the world – so that "all things needful" can, indeed, be provided for the Future of Man. The choice will be between Cooperation and Contention; between Justice and Injustice; between Good and Evil; between Peace and War; and between Life and Death. But if the final and fatal choice is, indeed, guided by smallness of spirit, by stupidity and by selfishness, then will the bodies of men, women and children lie strewn amid ruins charred and blackened by nuclear holocaust. The "handwriting is on the wall," where all may read.

War or Peace – a Biological Problem

by

EUROPAEUS

What I am going to say here does not claim to be exact science. It is a stringing together of thoughts, some of which have, for their complexity, even not been quite thought out, all of which, however, are meant to lead to one objective: Better relations between the different groups of nations and people, as the premise for content and peace within these groups.

In part they are thoughts which will probably need decades to mature, each within itself, or which demand the concurrent rethinking of many people who are at one with the author. In these days, when the most terribles of all wars are potentially a possibility, if not a probability, such a rethinking by many people has already become reality, and that is why these lines are written.

The suggestive force of the proverb which has brought about so much murder on a national scale "Si vis pacem, para bellum" – still retains its power. But slowly, the dawn of a new comprehension is rising – the comprehension that the problem "War or Peace" is basically a biological one, and that it must be regarded as such if it is to be solved.

This comprehension is spreading not only in a small circle, within the uppermost tops of science, but at long last also among statesmen – and naturally first among the greatest.

For thousands of years this murderous proverb, in one form or another, has been hammered into the human brain, and now we must begin to erase it or, better still, put another in its place, as suggestive as the old one: Si vis pacem – para pacem! And this problem is biological in nature, both regarded from within and from without:

Both instincts and conscious volition pull in both directions, the negative one towards war, and the positive one towards peace. But only *that* conscious volition which leads in the negative direction lies – at least for the greater part – outside the problem seen biologically.

It is that most energetic volition which we find accompanying business interests or power-political strivings of individuals and groups everywhere. These strivings, however, are from the first doomed to failure if they cannot gain control over the three other fields – and these lie plumb in the centre of biological science.

Both the negative instincts in man, to deny which would merely mean closing one's eyes before the fact of disease, and the positive instincts, but above all the congregated and ever increasing conscious volition which makes use of the other three fields in a planned manner so as to reach the goal in the positive way – all these lie within the sphere of biology in its wider meaning, comprising also psychology and sociology; and it is of decisive importance that first of all the biologists themselves should be clear on this point.

Let us try and marshal these power groups against each other.

The relevant *negative instincts* – a fact which in our day has almost become universally acknowledged – can probably be changed into positive instincts, and certainly into positive achievements, by the right education both of children and adults.

To take one example: We know how easy it is to change the combative spirit by competition into the spirit of sport – and also, as we readily concede, even more easily back again into the combative spirit. In the last analysis the creative instinct is surely something very positive – and yet closely related to the combative spirit. We can fight *FOR* something too, and this combat can just as well be for something spiritual or against something material, just as against other natural resistance, without seeing your neighbour as your main opponent.

What I see as far more difficult is the taming of the "Gruppen abwehr-Instinkt" (*repelling group instinct*), a phenomenon seen with animals as well as with humans. With men it can take the form of subconscious passive resistance or of conscious active opposition against the foreign and strange per se – with all grades in between these two extremes. Trying to understand this instinct or urge, we shall find that it belongs to the whole complex of instincts which have to do with the preservation of the species.

This dangerous primitive instinct, far more dangerous than the combative spirit, to which most distinguished men have often become a prey, can in my opinion be tamed only if we use all our powers of organizing and educating for the purpose of changing the psychically foreign and strange into something well known, and also to extend the natural egocentric small group as far as its maximum up to the species itself – that is all humanity.

In consequence of the unimaginable progress in technology we stand today at the beginning of an era in which what has so far been extremely foreign and strange can be brought near very quickly both psychically and physically. In fact, the beginnings of such an approach are already being made.

Airplane, Radio and cinema are already typical bearers of such an international mission. An *international language* for the purpose of international understanding should be the next step, to be taken as soon as may be.

But the central guiding hand is still missing, especially as regards the Radio and cinema. That air traffic will become a network of international understanding and union among nations, with or without or even against the War Offices of the different countries concerned, can be assumed with some certainty already.

Possibly the airplane more than anything else makes the existing political borders of states and groups of states become more and more constricted. In the last analysis traffic speed is the most important human standard for distance on earth, just as the speed of light is for space.

Seen from this angle, even most of the dwarf states of the Middle Ages were far larger than is today the whole of our earth, for from one border to the other it took longer to travel than today does flying to the antipodes.

The cinema, seen from our viewpoint, is still far behind the airplane. In fact, it often instigates instincts leading in the opposite direction to our conscious or unconscious goal. And yet the screen might have extraordinary possibilities for contributing to the vital goal, bringing the different groups of people near to each other, making them appear less strange one to the other. Here UNESCO has an immense field of activity which may well be of decisive importance. Thus they might, f.i. organize committees to investigate the educative value of films, in order to connect positive ones with material advantages and conversely, what is almost as important, disadvantages for negative films.

The third unifying item, and perhaps the most important in the fight against the repelling group instinct is a truly *international* language. Here we touch on a sore point in the history of mankind, a complex of questions which has ever since prehistoric times occupied the best minds. The biblical legend about the tower of Babel has lost nothing of its urgent topicality in our days.

Different experiments have been made, partly with regional success, to make some existing and widespread language into the international means of communication; in our times, even artificial languages have been constructed for the purpose. In Babylonian times, to take an ancient instance,

Aramaic was such a unifying language for the whole of Western Asia, Greek in Hellenistic times joined all the educated of the Mediterranean world at the time when actually the Romans were the Imperial Power; Latin became an international language only because of the Vulgate (the Latin version of the Bible of the 4th century) and remained supreme all through the Middle Ages and Modern times, for the European Cultural world, until the nineteenth century.

We have a similar development as Latin gained by means of the Vulgate, becoming an international language, for Arabic, which in consequence of the Koran united the different Moslem peoples from the Atlantic Ocean to India. A third example is the prevalence of German by means of LUTHER's translation of the Bible, for Central Europe. In science and research Latin remained the predominent language long after LOUIS XIV of France, when the international language of diplomacy and the upper crust of society had become French.

With the splitting of science into national units, the chaos in language began, actually becoming the strongest brake on scientific development – in the second half of the nineteenth century. It has only been since the Second World War that it has become quite unbearable, in many cases ruinous. The reason is that national consciousness as regards most European nations, on a scale unknown before, drove all other considerations into the background. One consequence was that there was a strong urge to put their own language in the foreground even as regards science, often enough at the price of publicity and sometimes even of comprehensibility.

The so-called purificators of the German language who might in one sense be called the precursors of the National-Socialist movement, have found slavish imitators among many nations. As this tendency towards isolation, often enough an unconscious one, still exists in strong measure today, and as it is a concealed and therefore all the more dangerous fact for humanity in general and for science especially, I think a few remarks on the subject may not come amiss.

There are endeavours at work with many peoples, aiming at the replacement of words, even internationally and quite regularly used words, by national expressions, often enough even at the cost of achieving the correct shading which alone makes for the wealth of a language.

We are here faced with an essential error. This error consists in the widespread belief that by exchanging such a "foreign word," which is in reality very well known, with a new word in the national language, this own language is being enriched. A language can be enriched only by widening its scope of expression by new concepts or shadings of concepts, but not by the purely phonetic exchange of one word for another. Let us try and understand the real effect of such an exchange quite clearly.

Actually, the result of such changes is merely that the relevant language is not in the least enriched, but the nation most essentially impoverished by having once more lost part of a means of communication with other peoples – in every case with the far, far greater part of humanity outside the special narrow national limits.

Isolation is thus increased, and the natural repelling group instinct is strengthened on both sides by this socalled "purification" of the language.

I think it right to express this once for all, even if it brings the danger of being called an enemy by the diverse enthusiastic defenders of linguistic purity among diverse nations, enthusiasts or fanatics who in every other respect may be quite excellent men or women.

As such words as I refer to are generally known, the term "foreign" word is wrong, they are in truth "*loan-words*" or borrowed words, and this type of borrowing is probably the only one in the world which brings substantial interest to both giver and taker, loaner and borrower.

It is to be hoped that humanity will find its way through all these thickets to achieve a united and unifying language, existing, at least in the beginning, beside the national languages. It would indeed be an irreparable loss if the countless specific concepts existing in the individual languages, and which often enough are not even translatable by circumlocution, should be lost.

But surely it is not too much to hope that such a second unifying language, supported by the growing contact between nations, should in time absorb the specific concepts of the individual languages and use adequate expressions for them, so that in the course of several or many generations for all civilized peoples with a high cultural level this second language may become the main one.

We have already seen such examples if only on a small scale. The Scots and the English are two ethnically very different peoples who have a common mothertongue, certainly to the advantage of both. I do not believe that the Scots think otherwise. That the original popular language can go on being cherished, either from historical, sentimental or whatever reasons, is proved by the Gaelic Speech Circles.

But what I wish to stress with all possible emphasis is that the first and decisive step in this direction towards a common language can and should originate with science. Every other way is impassable.

Within biological science these endeavours have in the last two decades led to quite concrete attempts. In the first analysis they were not suggested by highflying and partly still utopistic thoughts about the development of mankind, the impulse for these attempts was and is the iron necessity, increasing every day to face the terrible threat to the single branches of science, inherent in their unlimited specialization.

The urge towards synthesis in the biological sciences, the development of border sciences, and the urge towards a uniform language are all parallel functions of the fear of disaster, common to all far-seeing scientists. Today we have learned that each single branch of science can also be split into its atoms – and this is the moment when we must do everything in our power to learn how to build up a new and better world by means of the vast forces at our disposal, for the good of humankind, and taking the constructive path of evolution.

The knowledge that only devoted common work towards this goal gives any hope has already entered the minds of very many scientists in great measure; that the most important tool for achieving this goal would be a common language is clear to all – but here we have many obstacles in our path still.

Let us try and tackle the ungrateful task of seeing this complex of problems objectively.

What we need is not so much an international language as a common intercontinental language. We have quite a number of international languages, that is such as are being spoken by different peoples (racially different peoples also) as their mothertongue. English, German, Russian, Spanish are some examples. On the other hand there are some continental languages which are the mothertongues of a very much greater number of individuals than some of the international languages just mentioned, such as Russian or Chinese.

From the viewpoint of scientific publications English, Russian, German and French probably head the list by far.

If we try and balance all the necessary viewpoints one against the others objectively, we must approach the view that just at this moment the time has come to introduce the one language as a common international and inter-continental one which we are used to call English. (See the Note at the end). The name is rather misleading, as the English People form only a tiny minority among the peoples speaking English as their mothertongue.

Furthermore, this language is the mothertongue or at least the speech of about 250 million people – but that is of less importance. What gives weight to the proposal to make use of this tongue is the fact, that already it is the means of scientific and political communication between the most diverse nations in all continents. It is significant, for instance, that the first Panasiatic Conference, mostly covered by delegates of anti-British peoples, had to choose English as the only possible language of the meeting.

It is true that imponderables no less than certain power-political interests from different sides weigh in the balance against this solution. I am not thinking merely of the Russian sphere of power. The great endeavours and achievements of the Russianspeaking nations in all fields including the one which for us is objectively the decisive one – that of scientific literature – make it imperative that Russian together with French and German should be used as the objectively justified languages beside English, as far as science is concerned.

I am convinced that it will be possible to find, at least for a certain time of transition, a compromise, arrived at in a general discussion, of a kind that will obviate any possible Russian umbrage. When we enter these discussions, let us always remember: there can scarcely be anything more conductive to peace than having such a common tongue as a means of understanding each other. And it is in this sphere that science more than anything else is fit to become the vanguard.

At all the coming congresses and meetings, not only within but also beyond UNESCO, the problem of a common language must be brought to a solution as soon as may be.

It is the greatest service that science can do to mankind, and no discovery or invention, be it what it may, can come near this step in its importance.

At the beginning of these remarks we set up a sort of plan, a parallelogram of four psychological groups of forces, two of which are pulling mankind in a negative direction, two in a positive one.

The negative forces were:

a) The negative instincts (f.i. atavistic sadism, or the fighting instinct of the male, or the repelling group instinct common to all creatures, etc. etc.). Once these urges are realized to be biologic in nature, it is not very difficult to defeat or to change them.

b) The negatively directed conscious volition, finding its expression in certain power-political endeavours, or in business vested interests. – It needs to control the three other groups, before it can achieve its aims.

The positive forces mentioned were:

a) The positive instincts such as the self-preservative group instinct which comprises within itself many good instincts, f.i. the mother instinct, the urge to help and the satisfaction gained from such help. – The thirst for knowledge which must be guided in the right direction and others.

b) The positively directed conscious volition, which after the First World War led to the setting-up of the League of Nations and after the second to the foundation of UNO and its Specialized Agencies.

This volition, as far as an outsider can judge, seems to be the basic concept of the great statesmen of the West as of the East, even if single factors some times seem to contradict this; and it is also the foundation for the different planning schemes on a vast scale which are approaching concrete realization.

This parallelogram of forces can only be changed so that its resultant leads to the positive goal with certainty, if we, that is the scientists and especially the biologists, are filled with this urgent volition in the positive direction.

It is we who have the duty of knowing these instincts for what they are, it is we who must show the way to master them, and above all it is we who must in common endeavour, as a sort of giant symposion, try to seek and to find the way to such productivity on earth that all men of today – and of tomorrow even more – should be warranted a life of contentment: Free to think, free to believe, free of need, and free of fear.

The politicians can do no more than aid by providing the

means for reaching this goal. It is *the* biological problem of the present and of the future, to create the foundations for making this possible.

It is our guilt that in the past it was not so.

And here I must refer to the wonderful manifesto of VERDOORN's (Scientific Fiasco, Chron. Bot. V: 325), written at the time when the war began, in 1939 (!), a trumpet call which sparked in so many of us the understanding that we, the biologists, bear so great a part of the guilt – the guilt that such a war could begin at such a time.

We kept well away from all key positions, leaving the solution of biological problems to the politicians. And our guilt is not lessened by the fact that we failed to make the politicians understand how the problems before them were biological, simply because we ourselves did not see this clearly.

That a politician can solve a biological problem only in an amateurish way is a matter of course, and nobody can reproach him with it. The tragic moment lies in the fact that these problems involved the fate of nations, and that they hold within themselves the development towards war or peace.

In a little article written during the Second War (Chron. Bot. IX: 86) the attempt was made by H. BOYKO to show a passable way for realizing the thoughts contained in VERDOORN's manifesto in sober fact. The article suggested that by slow stages an international organization for a certain biological purpose (The International Network of Plant-sociological (= ecological) Stations) should gradually be changed into an organization of all the scientists of all the world. Its leading motive should be work on world-wide biological problems, problems which could only be solved by the common work of all, which would prove to be a means joining and uniting the peoples of the world, and which would be furthered and aided by the emotional and tense interest of all members of civilized nations. It would mean the creation of a symposium on a world-wide scale.

What at the time was supposed to take many decades to mature, is now in process of becoming reality through the conscious volition of many people thinking as one.

Boyko himself began to organize the cooperative work on such a problem: Arid Zone Research with the aim of productivizing the deserts. (General Assembly of IUBS, Amsterdam 1947). The result was a symposium on these problems in the framework of IUBS and a proposal of the Indian Government to Unesco, to erect a Central Institute for this line of research. The proposals led gradually to the great "Arid Zone Project" of UNESCO, now carried out in close cooperation with the other Specialized Agencies of UNO and many of the adhering countries.

A few years after these proposals the big plan of a global "Geo-physical Year" was proposed and carried out with great devotion of many hundreds of scientists from West and East as well. The possibility of a wholehearted global cooperation in the fields of science to the advantage of all humanity has been proved by this beyond any doubt.

However, we should do wrong to underestimate the forces ranged against us. Still today there already exist statesmen who see with the eye of the biologist, and biologists with statesmanlike qualities, and when the words scientific planning are pronounced, even such statesmen will support it as are in other respects still far removed from regarding things with the biologist's eye.

Our task today is the education – including the education of statesmen – of the world towards this understanding, and above all – the example.

Let us create as swiftly as possible the organizatory carrying out of certain biological tasks of great importance and general interest. Let us see to it that the world takes part in our work, sharing not only our successes but also our failures, which also will be of educational value. Not in terror of its result – as was the case with the atombomb – but in hopes of a better future. Many of us are deeply concerned with problems of vital importance for all planned development, or of interest for all. The great majority of men is most sensitive to our scientific researchwork and eager for scientific knowledge in general, most of all for natural science.

I am convinced – and I am not the first to give utterance to this conviction – that for instance the problem of cancer would have been solved long ago if as much centralized energy and means could have been used for it as has been put at the disposal of the atombomb problem. Other examples are the problems of the function of brain cells, productivizing the deserts, control of the treasures in the oceans (including breeding instead of mere fishing), irrigation with Seawater, and so on.

Each of us will readily have other examples of the kind at disposal. Let us begin and work! Let us give the example!

First of all *let us create* the common language, at the beginning for the use of science. Having achieved this, we shall see that the speed of air traffic and its increasing density will make it the common language for all civilized peoples, as their second tongue in use beside the mothertongue.

Let us comprehend, ourselves, first of all, the decisive importance of biology for the development of mankind, in the positive direction, in the direction towards peace, in the direction away from war, and we shall, working together, have the strength to transmit this comprehension to the others.

Let us subordinate ourselves voluntarily to an objective, global organizational instrument which has this object in view, as an universal World Academy of Science.

Let us do this and we shall reach our goal more quickly than we ever dreamed of.

It is the goal recognized by all the great religions, by all the great philosophers, by all the great statesmen as the only one truly worth striving for.

It is for us scientists, and especially us, the biologists, to point the way. That it has taken us so long to see the scientific possibilities for it, is our paltriness; that we can see them today, our greatness.

APPENDIX

I have tried to achieve as objective a scale of priorities as is possible, by evaluating the most important criteria of such a common scientific language in points. The result is given in the following table. Some people may wonder at my including the Bantu language. At this moment in time such a wonder may still have its justification, but we should not disregard the extremely swift development taking place in Africa.

It might be a good beginning, if every scientist would write down such a table, trying to be as objective as is humanly possible.

The author would be grateful to compare many such tables with his own, in order to diminish its natural subjective weakness.

Letters to the author should be sent c/o Dr. W. Junk Publishers, 13, van Stolkweg, The Hague, The Netherlands.

	Scale	English	French	Russ. and related lang.	German	Spanish and Port.	Chinese	Italian	Japanese	Malay	Bantu group
International	(1–5)	5	5	3	3	3	2	2	2	3	3
Inter-continental	(1–5)	5	4	2	2	3	3	2	2	2	1
Inter-racial	(1–5)	5	4	3	2	3	1	1	1	1	1
Mothertongue (each 100 million and part of one hundred = 1 point)		4	1	3	2	2	6	1	2	2	2
Highly developed as scientific language	(1–5)	5	5	5	5	5	5	5	5	1	1
Highly developed as script	(1–5)	3	5	4	5	5	2	5	2	2	1
Scientific publications	(1–5)	5	3	4	4	3	2	2	2	1	1
Scientific abstracts	(1–5)	5	4	5	3	2	1	2	1	1	1
Tradition as scientific language	(1–5)	5	5	3	4	4	5	4	3	1	1
		42	36	32	30	30	27	24	20	14	12

The priority list thus shows the result:[1]

English	42	points	Chinese	27	points
French	36	,,	Italian	24	,,
Russian	32	,,	Japanese	20	,,
German	30	,,	Malay	14	,,
Spanish	30	,,	Bantu	12	,,

According to this list we should, during the time of transition, teach – apart of the mothertongue – English and French and maybe later only one of them, for the full time of study (fifteen years), and use them as the only authoritative language(s). Summaries in one of the two international languages should be added even to those scientific papers which are only of limited local significance, and therefore written in the respective national language.

1. I tried also to evaluate Latin by this point-method and came to the rather high figure of 30 (5, 5, 5, 0, 3, 5, 2, 1, 4). I did, however, not include it in the table, because, during the last hundred years Latin has lagged far behind the development of science and even more so of technology. It could, however, be included for more or less political reasons as a completely neutral language; but in this case a much longer transition period will have to be allowed in order to achieve a better linguistic adaptation to modern science, and modern civilization and culture in general.

Science and Modern Civilization

by

I. Berenblum

Unlike the slow biological evolution of animal species, measured in terms of millions of years, the phenomenal progress of human civilization, from primitive society to modern times, covers little more than six thousand years. This is all the more impressive when one remembers how erratic the course of human progress has been, with centuries of almost imperceptible change punctuated by intermittent periods of violent social upheavals.

Yet, to imagine each upheaval as an unfortunate set-back in an otherwise progressive trend, would be too superficial an interpretation of history. More often than not, such an upheaval was the climax of a fundamental conflict between the old and the new – a conflict that arose from the impact of a revolutionary idea upon a previously stable society. Whether the "revolutionary idea" took the form of a change in man's mode of life (e.g. from the nomadic to the settled state through the introduction of land cultivation), or a new foundation for religious belief (such as the Jewish concept of monotheism or the advent of Christianity), a new method of disseminating knowledge (with the discovery of written language or, later, of the printing press), or a new standard of human values (as in the formulation of the equality of human rights), it usually led to a new level of civilization, however disturbing its effects may have been at the time. The emergence of twentieth century civilization owes more to the catalytic effects of these rare germinal ideas than to any sustained efforts at improving human society.

In the light of this, how is one to interpret the instability of our present civilization? Is it another example of "a conflict between the old and the new," and, therefore, a necessary step in the forward march of civilization, with science acting this time as the catalyst or revolutionary idea? Or is the world actually on the verge of a catastrophic retrogression which humanity may not be able to survive?

Whatever the answer to this question may be, there seems little doubt that the rapid growth of science is closely connected with the problem. A dispassionate assessment of its scope and influence should, therefore, help us to understand what is happening to our civilization.

Based on ancient principles of logic, and fostered for centuries in the restricted fields of mathematics and astronomy, the "scientific method" received its first effective opportunity at about the time of the Italian Renaissance. Since then, the waning influence of medieval mysticism, the rapid diffusion of knowledge through the introduction of printing, and the social and political changes associated with the French Revolution, all contributed towards its coming of age. Not until a century ago, however, did science really begin to impose itself on the varied aspects of human activity, the Industrial Revolution being but the outward manifestation of man's acceptance of science as a guiding force in human affairs.

Being in the midst of this period of phenomenal progress of scientific achievement, we are rather apt to make a distorted evaluation of the advances, and perhaps to lay undue emphasis on the *practical* applications of science.

We see the amazing speed and efficiency of travel by land, sea and air, the intricate mechanization of industry, with the harnessing of various forms of energy for elaborate systems of heating, lighting, and power; the improved utilization of mineral and vegetable resources of the soil, with advances in breeding of livestock, perfection in methods of cultivating the land, and exploitation of the chemical riches of the earth, the prevention and cure of diseases previously responsible for untold suffering, and the control of epidemics which, in the past, used to ravage the world, and a thousand and one other examples by which the hardship of life has been overcome, and nature's wealth brought to the service of man.

But the wonders of science are by no means restricted to these practical applications. Behind the façade of hydro-electric plants and ocean liners, of airoplanes and submarines, of films and television, of penicillin and D.D.T., lies the realm of fundamental research, inspired, partly at least, by the disinterested search for knowledge. This basic kind of scientific pursuit has led to a prodigious expansion of our knowledge of inanimate matter and a growing understanding of the intricate functioning of life itself.

To be able to estimate the weight of a planet millions of miles away, or measure the infinitesimally small distances between the invisible atoms in a molecule, to have the means of analysing the chemical composition of a distant star, or mapping out the positions of the genes within the chromosomes of a microscopic living cell, to "see" in total darkness, and to "hear" across oceans, to determine the age of a fossil millions of years old, or to predict the existence of a new chemical element prior to its discovery, to be able to count single electrons, or to comprehend the laws governing heredity, these are indeed achievements which our forefathers would have deemed miraculous. And with it all has now come the discovery of nuclear energy, making available for man's use tremendous sources of power which, for billions of years, have remained confined within the atom.

The conquest of nature, once an idle dream, has now become almost an understatement.

Few people take the trouble to ask themselves how it is that after thousands of years of futile endeavour to gain control over our surroundings, success should suddenly have become so readily available, and that the rate of progress should have become so rapid. There is, after all, no evidence to suggest that the capacity of the human mind has increased in the last few centuries, or that individuals of genius are being bred in greater numbers now than in the past. Yet man now performs acts and acquires knowledge altogether debarred from previous generations.

The truth of the matter is that the perfection, as manifested by modern scientific achievements, lies not in any change in man himself, but in the new technique he has adopted – *the scientific method of approach.* Without its use, men of even outstanding ability found themselves incapable of solving the most elementary problems concerning the material universe; but with the aid of the scientific method of approach, .progress is possible for all who care to make the effort, while in the hands of a genius, the scientific method acquires almost the properties of a magic wand.

In short, the "scientific method" is nothing more nor less than a mental tool of exceptional efficiency.

But is efficiency enough? Does it necessarily follow that the ever-increasing rate at which discoveries are being made must inevitably increase human happiness, or enable man to live a fuller life, or lead to a commensurate advancement in human civilization? On this point, opinion is divided.

There are those who blame science for all the evils of modern society and fear that the exploitation of the knowledge thus acquired must inevitably lead to disaster. They believe that science carries the germ of its own destruction, and that the material comforts and benefits it provides are obtained at the expense of all the finer qualities of our past civilization, tending to destroy the spiritual and religious heritage of man, arrest his aesthetic achievements, and undermine his morality. How, they argue, can science be identified with human progress if, in mastering and dominating the world, it destroys humanity itself? Those who hold this pessimistic view look back nostalgically to the more leisurely way of life which, with all its faults, was able to satisfy man for thousands of years, and to provide a measure of spiritual peace altogether lacking in contemporary civilization.

There are others, however, who take the opposite view. Science is, to them, neither good nor evil, but merely a method of approach that can be used for either purpose according to man's desire. To blame science for the evils of modern society is, to their way of thinking, reminiscent of the child's urge to smack the table against which he has hurt himself. They see in the continued application of science great possibilities for constructive effort, with undreamt of benefits to mankind. They are fully aware of the disturbing influence science is having at the present time, but they interpret this as a transition phase in the gradual establishment of the truly scientific age. They have faith in man's ability to weather the storm inherent in the present conflict, and foresee the time when man will emerge triumphant, with the creation of a new civilization that will be as far ahead of the pre-scientific era of a few centuries ago as the latter was ahead of the primitive society of our cave-dwelling ancestors.

When two diametrically opposite views are presented for dispassionate appraisal, each supported by, what appears to be, quite convincing arguments, one is tempted to conclude that some essential factor has been missed, or intentionally ignored, by both sides.

What, in fact, is the potential limit of scientific achievement? To answer this requires an understanding of the nature and scope of the technique employed: – *the scientific method.*

In essence, the scientific method is very simple: – It is, first, to ask one question at a time, for only then can the answer be free from ambiguity; secondly, to rely on precise data, and where these cannot be acquired by simple observation, to devise experiments for eliciting the information; and thirdly, since the human mind finds it difficult to assess shades of inferences, to insist on quantitative rather than qualitative values, obtained, if possible, by objective recordings. (The simplicity of the scientific method is, in a way, deceptive, since it requires great self-discipline to frame problems in such a way that only one question is asked at a time; it calls for considerable ingenuity to plan appropriate experiments for eliciting reliable data; and it needs long training and experience to obtain accurately recorded quantitative data. Nevertheless, *in essence*, the scientific method is remarkably simple.)

This is the whole secret of the efficiency of science as a tool for the search for knowledge. But herein also lies its limitations: – For, clearly, not all human problems lend themselves to quantitative treatment, nor can they all be resolved into single questions. Indeed, the division of human preoccupations into *material* and *spiritual* spheres, roughly correspond to the human problems that *can*, and those that *cannot*, be readily solved by the application of the scientific method.

Such spiritual values as ethics and morality, the constant striving for intellectual and aesthetic achievement, the passionate desire to fathom the purpose of man's existence, and the elusive search for lasting happiness have always served as the corner-stones of human endeavour in the progress of civilization. For thousands of years, man has been grappling with these spiritual problems; and though progress in this search has been slow, it has at least kept pace with progress in the material sphere, that is to say, in the fight for physical survival against the forces of nature, and the attempt to husband these forces for man's particular needs.

The situation has now changed. With the application of the

scientific method for the solution of man's material problems, his mastery over the elements has developed with prodigious speed, leaving his spiritual values more or less where they were. His power over the universe has outstripped his understanding of himself.

Here lies one of the major causes of conflict, or disharmony of contemporary civilization for which a solution is so feverishly being sought. The fault of the disharmony is not with the scientific method, which has contributed all that could be expected of it, but with the fact that the human mind has so far failed to devise a "mental tool" of comparable efficiency, suitable for the solution of man's spiritual problems.

Having reached this disquieting conclusion, the first inclination might be to call a halt to scientific progress – a moratorium for, say, a century, by which time man may have discovered the means of solving some of his other problems, so that the fruits of science could then be integrated in harmony with his inner, spiritual life, in the true march of progress.

Little attention need be paid to this proposition, for it is a counsel of despair, as impractical as it is illogical. It would be a denial of freedom of thought and the negation of progress – the blaming of what is potentially good, for the stupidity of those who prostitute it to base purposes. It presupposes that man, having once savoured perfection in the method of searching for the truth, would willingly abandon it in the interest of an abstraction of dubious value.

Finally, since restrictive measures of this sort would only be obeyed by honest men (whose use of science is calculated to be for the benefit of mankind), while the more unscrupulous and dishonest would secretly continue to exploit its use for evil purposes, the policy would actually increase the very instability which the measure seeks to eradicate.

An alternative approach would be to look towards science itself for a solution. If the scientific method is indeed so efficient a mental tool for the solution of material problems, could it not be adapted in some way for the solution of spiritual problems? Are there not, in fact, examples of the successful application of scientific principles to problems that are too complex to be resolved into single questions, or which do not lend themselves to quantitative treatment?

The answer to this is partly in the affirmative, and this might, at first sight, offer a ray of hope. The study of the mechanism of mental activity is just such a problem, and it must be admitted that the application of scientific methods to this problem has met with at least partial success, from two different directions.

Pavlov made a serious attempt to apply the scientific method to the study of mental processes. Realizing the need for a quantitative approach, he sought for *the unit* of mental activity, and this he achieved in his brilliant discovery of the "conditioned reflex." From simple mental processes in dogs, involving single conditioned reflexes, he passed on to somewhat more complicated mental processes in dogs, and hoped finally to probe into the elaborate workings of the human mind. However, the success of his experiments is destined, in all probability, to remain a *tour de force*, with no prospect of extension to the realm of complicated thought. The reason for this is that, in insisting on the use of rigid scientific principles, he was aiming at the impossible; for while succeeding in bringing mental activity down to a quantitative level, he was unable to achieve the other essential of scientific study, namely, of reducing every problem to the level where there is only one variable to be investigated at a time.

Freud's approach was different. He accepted the fact that the human mind was far too complex and dynamic to be approached by exacting scientific principles; and instead of trying to simplify the mind in order that the scientific method could be rigidly applied to it, he modified the scientific approach itself. If Pavlov's was the synthetic approach (i.e.

starting from the simplest unit of mental activity, and working upwards), FREUD's, on the contrary, was the analytical approach (i.e. starting from the most complex – the behaviour and emotions of the adult who has failed to fit into his elaborate surroundings – and working downwards.) The "science" in FREUD's approach consisted simply of the recognition and use of *observation* for the acquisition of data, freed from the thoughts and feelings of the observer. It had, surprisingly enough, never before occurred to anyone that this could only be achieved if the observer succeeded in ridding himself of the role of judge or moralist, of healer or confessor.

Naturally, FREUD's method lacked precision. It dealt with intricate complexities in apparent confusion, not amenable to quantitative treatment. All the same, his method proved more successful in analysing mental activity than anything previously attempted, and led to the momentous discovery of the existence and significance of the subconscious mind – that mental process, determined by forgotten experiences, which unconsciously influenced most of our irrational, and even of some of our rational, behaviour.

Two lines of criticism might be levelled against Freudian psychology, in so far as it affects the subject under discussion: – first that psychoanalysis achieves, at best, the eradication of a subconscious conflict, without any attempt at putting anything positive in its place and secondly, that psychology is essentially a study of the isolated individual, while the major problems of contemporary civilization are concerned with integrated society as a whole.

As regards the first criticism, it must be admitted, that, *as a therapeutic measure*, psychoanalysis has this negative function of eradicating undesirable conflicts. However, the knowledge thus acquired ultimately makes it possible to avoid some of these conflicts from ever arising, through sounder principles of parental care and educational upbringing of children, and through a more sympathetic awareness of the causes and origins of troubles in adult human relationships. In this sense, at least, psychology should, in time, be able to contribute towards the creation of a more stable society.

As for the second criticism – that psychology is essentially a study of isolated individuals – one must remember that the same semi-scientific principles that proved so effective in the psychoanalysis of the individual, can be, and are being, applied to integrated groups and whole societies as well. Social anthropology is to the community what psychology is to the individual. It, too, is based on dispassionate analysis and observation, aiming to discover the deeply rooted, subconscious motives that determine the *collective* behaviour patterns of integrated societies.

It is, perhaps, too early to assess the efficacy of these new methods of study, or to judge the full scope of the impact of the knowledge thus acquired in the reshaping of the collective character of a society. Social anthropology is, as yet, a very young subject, and still suffers from many of the crudities of an immature science. However, there are already sufficient indications to show what far-reaching results may be obtained from a scientific study of the habits, customs, religious observances, methods of education, etc., of past and present civilizations. If this were, indeed, to provide a deeper understanding of the origins and developments of specific patterns of collective behaviour (and that is, after all, what we mean by "civilizations") it should theoretically enable future societies to reshape their own civilizations *at will* into any desired mould.

Whether such a society would, in fact, make the necessary effort to reshape its collective pattern of living, is another matter. This brings us to the core of the problem. While a correct evaluation of history may provide an understanding of the developmental errors of an unstable society, and while the fruits of psychology, anthropology and other social sciences, may show the way to alter the existing pattern of society, it does not necessarily follow that mankind would be ready to execute the changes called-for and accept all the consequences involved. Science may be able to show the way, but other human attributes and qualities must serve as motives.

Earlier, in dealing with the limitations of the scientific method, it was pointed out that, broadly speaking, the division between material and spiritual spheres of human preoccupations roughly correspond to the human problems that can, and those that cannot, be readily solved by the application of the scientific method. We now perceive another, and more fundamental, limitation: science can only serve as a method, not as a motive or inspiration of human activity. The fruits of science may serve as a stimulus for further endeavour; the habit of scientific thinking may seep into our daily lives and influence our thinking in other spheres; but even the best of methods is useless if misapplied, or not applied at all.

What, then, should serve as the motive force? A return to religion? Or some political philosophy? Or, perhaps, a new ethical principle that may emerge spontaneously as a consequence of the continued spread of culture?

Before even attempting to answer this important question, one must try (1) to understand why it is that religion is no longer a dominant influence in human affairs today, and (2) to evaluate the function and limitations of political philosophy as an inspirational force.

Faith is the basis of religion; reason is the underlying principle of science. When faith is artificially bolstered by false reasoning, or when reason is irrationally circumscribed by faith, chaos and confusion is the inevitable consequence.

To people who have become accustomed to dispassionate appraisal of evidence and to the habit of scientific thought, the rigid dogmas and creeds of established religions must inevitably lose their hold, especially if they obliterate, in time, the underlying ethical principles on which such religions were initially founded. Moreover, the biblical account of the Creation, the succession of miracles that defy the normal laws of nature, and the anthropomorphic conception of God and his ministering angels, however attractive they may be as poetry or allegory, cannot much longer be expected to serve as the foundation of man's belief.

That is not to say that there is necessarily a conflict between science, and a belief in a divinity that can serve as an inspiration to higher ethical ideals. On the contrary, in helping to dispose of the artificial encumbrances of existing religions, science may even contribute towards a reawakening of a pure religious belief. SPINOZA saw this clearly enough three hundred years ago. But meanwhile, there is little evidence of the emergence of a worldwide religious revival which could serve as a powerful force in directing the future progress of civilization.

Without wishing to draw too close a parallel, it may be said that, in a sense, political movements play the part today that established religions did in former times. Political theory calls for selfless devotion to the betterment of mankind in the name of justice and ethical idealism; but it can, in time, also become an object of blind worship, divorced from its initial moral values, impervious to logical reasoning, and tyrannical in its demands. Indeed, in the course of time, as the moral principles underlying a political philosophy become forgotten by its adherents, or wilfully abused by its leaders, rational thought becomes replaced by fears and hatreds in a spirit of prejudice.

One must not, however, fall into the error of condemning political philosophy on the grounds that it lends itself to abuse, any more than one is prepared to deny the benefits of science because of its potential misapplication for evil and destruction, or to condemn sincere religious belief because it has so often been debased in the past. Political theory, as a potential force in directing civilization, must be judged on its merits.

We are, of course, not dealing here with political philosophy in general, but only with the contemporary patterns and even here, we are not so much concerned with the political creeds of the opposing systems, as with *the features they have in common*, as an index of man's political aims in contemporary society.

The existence of such a common denominator is apparent from the extent to which Marxian principles intrude in the political thinking of even the most conservative upholders of capitalistic societies and conversely, from the degree to which socialistic and even communistic societies accept some of the most cherished principles of capitalism as necessary techniques in the government of a modern State.

This common denominator stems from a blend of eighteenth century liberalism and the Marxian materialistic concept which equates human happiness with freedom from hunger and want. The principle of eighteenth century liberalism, aiming at individual freedom and suffrage, has become so deeply ingrained in contemporary society that even a modern dictator finds himself obliged to pay lip service to it, while attempting, in fact, to destroy it. The Marxian emphasis on freedom from hunger and want *as almost the sole function of human striving*, is also becoming accepted as if it were an axiomatic truth.

No rational person would deny that hunger and want must be eradicated, and that the individual in a civilized society must be given as much freedom as possible to express his thoughts and desires in shaping its affairs. But that is no more a recipe for a civilized society than to say that an adequate supply of air is the means for maintaining the complete health of an individual. Man may live in luxury and exercise his voting rights at elections, and yet be acutely unhappy.

All the same, serious attention must be given to the practical question of the *physical* needs of mankind. History has ceased to be an account of Machiavellian rulers and of battles. We know, for instance, that more casualties have been suffered through typhus and other epidemics than by actual warfare; and that the results of victorious wars have more often been determined by failures of food crops than by decisions at Peace Conferences. It needs but a slight change in the statistical ratio between birth-rate and death-rate to cause, in less than a century, a complete change in the face of a whole continent, regardless of political movements or national aspirations.

While birth-rates and death-rates, food supplies and epidemics, have, in the past, been left to chance and the Will of God, these are now factors amenable to scientific control. The population of the world is increasing at quite an alarming rate; but given the chance, science could cope with the resulting increased demand for food supply. The inequitable distribution of the available food throughout the world has led to mass starvation in some areas and overabundance in others. The solution of this fantastic situation could also be achieved by science, if it were not complicated by political issues. The population can itself be checked by birth-control.

One is, in fact, confronted again and again with the proposition, mentioned above, that while most of the formidable problems of contemporary civilization are potentially soluble by the application of science, the motive that would drive society to achieve the desired objectives lies within man himself.

It is, perhaps, in this direction that contemporary civilization is most in need of salvation. The spread of education has eradicated illiteracy in western society, but has, so far, failed to show how people can use their newly-acquired literacy to appraise their knowledge in a logical and unemotional fashion. The failure of education lies in the sacrifice of quality and content for quantity. We pride ourselves that the percentage of illiteracy is continually falling, that the proportion of university graduates is continually rising, and that the tonnage of printed matter read by the public is increasing at a prodigious rate. Yet learning is less and less respected for its own sake; the teaching profession, in whose hands the subsequent generation is moulded, stands low in the social hierarchy; and the average man is far more bewildered than his illiterate forefathers. The fault lies not with religion, politics, or science; *it stems from a distorted sense of values.*

We have developed a thirst for facts and figures, but not an appreciation of their value and significance. We no longer prize creative achievement; we only worship success. The art of memorizing and the quoting of statistics have become a lazy substitute for thinking: arguments are pigeonholed and people are branded by the use of catch-phrases ("bourgeois," "decadent," "reds") instead of being judged on their merits. While the practical fruits of man's achievements are becoming more and more abundant, human relationships continue to deteriorate. Race-hatred and other forms of intolerance continue, despite our progress in civilization, and though the targets change from time to time, the evil grows in intensity. People are learning to get on with one another individually, but more and more to hate each other collectively.

This is the sorry state of contemporary civilization in its spiritual spheres, and the blame must be laid on the educational system we have chosen, using "education" in its widest sense as *the model of society we encourage our next generation to adopt.* It is here that science may, after all, save civilization – not science as a profession, nor scientists as individuals, nor even the fruits of science, with the material benefits they may provide for mankind, but *the scientific method, applied to all walks of life.*

The world is torn by opposing ideologies of socialism and capitalism, each claiming that it can bring peace, happiness and prosperity to mankind. Assessing the relative merits of these two rival claims is surely a matter for scientific analysis, and not for decision by threat of warfare. Either of these two opposing ideologies may be maintained by authoritarian or democratic means. These are essentially techniques (as distinct from the ideologies they happen to sponsor), and as techniques, they can also be evaluated by an analysis of the evidence, free from preconceived notions.

In the past, man was very conscious of the enormity of the universe and of his own relative insignificance in relation to it. He, therefore, held on to tradition for his stability; and when faced with problems that were beyond him, he turned to a supernatural source for inspiration and guidance. In more recent times, with all the scientific achievements affecting the material universe, man acquired a certain degree of emancipation and self-reliance: he no longer felt the need to propitiate an angry deity when confronted with calamities that were now explicable by scientific laws of nature. Yet his uncertainty persisted, as manifested, at moments of stress, by worship of human instead of superhuman leadership and demagogy. The next stage in the development of civilization will have to be towards a more assured sense of collective self-reliance, man's destiny being controlled by his understanding of the problems that face him – freed from prejudice and hysteria, and from the ever-growing power of the propaganda machine.

How will the change come about? No one can tell yet.

With the growing disharmony of contemporary civilization, the collective will for survival will presumably play a part in stirring humanity out of its traditional grooves. But the spiritual "message" that will act as the motive force may prove as remote from religion or politics (as we understand them today) as the latter are from the tribal taboos of primitive societies. Until then, science will supposedly continue to add to the material comforts of man, while continuing to widen the gap between his growing prosperity and his diminishing peace of mind.

New Ways with Science as Leader

by

WILLEM CAREL DE LEEUW

The interrelations which face terrestrial mankind today are chaotic: morally, sociologically, politically. No sincere thinker will deny this. Thousands of people in this fear-ridden world are trying today to find a way out, in order to provide happier conditions along many different lines, proposing many explanations and remedies – more or less strongly objectively coloured. The latter – in so far as materialistic or emotional – by far the most – will bring only incidental, no lasting relief. However, they all concur herein, that man's environment is considered as not conducive to his well-being and that it demands fundamental improvement; whereas it is now at least unsatisfactory, not to say fraught with danger and is threatening human existence.

Where lies the cause of all this? Certainly not with Man's environment. It was the present and earlier generations, that brought it into being and the fault must lie with the creator, Man himself. His inner attitude has been wrong, being ignorant of his origin, his place and his task in the cosmic conditions in which he finds himself. The basis of all his activity on his habitat needs complete reformation or remoulding.

The Universe in which terrestrial Man and his Globe have their place – and a very modest one at that – is one of integral Law and Order. No Law of Nature is autonomous or self-sufficient. If this were the case, the Universe would not be a Kosmos, but a Chaos, or might at any moment become so. Man is part of this grand Whole. It is his duty to live in harmony with the gradual unfolding, the Evolution of it. This means submission to the lines of that Evolution, laid down at the beginning of every new manifestation of the Unique Unknown and Unknowable Reality, of which Law and Order are but the reflections on the phenomenal plane in each successive Universe.

Now the great majority of men have not the slightest idea of such submission. They live egotistically, if not egocentrically, or extremely selfishly. They see themselves, not as humble cogs in the great cosmic machinery, but they place themselves autonomously or even antagonistically opposite of Nature. They consider it their right to subdue and exploit her to his needs (as "authorized" by Genesis I, 28). They thus create disturbance in the unfolding of the cosmic scheme. This has been going on on this Earth for countless ages, since manlike animal became a thinking, planning tyro, however stumbling. And the present global conditions are the accumulated outcome of this long-protracted maltreatment of Nature and the violation of her Laws. Viewed from a spiritual point of view her resources have been wasted lately in a terrific, and accelerated tempo.

If ever there should dawn improvement, this must start with Man's mutual relations, as well as those of Man with Nature, in the way of generating a profound change of human attitude. Man needs knowledge to bring about this change. Being of an intellectual nature his knowledge belongs to the realm of Science. It is to her, that we must look for help. The present Religion and Philosophy of the West are contemplative and can not help directly in his remoulding of attitude; but they can do it indirectly, be it that they may benefit or even inspire Man's search after the causes of Man's present moral decline. It is ratiocinative intellect that rules this era and it appeals particularly to the modern man.

This is not contemplative, but in the first place extrovert. And this extroversion, followed by gestation and reconsideration of present values is what man thinks he needs now.

The omnipresent validity of Law and Order and their harmonious interrelation point to a final cosmic Unity of intellectual nature. This intellectuality is not of a shifting nature, progressive like human knowledge, but is established and its field laid down once and forever for every new cosmic manifestation. Hence there is Coherence, Unity in Nature. Only Man, with his unripe intellect, can disturb it, but only temporarily. If he continues his mistakes long enough, the evolutionary trend towards Unity will sweep him, individually or groupwise, away. Nations have gone out like a torch dipped in water.

Lack of awareness of this Unity and its ethical consequences is the main cause of the present bewilderment. In our era of ratiocinative intellect it is, as said above, Science that is best capable of reaching the masses. The way of the mystic which leads as well to a realization of the Unity, is not effective for the average man of our time. Yet in millions of people, even in those who are not particularly religiously inclined, Unity is felt vaguely as an intuition – religious instinct, that lies at the root of all ethics. In this intuition lies the hope for salvation.

It would mean a formidable step forward towards improvement if the reality of Unity and its implications would gradually dawn on the inner life of Man. It would mean a deep change in the moral attitude of the many and bring about an outlook on life diametrically opposed to the present general way of life. Such men would view themselves as part of a great whole and feel their responsibilities towards their own Inner Life, toward Mankind and all Nature. Altruism need no longer be based on commandments, fear or emotions, however good, but would become to be viewed as a cosmic necessity. Having attained to this as a firm conviction, Man's consciousness will then enable him to realize and to live up to the bond which holds together all Nature and binds him to all, which compells to exercise his duty as a helper at the frontline of Evolution and assist in the expression of its universal trend.

By broadening and deepening its correlations to such extent, that Unity becomes manifest in all her departments, thus furnishing a final correlation, Science can give to the World a coherent, intellectual expression to the prevailing intuition of Universal Unity. Science herself will also benefit greatly from that: from compartmental it will become unified. Scientists progress on the borderline of the human field of consciousness and in a unified science they will be compelled to keep, in postulating correlations, their inner views always directed towards the Centrum, from which Unity emanates. By combining induction and analysis with deduction and synthesis they will be able to detect and establish the validity of the Law of Unity throughout the Kosmos. No longer relying on the pseudo-reality of sensorial observation Science will become a whole: knowledge wedded to universal Philosophy and Ethics. Now the former is neglected; the latter completely ignored.

In the way in which more and more individuals realize the existence of Unity, as unveiled by Science, they will see the necessity not merely to value it as a mental conception, but to *assimilate* it in their inner life and then to turn outward and *apply* it in their behaviour. This then will be the initial effort towards Spiritual Evolution by trying to adopt altruistic standards. This means inner conflicts and they constitute the greatest of all wars, waged within Man's breast: two souls, as it were, in constant conflict, as GOETHE said. That evolution has become complete only in rare individuals.

It is Science, if well directed, that can call forth the initial effort towards it: a grand task indeed! Its outcome will go far beyond the present certainly wonderful achievements of Science. It will provide a remodelling of the general way of life. Many thinkers, revolting against mere lip-confession of ethics have tried in vain to establish the beginnings of a better world along emotional lines. Would Science try it in her way?

Per Aspera ad Astra[1]

by

Bertrand Russell

CURRENT PERPLEXITIES

The present time is one in which the prevailing mood is a feeling of impotent perplexity. We see ourselves drifting towards a war that hardly anyone desires – a war that, as we all know, must bring disaster to the great majority of mankind. But like a rabbit fascinated by a snake, we stare at the peril without knowing what to do to avert it. We tell each other horror stories of atom bombs and hydrogen bombs, of cities exterminated, of Russian hordes, of famine and ferocity everywhere. But although our reason tells us we ought to shudder at such a prospect, there is another part of us that enjoys it, and so we have no firm will to avert misfortune, and there is a deep division in our souls between the sane and the insane parts. In quiet times the insane parts can slumber throughout the day and wake only at night. But in times like ours they invade our waking time as well, and all rational thinking becomes pale and divorced from the

1. This article represents the main lines of the author's book: "New Hopes for a Changing World."

The text has been put at our disposal by the author with the kind permission of the publishers George Allen & Unwin Ltd., London and Simon and Schuster Inc., New York.

Earl Bertrand Russell is one of the first Chartermembers of the World Academy of Art and Science.

will. Our lives become balanced on a sharp edge of hypothesis – if there is to be a war one way of life is reasonable; if not, another. To the great majority of mankind such a hypothetical existence is intolerably uncomfortable, and in practice they adopt one hypothesis or the other, but without complete conviction. A youth who finds scholastic education boring will say to himself: "Why bother? I shall be killed in battle before long." A young woman who might live constructively thinks to herself that she had better have a good time while she can since presently she will be raped by Russian soldiery until she dies. Parents wonder whether the sacrifices called for by their children's upbringing are worth while since they are likely to prove futile. Those who are lucky enough to possess capital are apt to spend it on riotous living, since they foresee a catastrophic depreciation in which it would become worthless. In this way uncertainty baulks the impulse to every irksome effort, and generates a tone of frivolous misery mistakenly thought to be pleasure, which turns outward and becomes hatred of those who are felt to be its cause. Through this hatred it brings daily nearer the catastrophe which it dreads. The nations seem caught in a tragic fate, as though, like characters in a Greek drama, they were blinded by some offended god. Bewildered by mental fog, they march towards the precipice while they imagine that they are marching away from it.

It must be said that the purely intellectual problems presented by the world of our day are exceedingly difficult. There is not only the great problem: can we defend our Western world without actual war? There are also problems in Asia and problems in Africa and problems in tropical America which cannot be solved within the framework of the traditional political ideas. There are those, it is true, who are quite certain that they can solve these problems by ancient methods. One of the painful things about our time is that those who feel certainty are stupid, and those with any imagination and understanding are filled with doubt and indecision. I do not think this is necessary. I think there is a view of man and his destiny and his present troubles which can give certainty and hope together with the completest understanding of the moods, the despairs and the maddening doubts that beset modern men. It is my hope to set forth such an outlook in the following pages in a way that shall be convincing and overwhelmingly encouraging, that shall enable men of goodwil, to work with the same vigour which of late has been the monopoly of cruel bigots; to take away from our Western mentality the reproach that we have nothing to offer inspiring the same firm conviction and the same solid body of belief as is offered by the disciples of the Kremlin. But I anticipate. And after this digression into hope I must return to the causes of its opposite, which have all too much sway in the reflections of thoughtful men. If we forget MAC ARTHUR, what are we to think about Asia? From the time of VASCO DA GAMA until the Russo-Japanese war, the Western world did not think seriously about Asia. No doubt, it was a picturesque continent, and amid our progressive schemes we enjoyed talking about the unchanging East. Philosophers with kindly contempt, and missionaries with reforming zeal, studied what we were pleased to call their superstitions. We enjoyed their military incompetence, and their incapacity to extract high wages. For all these reasons we rather like them. We realized, of course, that the inhabitants of Asia did not all form one community. There were Mohammedans and Hindus and Buddhists, and it was our hope that they would continue to hate each other for ever. And on this ground the more enlightened among administrators deprecated the work of missionaries for fear lest it should diminish the virulence of "superstition."

The first country of Asia to cause misgivings in Europeans was Japan. At first, after Commodore PERRY had opened the country to our curiosity, we admired the cherry blossom, Bushido, and the chivalrous virtues of the Samurai. We like the temples and the art, and our aesthetes imagined the Japanese to be kindred souls. But gradually a change came over the spirit of our dream. It may be seen in the works of LAFCADIO HEARN. At first he was enthusiastic about the Japanese, but his last book, Japan, an Interpretation, has begun to be aware of things slightly more serious than cherry blossom. The Japanese refused to stay put. They set to work to imitate the West, and in the measure in which they succeeded they inspired hatred in Western minds.

The Japanese for the moment encountered disaster; they mastered our brutalities, but not our suppleness. But they left to the rest of Asia a legacy of war-like rebellion against Western insolence. Western men of liberal outlook cannot but sympathize with the wish of Asia to be independent, but it would be a pity if this sympathy were to blind Western thought to certain matters of the gravest import. The Western world has achieved, not completely but to a considerable extent, a way of life having certain merits that are new in human history. It has nearly eliminated poverty. It has cut down illness and death to a degree that a hundred years ago would have seemed fantastic. It has spread education throughout the population, and it has achieved a quite new degree of harmony between freedom and order. These are not things which Asia, if it becomes quickly independent, can hope to achieve. We, in the West, aware of the appalling poverty of South-East Asia, and convinced that this poverty is a propaganda weapon in the hands of the Russians, have begun to think for the first time that some thing ought to be done to raise the standard of life in these regions. But their habits and our beliefs between them make the task, for the present, a hopeless one. Every increase of production, instead of raising the standard of life, is quickly swallowed up by an increase in population. Eastern populations do not know how to prevent this, and Western bigots prevent those who understand the problem from spreading the necessary information. What is bad in the West is easily spread: our restlessness, our militarism, our fanaticism, and our ruthless belief in mechanism. But what is best in the West – the spirit of free inquiry, the understanding of the conditions of general prosperity, and emancipation from superstition – these things powerful forces in the West prevent the East from acquiring. So long as this continues, Eastern populations will remain on the verge of destitution and in proportion as they become powerful, they will become destructive through envy. In this they will, of course, have the help of Russia, unless and until Russia is either defeated or liberalized. For these reasons, a wise policy towards Asia is still to seek.

In Africa the same problems exist, though for the present they are less menacing. [2] Everything done by European administrators to improve the lot of Africans is, at present, totally and utterly futile because of the growth of population. The Africans, not unnaturally, though now mistakenly, attribute their destitution to their exploitation by the white man. If they achieve freedom suddenly before they have men trained in administration and a habit of responsibility, such civilization as white men have brought to Africa will quickly disappear. It is no use for doctrinaire liberals to deny this; there is a standing proof in the island of Haiti.

It must not be supposed that there is any essential stability in a civilized way of life. Consider the regions overrun by the Turks and contrast their condition under the Turks with what they were in Roman days. Over great parts of the earth's surface, similar misfortunes are not impossible in the near future. On the other hand it must be admitted that until we include birth-control in our African policies every increase in efficiency and honesty and scientific skill on the part of European administrators will only increase the sum of human misery.

The population problem is similar in Central and South America, but it does not there have the same political importance.

2. Remark: this was written in 1951.

I have been speaking hitherto of public perplexities, but it is not these alone which trouble the Western mind. Traditional systems of dogma and traditional codes of conduct have not the hold that they formerly had. Men and women are often in genuine doubts as to what is right and what is wrong, and even as to whether right and wrong are anything more than ancient superstitions. When they try to decide such questions for themselves they find them too difficult. They cannot discover any clear purpose that they ought to pursue or any clear principle by which they should be guided. Stable societies may have principles, that, to the outsider, seem absurd. But so long as the societies remain stable their principles are subjectively adequate. That is to say they are accepted by almost everybody unquestioningly, and they make the rules of conduct as clear and precise as those of the minuet or the heroic couplet. Modern life, in the West, is not at all like a minuet or a heroic couplet. It is like free verse which only the poet can distinguish from prose. Two great systems of dogma lie in wait for the modern man when his spirit is weary: I mean the system of Rome and the system of Moscow. Neither of these gives scope for free mind, which is at once the glory and the torment of Western man. It is the torment only because of growing pains. The free man, full grown, shall be full of joy and vigour and mental health, but in the meantime he suffers.

Not only publicly, but privately also, the world has need of ways of thinking and feeling which are adapted to what we know, to what we can believe, and what we feel ourselves compelled to disbelieve. There are ways of feeling that are traditional and that have all the prestige of the past and weighty authority, and that yet are not adapted to the world in which we live, where now techniques have made some new virtues necessary and some old virtues unnecessary. The Hebrew prophets, surrounded by hostile nations, and determined that their race should not be assimilated by Gentile conquerors, developed a fierce doctrine in which the leading conception was sin. The Gentiles sinned always and in all their ways, but the Jews, alas, were only too apt to fall into sin themselves. When they did so they were defeated in battle and had to weep by the waters of Babylon. It is this pattern which has inspired moralists ever since. The virtuous man has been conceived as one who, though continually surrounded by temptation, though passionately prompted to sin, nevertheless, by almost superhuman strength of will, succeeds in walking along the straight and narrow path, looking meanwhile disdainfully to the right and left at those inferior beings who have loitered to pluck flowers by the way. In this conception, virtue is difficult, negative, and arid. It is constrictive and suspicious of happiness. It is persuaded that our natural impulses are bad and that society can only be held together by means of rigid prohibitions. I do not wish to pretend that society can hold together if people murder and steal. What I do say is, that the kind of man whom I should wish to see in the world is one who will have no impulse to murder, who will abstain from murder not because it is prohibited but because his thoughts and feelings carry him away from impulses of destruction. The whole conception of sin has, as it were, gone dead, so far, at least, as conscious thought and feeling are concerned. Most people have not thought out any other system of ethics, and have not, perhaps, theoretically rejected the old system. But it has lost its hold on them. They do not murder or steal as a rule, because it would not be to their interest to do so, but one cannot say as much for their obedience to the Seventh Commandment. They have, in fact, no wish to conform to the ancient pattern. The Publican thanks God that he is not as this Pharisee, and imagines that in so doing he has caught the point of the parable. It does not occur to him that feeling superior is what is reprehended, and that whether it is the Publican or the Pharisee who feels superior is an unimportant detail.

I should wish to persuade those to whom traditional

morals have gone dead, and who yet feel the need of some serious purpose over and above momentary pleasure, that there is a way of thinking and feeling which is not difficult for those who have not been trained in its opposite, and which is not one of self-restraint, negation and condemnation. The good life, as I conceive it, is a happy life. I do not mean that if you are good you will be happy; I mean that if you are happy you will be good. Unhappiness is deeply implanted in the souls of most of us. How many people we all know who go through life apparently gay, and who yet are perpetually in search of intoxication whether of the Bacchic kind or some other. The happy man does not desire intoxication. Nor does he envy his neighbour and therefore hate him. He can live the life of impulse like a child, because happiness makes his impulses fruitful and not destructive. There are many men and women who imagine themselves emancipated from the shackles of ancient codes but who, in fact, are emancipated only in the upper layers of their minds. Below these layers lies the sense of guilt crouching like a wild beast waiting for moments of weakness or inattention, and growling venomous angers which rise to the surface in strange distorted forms. Such people have the worst of both worlds. The feeling of guilt makes real happiness impossible for them, but the conscious rejection of old codes of behaviour makes them act perpetually in ways that feed the maw of the ancient beast beneath. A way of life cannot be successful so long as it is a mere intellectual conviction. It must be deeply felt, deeply believed, dominant even in dreams. I do not think that the best kind of life is possible in our day for those who, below the level of consciousness, are still obsessed by the load of sin. It is obvious that there are things that had better not be done, but I do not think the best way to avoid the doing of such things is to label them sin and represent them as almost irresistibly attractive. And so I should wish to offer to the world something scarcely to be called an ethic, at any rate in the old acceptation of that word, but something which nonetheless, will save men from moral perplexity and from remorse and from condemnation of others. What I should put in the place of an ethic in the old sense is encouragement and opportunity for all the impulses that are creative and expansive. I should do everything possible to liberate men from fear, not only conscious fears, but the old imprisoned primeval terrors that we brought with us out of the jungle. I should make it clear, not merely an as intellectual proposition, but as something that the heart spontaneously believes, that it is not by making others suffer that we shall achieve our own happiness, but that happiness and the means to happiness depend upon harmony with other men. When all this is not only understood but deeply felt, it will be easy to live in a way that brings happiness equally to ourselves and to others. If men could think and feel in this way, not only their personal problems, but all the problems of world politics, even the most abstruse and difficult, would melt away. Suddenly, as when the mist dissolves from a mountain top, the landscape would be visible and the way would be clear. It is only necessary to open the doors of our hearts and minds to let the imprisoned demons escape and the beauty of the world take possession.

THE HAPPY WORLD

I have been concerned in my book "New Hopes for a Changing World," to set forth certain facts, and certain hopes which these facts render rational. The facts concern the unification of mankind through modern technique, and the liberation of mankind from bondage to excessive toil which the inadequate technique of the past rendered unavoidable. The hopes that are based upon these facts are hopes as to the general well-being that may be realised if mankind learned to practice the cooperation which modern techniques demand. There are, it is true, correlative fears, for which there is perhaps as good basis in the present state of the world as for the hopes that I have been setting forth. The technical unification of the world not only makes possible much greater general well-being than at any former time, if it is accompanied by economic and political unification; it also makes possible greater disasters than any known to even the worst of former times, if our technical skill continues to be devoted to disunity rather than unity. I have not, however, in this book dwelt much upon the reasons for fear, since I do not think that it is through fear that we shall avoid the dangers that threaten us. Our world has too much of fear, and emphasis upon dangers is apt to lead to apathetic despair. What our world needs is the opposite; it needs rational creative hope; it needs something positive to live for. It needs "yes" feelings rather than "no" feelings. If the "yes" feelings are as strong as a purely rational consideration allows them to be, the "no" feelings will melt away and become unnecessary. But if we dwell upon "no" feelings too much, we shall never emerge from despair.

I shall assume in what follows that mankind, whether through the lessons of a third world war or through some less painful process, will have come to understand the community of interest which unites the human family. And I shall try to portray the kind of world that will result from this understanding. I shall consider that public institutions can do to bring about a happy issue in the three age-long conflicts of men: with nature, with each other, and with themselves.

Let us begin with the conflict with nature.

There will have to be an international authority controlling the production and distribution of food and raw materials. This authority must have power to prevent such wasteful agricultural methods as have produced the deserts in North Africa and the Dust Bowl in the United States. The present cultivators of the soil must not be allowed to enrich themselves by using up wastefully the natural capital upon which future generations will have to subsist. It must come to be realized that whoever destroys the fertility of the soil in any region is doing an injury to mankind as a whole, and that this is not the sort of injury that private persons, or even whole nations, have a right to inflict. The agricultural authority, in addition to insisting upon soil conservation, will have to give advice on scientific agriculture and to make all knowledge on this subject easily available to every cultivator. But I do not think that cultivators need be compelled to adopt the latest scientific methods, except in cases where the old methods are permanently destructive to fertility.

Somewhat similar considerations apply to raw materials. As I write a dangerous dispute is in progress concerning Iranian Oil. The Persians say that it belongs to them, the British and Americans say that it belongs to them, the Russians, in the background, are hoping that it will soon belong to them. But by what right should it belong to any of these contending parties? It was not they who put it there, and it is not they alone who will use it. It should be viewed as the common property of all nations. Socialists have become aware of the evils of private property in land, when the private landowner is a citizen whose interests may be opposed to those of other citizens of his state, but they have not yet become aware of the evils of national private property – I mean property vested in one nation to the exclusion of others. With the unification of world economy, this kind of private property becomes increasingly harmful, and is a constant incentive to war. It is because of this kind of private property that Czechoslovakia has to have a Communist Government, since otherwise Russia would not be able to use its uranium in the manufacture of atom-bombs. For such reasons it is not enough that raw materials should be nationalized; they must be internationalised, and rationed to possible users on some system that has international sanction.

As we have seen, the problem of adequately nourishing the

human family cannot be solved while the population continues to increase rapidly. Rapid increase has been checked in the past by famine and pestilence, but these are painful methods. Moreover, their effectiveness is diminishing; medicine is coping with pestilence, and philanthropy is causing famine to be a less localized phenomenon than it used to be. The population problem, therefore, if the world is to flourish in spite of scientific medicine and economic justice must be dealt with by means of universal birth-control. Whatever this may involve in the way of education, industrialization and increase of prosperity in the poorer regions of the world must be undertaken at no matter what cost, if a scientifically unified world is to be stable, and is not to sink to continually lower levels of subsistence.

I come now to the conflicts of man with man. Here the first thing to be coped with is war. While mankind are subject to the threat of war, especially by the deadly methods which science is perfecting, nothing good can be secure. There is only one way of making the world safe against war, and that is to have only one armed force in the world. There might be local police forces with minor weapons such as could cope with unarmed civilians, but all the really serious weapons of war must be concentrated in the hands of one single authority. When this has been achieved, there will no longer be danger of serious wars, unless they were to take the form of civil wars between different parts of the international force. To prevent this, measures which are not purely military will be required. There will need to be control over education, in the sense that no country must be allowed in its schools to teach a predatory nationalism. The teaching of history everywhere should lay more stress upon the progress of man than upon national victories of defeats in contests with other nations. The books used in the teaching of history should everywhere be such as have been sanctioned by the international authority, and have been certified to be free from nationalistic falsehoods. There should also be a very widely diffused teaching of sound economics – the economics, I mean, which emphasizes the much greater part played by co-operation than by competition in an intelligent modern technique. There should be a gradual approach to universal free trade. There should be complete freedom of travel, as there was in most countries before 1914. There should be interchanges of students, so that many people, while still young enough to be not hardened in habits and prejudices, should become intimate with people of other countries and with their ways of thought and behaviour. The edifice of internationalism in education should have at its apex an *international university*, open to able students from all countries, containing professors to whom the international ideal appeared important, and affording a refuge to able men who, like EINSTEIN, were found displeasing to their compatriots. One might hope that in such a university a free community might grow up of men capable, not only of overcoming nationalism in their thoughts by deliberate effort, but of genuinely feeling the unity of man and of the common tasks to which a wise humanity should devote itself.

I come last to the protection of the individual, both against the hostility of the herd and against his own fear. These two are more closely connected than is sometimes thought, for herd hostility is usually the result of fear, and the fear that it expresses though nominally directed outwards, has, as a rule, its root in a fear which the intolerant individuals feel of a part of themselves. I have spoken in previous chapters of what education in the very early years can do to prevent the growth of underground terrors, such as psycho-analysis lays bare. Affection and security are what is mainly needed in the early years. A population wisely handled in youth will be less liable to herd hostilities than is now common in most parts of the world. Nevertheless, it must be expected that herd hostilities will be sometimes aroused in cases in which to the outsider there seems no just ground for such hostilities. The best way of dealing with such cases would be to provide places of sanctuary, as was done in the Middle Ages; those who had fled to such places should be examined by a neutral authority and should be protected if that authority pronounced them blameless.

Regimentation and uniformity are dangers that an organized industrial world will have to fear, and against which it should take deliberate measures. There should be opportunities for exceptional individuals, such as poets and artists, who would be like to fail in any attempt to win the approval of elderly bureaucrats. I should have academies for such men, not as a reward for achieved eminence, for then it is too late, but as expressing the favourable opinion of young men engaged in similar pursuits. I would have election to such academies only possible for men under twenty-five, and I would confine the voting for election to members of the Academy concerned who were still under thirty-five. Such regulations might make it possible for the academy not to become an ossified collection of old fogies, as academies too often are.

There would still be some whose work would be too anarchic or too much opposed to the fashion to win the approval even of the young. BLAKE, for example, would not have secured the suffrages of contemporary poets or painters. Such men would have to make their living by work that left them a certain amount of leisure, and if they were content to live simply this should be possible. There should be for everybody considerably shorter hours of work then are now customary, and much longer holidays than are now enjoyed by anybody except university professors. Some people are afraid that in such a community life would be too tame and unadventurous, but this need not be the case. There are innumerable forms of adventure which could be open to everybody who desired them, if holidays were as long as they easily might be. For those who wish at all times to live strenuously, and to whom a soft life feels disgusting, it should be possible to find a quite sufficient outlet in some really difficult work, whether of artistic creation or of scientific research. Such work stretches men's powers to the very utmost, as much in its way as an attempt to climb Everest; but for those who do not find it adequate, Everest still remains to be conquired.

Unusual individuals whom subsequent ages, but not their contemporaries, have regarded as meritorious, have been possible in the past if they had the good fortune to inherit money. MILTON, BYRON, SHELLEY and DARWIN were all rendered possible by this piece of good fortune. But there is no social system imaginable which will enable everybody to inherit a fortune, and in the society of the future, if exceptional individuals whose merit is not recognized while they are young are to be enabled to do their work, there must be definite institutions designed for this purpose. If this is not done, fundamental progress will cease, and men will tend to look back to the intellectual or artistic giants of former times as something beyond the capacity of the present age.

No society can be great without great individuals, and I should not think much of a world which had secured universal safety at the price of universal mediocrity. I think, however, that universal security, if it were attained by the kind of means that I have spoken of, would so much diminish envy and fear of eccentricity that the recognition, even in the young, of possible exceptional merit would not encounter the psychological resistance which it now has to meet in the great majority of mankind. If this is indeed the case, and if such institutions as I have spoken of can be established, the happy world that I am envisaging can be not only happy but glorious. I cannot believe that what is dark and dreadful and destructive in the souls of men is essential to the production of great works of imagination. I believe, on the contrary, that it lies within the power of man to create edifices of shining splendour, from which the glory and greatness of which human thought and feeling are capable shall spread a light unmixed with darkness, filling men's hearts with joy and their thoughts with clarity. Such a world is possible. It rests with men to choose whether they will create it, or allow the human race to perish in anger and sordid hate.

Man, in the long ages since he descended from the trees, has passed arduously and perilously through a vast dusty desert, surrounded by the whitening bones of those who have perished by the way, maddened by hunger and thirst, by fear of wild beasts, by dread of enemies, not only living enemies, but spectres of dead rivals projected on to the dangerous world by the intensity of his own fears. At last he has emerged from the desert into a smiling land, but in the long night he has forgotten how to smile. We cannot believe in the brightness of the morning. We think it trivial and deceptive; we cling to old myths that allow us to go on living with fear and hate – above all, hate of ourselves, miserable sinners. This is folly. Man now needs for his salvation only one thing: to open his heart to joy, and leave fear to gibber through the glimmering darkness of a forgotten past. He must lift up his eyes and say: "No, I am not a miserable sinner; I am a being who, by a long and arduous road, have discovered how to make intelligence master natural obstacles, how to live in freedom and joy, at peace with myself and therefore with all mankind." This will happen if men will choose joy rather than sorrow. If not, eternal death will bury man in deserved oblivion.

The Authors

Lord JOHN BOYD ORR, F.R.S., F.R.S.E., LL.D., D.Sc., M.D.; Physiologist. Apart of his extensive research and organisatory work in animal and human nutrition in the service of the British Commonwealth, he taught as Professor of Agriculture at the University of Aberdeen. He is the founder and former Director General of the United Nations' Food and Agricultural Organization. For his fight against hunger on a global scale he received the Nobel Peace Prize in 1949.

Lord BOYD ORR is one of the Charter Members and the first President of the World Academy of Art and Science. (see the Manifesto on page 367).

Adress: Newton of Stracathro, Brechin, Scotland.

ALBERT EINSTEIN, 1879–1955. The visionary words quoted here, are words of his early life as scientist. During his whole life, however, his thoughts and his work were directed to a global cooperation – and not only in science. He inspired the idea of the World Academy of Art and Science, but died to early to witness its materialization.

HUGO N. BOYKO, Ph.D., born in Vienna, Austria, where he introduced plant sociology at that University. At present he is Ecological Advisor to the National Research Council of

Israel, Prime Minister's Office. His numerous publications contain several new lines of research, three natural laws, and about fifty new methods in plant ecology. His main scientific activities are at present in the field of ecological climatography and of fundamental research for productivizing deserts and waste lands, continuing also his and his wife's successful experiments of direct irrigation with sea water.

He holds several leading positions in international organizations of science and is Secretary General of the World Academy of Art and Science.

Address: 1 Ruppin Street, Rehovot, Israel.

ROBERT OPPENHEIMER, D. Sc.; formerly Professor of Physics at the University of California and at the Californian Institute for Advanced Study in Princeton, N.J. As Chairman of the Atomic Energy Commission (1946–1952) he organized the research work in this field in the United States of America.

He achieved world fame as scientist and teacher, as well as for his striving for peaceful use of atomic energy. A close co-worker of EINSTEIN, ROBERT OPPENHEIMER is one of the outstanding educationists of international influence teaching the humanitarian obligations of science, wherever the opportunity is given.

Address: Institute for Advanced Study – Princeton, N.J. U.S.A.

W. F. G. SWANN, M.A., D.Sc., A.R.C.S.; Physicist and Philosopher, worked first at the Carnegie Institute of Washington (1913). Then in succession he became Professor of Physics at the University of Minnesota, the University of Chicago and Yale University, where he was Director of the Sloane Laboratory. In 1927 he became Director of the Bartol Research Foundation of the Franklin Institute, from which position he retired in 1959 to become Director Emeritus.

He is a member of numerous scientific societies and was President of the American Physical Society in 1931–1932. Professor SWANN is the author of some 250 scientific publications, and his outstanding contributions to science as well as his stimulating efforts towards progress in research during the last decades have won him many honorary degrees and awards in America and abroad.

Address: Bartol Research Foundation, Whittier Place, Swarthmore, Pa., U.S.A.

HERMANN JOSEPH MULLER, M.A., Ph.D., D.Sc.; Leading Geneticist; Professor of Zoology at the Indiana University, Bloomington, U.S.A.; Distinguished Service Professor since 1953; his international fame is based not only on his outstanding scientific work but also on his humanitarian activities. In his own field of research he won many international honours, among them (in 1946) the Nobel Prize in Physiology and Medicine for the "discovery of the production of mutations by means of X-rays."

He is Charter Member of the World Academy of Art and Science, and Vice President of its first Presidium.

Address: Department of Zoology, Indiana University, Bloomington, Ind., U.S.A.

HAROLD D. LASSWELL. Ph.D.; Professor of Law and of Political Science, Yale University. He taught his new lines of research at various Universities in the East and in the West of the U.S.A., as well as in China and Japan.

He is one of the co-founders of Political Science and Past President of the American Political Science Association. Professor LASSWELL is particularly known internationally for his leading research in the field of political sociology and psychology.

Address: Yale University, Law School, New Haven, Conn., U.S.A.

SOLCO W. TROMP, Ph.D.; Formerly Professor of Geology at Fouad I University, Cairo, Egypt; Geological Consultant of the United Nations Technical Assistance Program. At present he is Head of the Bioclimatological Research Centre, University Medical Centre at Leiden, the Netherlands, and Secretary of the Netherlands Society of Medical Geography.

Apart from his work in foreign countries and particularly from his exploration work in Afghanistan, which represents an important basis for the development of that country, he is – in the international teamwork of science – Secretary General of the International Society of Bioclimatology and Biometeorology.

Address: Hofbrouckerlaan 54, Oegstgeest, the Netherlands.

RICHARD MONTGOMERY FIELD, Ph.D. (Harvard); Professor Emeritus of Geology, Princeton University; Past President, American Geophysical Union; President-Director, American Institute of Geonomy and Natural Resources; etc.

An internationally acknowledged leading geologist, he worked many years in the framework of the International Union of Geodesy and Geophysics as Chairman of the International Committee for the Social Value of Natural Sciences. In this capacity he organized, together with the late JOHN A. FLEMING, the International Conference on Science and Human Welfare, Washington, D.C., 1956, which led to the election of the International Preparatory Committee for the World Academy of Art and Science.

Address: American Institute for Geonomy and Natural Resources, South Duxbury, Mass., U.S.A.

PIERRE DANSEREAU, Ph.D.; Born in Montreal, he received his doctorate in Europe (Geneva) and taught – until his appointment as Professor of Botany at his birthplace in 1955 – as Lecturer and as Professor in many countries (Canada,

Brazil, U.S.A., Spain, France, Portugal, New Zealand, etc.). He now works at the New York Botanical Garden.

His research work in all these countries has won him a leading position as plant geographer and – based on his worldwide experience – as ecologist.

Address: New York Botanical Garden, Bronx Park, New York 58, N.Y., U.S.A.

M. J. SIRKS, Ph.D., (Leiden); Professor of Genetics, Groningen University (1937–1960). (Since September 1960, Professor Emeritus).

A leading Botanist and Organizer of international cooperation in science, he was elected Secretary General of the International Union of Biological Sciences (1935–1947) and then its President (1947–1950). Since 1935, Member of the World Council of Botany. Honorary President of two International Botanical Congresses (Stockholm, 1950, and Paris, 1954).

Address: Genetisch Instituut, Haren (Gron.), the Netherlands.

PIERRE CHOUARD, D.ès Sc.; Professor of Plant Physiology at the Sorbonne University, Paris, he is one of the foremost leaders in Botany. As Director of the French Phytotron and Member of the French Academy of Agriculture, he is also closely connected with agricultural problems.

In the International Union of Biological Sciences (IUBS), he is President of the Division of Botany and Vice-President of the Union itself. For his activities in Desert Research, he was appointed by UNESCO as one of the nine members of the International Advisory Committee for Arid Zone Research.

Address: Laboratoire de Physiologie Végétale, 1 Rue Victor Cousin, Paris, France.

JOHN F. V. PHILLIPS, D.Sc., F.R.S.E., F.R.S.S.Afr.; Ecologist, Conservationist and Agriculturist; Formerly Professor of

Botany, University of Johannesburg; Professor of Ecology and Agriculture, University of Ghana; Consultant to FAO (Food and Agriculture Organization) and to the International Bank for Reconstruction and Development of the United Nations Organization. At present Chairman, Advisory Committee on African Agricultural Development, Southern Rhodesia.

His books on Africa's Ecology and Agriculture are acclaimed as basis for land use and agricultural development of Africa, South of the Sahara.

Address: 16 Fourth Avenue, P.O. Mabelreign, Salesbury, Southern Rhodesia.

Théodore André Monod, D.ès Sc.; Corresponding Member of the French Academy of Sciences, Professor at the National Museum of Natural History in Paris, and Director of the Institut Français d'Afrique Noire in Dakar. Théodore Monod is internationally acclaimed as one of the few encyclopedists of our time. Although his main field is Zoology, he is a leading scientist also in several other fields, as Geography, Geology, Archeology and Botany.

His famous recent journey through the length (!) of the Sahara from West to East on camelback, with two Beduins only as companions, enriched significantly our knowledge of deserts and desert life in many directions.

Address: Institut Français d'Afrique Noire, Dakar, Senegal, West Africa.

Henrik F. Infield, Ph.D. (Vienna); He taught Sociology at several Universities in Central Europe and in the U.S.A. and is at present Visiting Professor at the Hebrew University in Jerusalem.

His special field is Sociology of Cooperation, and his extensive publications in this branch of science have appeared in many languages. He is a member of the Board of Editors of the International Archives of the Sociology of Cooperation, and was in 1953 elected President of the International Council of this Research.

Address: The Eliezer Kaplan School, Hebrew University, Jerusalem, Israel.

LYLE K. BUSH, Professor of Fine Arts, Simmons College, Boston, Massachusetts, U.S.A.

Internationally known for his teaching philosophy, voiced particularly in his papers in the *Harvard Educational Review* and in the *Simmons Review*, where he regards current schisms between cultural and scientific criteria to be a major handicap to meaningful survival.

His active participation in the foundation of the World Academy has as its particular aim to help in building the necessary bridge.

Address: King Arthur Way, Duxbury, Massachusetts, U.S.A.

W. TAYLOR THOM, Jr., D.Sc.; Professor of Geology, Emeritus, and Chairman, Emeritus, Department of Geological Engineering, Princeton University, U.S.A. Born of an old Quaker family, he developed, already as a young geologist, how the matters of mineral-resources discovery, development and political geography have influenced the rise and decline of nations, of empires and of civilizations throughout historic times. During 1920 and 1921 he was charged with preparing an estimate of available American oil reserves, and soon achieved international fame by his work on mineral resources.

With RICHARD M. FIELD he is co-founder of the out-of-door summertime University, and organizer and co-worker of many important national and international teamworks in his scientific field. For his outstanding achievements he received the John Fleming Medal in 1957.

Address: 272 Snowden Lane, Princeton, N.J., U.S.A.

EUROPAEUS: As the language problem is closely connected with political problems, the author is of the opinion, that it may be of more advantage for an objective and scientific consideration of the subject if he remains anonymous.

ISAAC BERENBLUM, M.D., M.Sc.; At present Head of the Department of Experimental Biology at the Weizmann Institute of Science, Rehovot, Israel. Formerly on the staff of the Sir William Dunn School of Pathology at Oxford University.

His field is experimental cancer research with special reference to the mechanism of carcinogenesis. Professor BERENBLUM – besides his numerous scientific publications and invited lectures in all continents – is author of the book "Man Against Cancer", and his leading position in this field of research has won him many international honours and awards. But – as this essay also proves, and like most of the leading scientists – he does not confine himself to his specialized research only.

Address: Weizmann Institute of Science, Rehovot, Israel.

WILLEM CAREL DE LEEUW, has been for many decades a leading scientist in Botany, without being connected with a scientific institution.

His work is widely acknowledged internationally. He is Doctor honoris causa of the University of Amsterdam, and President of the International Society for Plantgeography and Ecology.

Address: Roodenburgerstraat 35, Leiden, the Netherlands.

EARL BERTRAND A. W. RUSSELL, O.M., M.A., F.R.S.; Philosopher, mathematician and educationist, the dynamic nonagenarian is one of the foremost spiritual leaders of our times, and a keen co-worker of the World Academy of Art and Science.

His idea of a World University (first published in 1951) is one of the major aims of the World Academy. The name BERTRAND RUSSELL has long become a symbol of man's struggle for real freedom and peace.

Among the visible acknowledgements are the Nobel Prize for Literature (1950) and the UNESCO Kalinga Prize (1957).

Address: Plas Penrhyn, Penrhyndeudraeth, Merioneth, U.K.

World Academy

of

Art and Science

Manifesto

In the Name of Science and the Future of Mankind.

The appeal of the International Conference on Science and Human Welfare has been realised – THE WORLD ACADEMY OF ART AND SCIENCE has been established.

This urgently needed forum has been created for distinguished scientists and scholars to discuss the vital problems of mankind, independent of political boundaries or limits – whether spiritual or physical; a forum where these problems will be discussed objectively, scientifically, globally and free from vested interests or regional attachments.

The World Academy of Art and Science will function as an informal "world university" at the highest scientific and ethical level, in which deep human understanding and the fullest sense of responsibility will meet.

The structure of the Academy and its goal are laid down in the first volume of its publications, "Science and the Future of Mankind," now in press.

The basic idea which led to the founding of the Academy stems from the following considerations:

All existing international organisations which decide on vital problems of mankind are constructed on the principle of national or group representation. *This* forum is international, or more truly trans-national.

From the dawn of mankind people have worked together to build the tower of knowledge, and no nation has failed to contribute to this marvellous building. The creative power of the human spirit is to be found in the first prehistoric digging stick for agriculture as in the motorised plough of our time. The first canoe is no less original in concept than the Archimedian principle; the first wheel no less than the first aeroplane – perhaps even more so.

The true object of all these achievements of the human spirit is to lighten the burden of life, to enrich it – and certainly not to make it more difficult or to destroy it. In the words of EINSTEIN who is one of the spiritual fathers of this trans-national forum: "The creations of our mind shall be a blessing and not a curse to mankind."

This is the fundamental aim of the World Academy: to rediscover the language of mutual understanding. It will work in close collaboration with the institutions of the United Nations. It will look for the true enemies of peace, and try to fight them:

These enemies are hunger and sickness, waste and destruction; the archenemies intolerance and ignorance, resignation and fear.

In International meetings and conferences, represented by group or nation, the intrinsic merits of the questions discussed have too often to be subordinated to considerations of national prestige or group-interests. The World Academy has no pre-established tasks to fulfil and no vested interests to serve. It is free to attack problems in the broad interests of mankind, and to seek solutions leading to hope, happiness and peace.

With the help of science and the support of all cultural and constructive forces of mankind, the World Academy will be able to dedicate itself to its objective – the aim of serving as an impartial and unpolitical adviser, complementing other organisations, in this difficult transition period, and contributing in leading mankind to an era of true progress, true human welfare, and true happiness.

Supported by the confidence and trust of a great number

of spiritual leaders of mankind, we herewith declare the World Academy of Art and Science founded.

For the Charter Members:

The President	–	Lord John Boyd Orr (Brechin, Scotland, U.K.)
The Vice Presidents	–	Hermann Joseph Muller (Bloomington, Ind., U.S.A.)
		Hugo Osvald (Uppsala, Sweden)
The Secretary General	–	Hugo Boyko (Jerusalem-Rehovoth, Israel).

24th December, 1960.

Manifeste

Au nom de la Science et de l'avenir de l'Humanité.

L'appel de la Conférence Internationale sur la Science et le Bien-être humain a été entendu. L'Académie Mondiale de l'Art et de la Science a été constituée.

Ainsi, ce forum dont le besoin se faisait sentir de façon pressante a été créé; des hommes de science et des savants de réputation internationale y délibèreront ensemble, hors de toute restriction ou frontière politique, des problèmes vitaux de l'humanité, qu'ils soient spirituels ou physiques; un forum où ces problèmes pourront être discutés objectivement, scientifiquement, dans leur ensemble et par delà tous intérêts acquis ou intérêts de groupes.

L'Académie Mondiale de l'Art et de la Science fonctionnera comme une "université mondiale" non formelle, d'un très haut degré scientifique et moral, où regneront une profonde compréhension humaine et un sens parfait des responsabilités.

La structure de l'Académie et son but sont exposés dans le premier volume de ses publications, "Science and the Future of Mankind" [Science et l'avenir de l'Humanité], actuellement sous presse.

Quelle est l'idée fondamentale qui a conduit à la fondation de l'Académie?

Elle provient des considérations suivantes: les organisations internationales qui, aujourd'hui, confèrent sur les problèmes vitaux de l'humanité et les tranchent sont toutes bâties sur le principe d'une représentation nationale ou de groupe.

Ce forum-ci est vraiment international. Il est même plus: il est trans-national.

Depuis l'aube de l'humanité, nous autres êtres humains avons travaillé tous ensemble à bâtir la tour de nos connaissances. Il n'y a pas de peuple sur notre planète qui n'ait participé de façon constructive à ce merveilleux édifice.

Le pouvoir créateur de l'esprit humain se retrouve aussi bien dans le morceau de bois qui servait à piocher la terre aux temps préhistoriques que dans la charrue motorisée de notre époque. La première pirogue n'est pas moins originale dans sa conception que le principe d'Archimède, la première roue que le premier avion; peut-être même l'est-elle davantage.

Le véritable objet de tous ces succès de l'esprit humain est d'alléger le poids de la vie, de l'enrichir-et certes non pas de la rendre plus difficile ou de la supprimer. Ou bien, pour reprendre les paroles d'EINSTEIN qui est l'un des pères spirituels de ce forum transnational: "Les créations de notre esprit doivent être une bénédiction et non pas un fléau pour l'humanité".

Ceci est le but fondamental de l'Académie Mondiale: essayer de trouver de nouveau le langage de la compréhension mutuelle.

Elle travaillera en étroite coopération avec les institutions des Nations Unies.

Elle reconnaîtra quels sont les véritables ennemis, le cartel des ennemis de la paix, et montrera comment les combattre.

Ces ennemis sont la faim et la maladie, le gaspillage et la destruction, et avant tout: l'intolérance et l'ignorance, la résignation et la peur.

Dans les réunions ou conférences internationales dont la représentation est soit de groupe soit nationale, les mérites intrinsèques des questions discutées sont trop souvent subordonnés à des considérations de prestige national ou aux intérêts des groupes.

L'Académie Mondiale n'a pas de tâches pré-établies à remplir ni d'intérêts acquis à servir. Elle est plus libre pour attaquer les problèmes dans le plein intérêt de l'humanité et pour chercher des solutions conduisant à l'espoir, à la joie et à la paix.

Avec l'aide de la Science et l'appui de toutes les forces culturelles et constructives de l'humanité, l'Académie Mondiale pourra se consacrer pleinement à son objectif, le but de servir de conseiller impartial et a-politique, suppléant ainsi d'autres organisations dans cette difficile période de transition, et contribuant à conduire l'humanité vers une ère de progrès véritable, de vrai bien-être de l'être humain et de véritable joie de vivre.

Soutenus par la confiance et l'espoir d'un grand nombre de chefs spirituels de l'humanité, nous déclarons fondée, par la présente, l'ACADEMIE MONDIALE DE L'ART ET DE LA SCIENCE.

Pour les membres de la Charte:

Le Président – Lord JOHN BOYD ORR
(Brechin, Scotland, U.K.)

Les Vice-Présidents – HERMANN JOSEPH MULLER
(Bloomington, Ind., U.S.A.)
HUGO OSVALD
(Uppsala, Suède)

Le Sécrétaire Général – HUGO BOYKO
(Jerusalem-Rehovot, Israel)

Le 24 Décembre 1960.

List of Co-Workers in the Preparatory Steps and of Charter Members of the World Academy of Art and Science

			Main International Organization (activities)
PIERRE CHOUARD	Paris	Ecologist	President, Division of Botany, I.U.B.S.
RITCHIE CALDER	Aberdeen	Science Writer	President, Int. Association of Science Writers
H. MUNRO FOX	London	Zoologist	Past-President of I.U.B.S.
JOSEPH NEEDHAM	Cambridge, U.K.	Biochemist, Historian, Orientalist	Co-Founder of UNESCO and first Director of its Dept. of Natural Sciences
GEORGE LACLAVÉRE	Paris	Geophysicist	Secretary-General of I.U.G.G.
G. LE LIONNAISE	Paris	Science Writer	Chairman, Round Table Conference of UNESCO
ROBERT OPPENHEIMER	Princeton	Physicist	

The following scientists have already sent their agreement to sign as charter members: –

PIERRE AUGER	Paris	Physicist	Advisor and former Director of UNESCO, Dept. of Natural Sciences
I. BERENBLUM	Rehovot	Biologist, (Cancer-Research)	
LORD J. BOYD-ORR	Brechin	Nutritionist	Founder and first Director General of FAO, Nobel Prize Laureate
H. BOYKO	Rehovot	Ecologist	President, ICE; Vice-President, ISBB
LYLE K. BUSH	Boston	Prof. of Art	Member, Int. Preparatory Commission of WAAS
G. BROCK CHISHOLM	Victoria	Medicine	Founder and first Director General of WHO
MAURICE EWING	New York	Geophysicist	President, Geophysical Union of America

Paul Fallot	Paris	Geologist	(died shortly after signing as Charter Member)
R. M. Field	South Duxbury	Geologist	Past President, Geophysical Union of Amerika, President, American Institute for Geonomy and Natural Resources
F. R. Fosberg	Washington, D.C.	Ecologist	Co-founder and Vice-President, Int. Association for Tropical Ecology
J. Heimanns	Amsterdam	Botanist	
A. Katchalsky	Rehovot	Physico-Chemist	Vice-President, Israel Academy of Science
Harold D. Lasswell	New Haven	Political Science	
W. C. de Leeuw	Leyden	Plant sociologist and philosopher	President, Int. Association of Plantgeogr. and Ecology
P. Maheshvari	Delhi	Botanist	
J. van Mieghem	Bruxelles	Meteorologist	President, Royal Flemish Academy of Sciences; Vice-President, Int. Commission of Aerology, WMO
Théodore Monod	Dakar-Paris	Zoologist	
Stuart Mudd	Philadelphia	Microbiologist	President, Int. Association of Microbiological Societies
Hermann Joseph Muller	Bloomington	Geneticist	Nobel Prize Laureate
Hugo Osvald	Uppsala	Agriculturist	
P. van Oye	Ghent	Hydrobiologist	Vice-President, Int. Association of Limnology
Francis Perrin	Paris	Physicist	
A. de Philippis	Firence	Forest Scientist	Vice-President, Int. Union of Forest Research Stations
John F. V. Phillips	Southern Rhodesia	Agricultural Ecologist	Advisor of World-bank in African Problems
Christian Poulsen	Kopenhagen	Mineralogist	President, Int. Union of Paleontology and Stratigraphy
B. Pregel	New York	Physicist	Past President, and Chairman, Board, New York Academy of Science
J. Rotblat	London	Physicist	Hon. Secretary of, and Liaison officer to Pugwash Conferences
Earl Bertrand Russell	U.K.	Philosopher	Nobel Prize Laureate
Arthur William Sampson	Calif.	Forest Scientist	
M. J. Sirks	Wageningen	Geneticist	Past President, I.U.B.S.
Harlan T. Stetson	Fort Landerdale, Florida	Astronomer	
W. F. G. Swann	Philadelphia	Physicist	Director Emeritus, Bartold Research Foundation of the Franklin Institute

W. TAYLOR THOM, JR.	Princeton	Geologist	Member, Preparatory Commission of WAAS
SOLCO W. TROMP	Oegstgeest	Bioclimatologist	Founder and Secr. General ISBB
HARLD C. UREY	Calif.	Chemist	Nobel Prize Laureate
FRANS VERDOORN	Utrecht	Botanist	President, Int. Commission for Biohistorical Science
WALTER W. WEISBACH	The Hague	Physician (Hygiene and National Economy)	

We miss the signatures of four great men who worked in this direction until their death:

Sir IAN CLUNIES ROSS, the famous Australian Biologist and Organisator of scientific research, who – full of enthusiasm – had just started to write his essay for our book "Science and the Future of Mankind", when sudden death ended his work

JOHN A. FLEMING, the former President of the International Council of Scientific Unions, who organized, together with R. M. FIELD, the First Internat. Conference on Science and Human Welfare in 1956, where the decision of this foundation was made

HOMER LE ROY SHANTZ, the great Ecologist, who encouraged the plan by word and letter through the 3 years 1955–1958, and last but not least

ALBERT EINSTEIN, the spiritual father of the idea.

All four we can call – Charter members "posthumus".

ABBREVIATIONS

FAO	Food and Agricultural Organization of United Nations Organization
ICE	International Commission of Ecology of International Union of Biological Sciences
Int.	International
ISBB	International Society of Bioclimatology and Biometeorology
IUBS	International Union of Biological Sciences
IUGG	International Union of Geophysics and Geodesy
UNESCO	United Nations Educational, Scientific and Cultural Organization
UNO	United Nations Organization
WAAS	World Academy of Art and Science
WHO	World Health Organization of United Nations Organization
WMO	World Meteorological Organization of United Nations Organization

Informatory Notes

1. General remarks:

   The World Academy of Art and Science intends to publish periodically the results of its official investigations and discussions on vital problems of mankind. These volumes will also contain general information about organizational developments of the Academy (member lists, working groups, etc.) as an Appendix.

2. Contents of the next volume (Vol. II):

   Academy members and others have been approached by Circular letter for their opinion regarding priorities out of a list of vital problems. As a result of this "voting" by correspondence the next volume will deal with the global population problem and related problems (e.g. birth control, etc.), and with recommendations for their solution. In accordance with this decision the Secretary General has invited leading experts to join an appropriate working group of the World Academy and to contribute to the forthcoming Volume II.

   In connection with these preparatory steps the Secretary-General has also been approached by leading personalities of "The International Conference on the World Population Crisis" and has been asked to include the proceedings of this important meeting into the forthcoming volume. This Conference took place in New York City, May, 1961, under the Chairmanship of Sir Julian Huxley with participants and lecturers from five continents, among them official representatives from various over-populated countries (Ceylon, China, India, Japan, Pakistan, etc.).

3. OFFICIAL NAME AND ADDRESS OF THE CENTRAL SECRETARIATE:

World Academy of Art and Science
(An Agency for Human Welfare),
1 Ruppin Street, Rehovot, Israel. P.O. Box 534.
Telephone: 951533
Bank Account No. 211588
Jacob Japhet and Co. Ltd., Bankers,
Jerusalem, Israel.